n c fo

LAND APPLICATION
OF WASTES
Volume I

LAND APPLICATION OF WASTES
Volume I

Raymond C. Loehr
Professor of Agricultural Engineering

William J. Jewell
Associate Professor of Agricultural Engineering

Joseph D. Novak
Professor of Science Education

William W. Clarkson
Research Associate

Gerald S. Friedman
Research Associate

College of Agriculture and Life Sciences
A Statutory College of the State University of New York
Cornell University

Van Nostrand Reinhold Environmental Engineering Series

VAN NOSTRAND REINHOLD COMPANY
NEW YORK   CINCINNATI   ATLANTA   DALLAS   SAN FRANCISCO
LONDON   TORONTO   MELBOURNE

Van Nostrand Reinhold Company Regional Offices:
New York   Cincinnati   Atlanta   Dallas   San Francisco

Van Nostrand Reinhold Company International Offices:
London   Toronto   Melbourne

Manufactured in the United States of America

Published by Van Nostrand Reinhold Company
135 West 50th Street, New York. N.Y. 10020

Published simultaneously in Canada by Van Nostrand Reinhold Ltd.

15 14 13 12 11 10 9 8 7 6 5 4 3 2 1

Library of Congress Cataloging in Publication Data

Main entry under title:

Land application of wastes.

   (Van Nostrand Reinhold environmental engineering
series)
   Includes bibliographies and index.
   1. Sewage disposal.   I. Loehr, Raymond C.
TD760.L22   628'.36   78-27646
ISBN 0-442-21705-6 (v. 1)

Van Nostrand Reinhold Environmental Engineering Series

THE VAN NOSTRAND REINHOLD ENVIRONMENTAL ENGINEERING SERIES is dedicated to the presentation of current and vital information relative to the engineering aspects of controlling man's physical environment. Systems and subsystems available to exercise control of both the indoor and outdoor environment continue to become more sophisticated and to involve a number of engineering disciplines. The aim of the series is to provide books which, though often concerned with the life cycle—design, installation, and operation and maintenance —of a specific system or subsystem, are complementary when viewed in their relationship to the total environment.

The Van Nostrand Reinhold Environmental Engineering Series includes books concerned with the engineering of mechanical systems designed (1) to control the environment within structures, including those in which manufacturing processes are carried out, and (2) to control the exterior environment through control of waste products expelled by inhabitants of structures and from manufacturing processes. The series include books on heating, air conditioning and ventilation, control of air and water pollution, control of the acoustic environment, sanitary engineering and waste disposal, illumination, and piping systems for transporting media of all kinds.

Van Nostrand Reinhold Environmental Engineering Series

ADVANCED WASTEWATER TREATMENT, by Russell L. Culp and Gordon L. Culp

ARCHITECTURAL INTERIOR SYSTEMS—Lighting, Air Conditioning, Acoustics, John E. Flynn and Arthur W. Segil

SOLID WASTE MANAGEMENT, by D. Joseph Hagerty, Joseph L. Pavoni and John E. Heer, Jr.

THERMAL INSULATION, by John F. Malloy

AIR POLLUTION AND INDUSTRY, edited by Richard D. Ross

INDUSTRIAL WASTE DISPOSAL, edited by Richard D. Ross

MICROBIAL CONTAMINATION CONTROL FACILITIES, by Robert S. Rurkle and G. Briggs Phillips

SOUND, NOISE, AND VIBRATION CONTROL (Second Edition), by Lyle F. Yerges

NEW CONCEPTS IN WATER PURIFICATION, by Gordon L. Culp and Russell L. Culp

HANDBOOK OF SOLID WASTE DISPOSAL: MATERIALS AND ENERGY RECOVERY, by Joseph L. Pavoni, John E. Heer, Jr., and D. Joseph Hagerty

ENVIRONMENTAL ASSESSMENTS AND STATEMENTS, by John E. Heer, Jr. and D. Joseph Hagerty

ENVIRONMENTAL IMPACT ANALYSIS: A New Dimension in Decision Making, by R. K. Jain, L. V. Urban and G. S. Stacey

CONTROL SYSTEMS FOR HEATING, VENTILATING, AND AIR CONDITIONING (Second Edition), by Roger W. Haines

WATER QUALITY MANAGEMENT PLANNING, edited by Joseph L. Pavoni

HANDBOOK OF ADVANCED WASTEWATER TREATMENT (Second Edition), by Russell L. Culp, George Mack Wesner and Gordon L. Culp

HANDBOOK OF NOISE ASSESSMENT, edited by Daryl N. May

NOISE CONTROL: HANDBOOK OF PRINCIPLES AND PRACTICES, edited by David M. Lipscomb and Arthur C. Taylor

AIR POLLUTION CONTROL TECHNOLOGY, by Robert M. Bethea

POWER PLANT SITING, by John V. Winter and David A. Conner

DISINFECTION OF WASTEWATER AND WATER FOR REUSE, by Geo. Clifford White

LAND USE PLANNING: Techniques of Implementation, by T. William Patterson

BIOLOGICAL PATHS TO ENERGY SELF-RELIANCE, by Russell E. Anderson

HANDBOOK OF INDUSTRIAL WASTE DISPOSAL, by Richard A. Conway and Richard D. Ross

HANDBOOK OF ORGANIC WASTE CONVERSION, by Michael W. Bewick

LAND APPLICATIONS OF WASTE (Volume 1), by Raymond C. Loehr, William J. Jewell, Joseph D. Novak, William W. Clarkson and Gerald S. Friedman

LAND APPLICATIONS OF WASTE (Volume 2), by Raymond C. Loehr, William J. Jewell, Joseph D. Novak, William W. Clarkson and Gerald S. Friedman

WIND MACHINES (Second Edition), by Frank R. Eldridge

PREFACE

Land treatment of municipal, agricultural, and industrial wastes and residues can be a cost-effective and efficient means of pollution control and resource recovery. Federal laws and regulations clearly indicate that Congress believes that this alternative approach must be considered, and should be favored wherever public funds are involved. When the first law (P.L. 92-500) emphasizing this technology became effective in 1972, only limited knowledge and experience were available to guide its application. In response to this lack of information, a multidisciplinary team was formed in 1974 in the College of Agriculture and Life Sciences (a statutory unit of the State University of New York) at Cornell University to develop an educational program beginning in 1974. The general goal of the program was to assemble state-of-the-art information to enable engineers, scientists, and pollution-control decision makers rapidly to determine the feasibility of using land application of waste. Financial support to develop this program was provided from 1974 through 1978 by the U.S. Environmental Protection Agency (Grant No. T-900500), and also during 1977 and 1978 by the U.S. Army Corps of Engineers. *Land Application of Wastes* represents a comprehensive summary of scientific and engineering fundamentals and design information of this technology.

The text of this two-volume set represents the bulk of the material developed by the Cornell team. However, it is only one component of a learning program that was produced to provide rapid, intensive, and comprehensive information to decision makers in wastewater pollution control. Additional components of the program include self-paced slide and tape modules ("audio-tutorial lessons") that reinforce and supplement material contained in the written modules. In addition to the written material, support materials that were developed included over 1000 slides, 16 cassette tapes, and an Instructor's Program. These are available at cost (without royalties to the authors). Information may be obtained from Instructional Materials Service, Stone Hall, Cornell University, Ithaca, New York 14853.

In addition, the authors would like to alert the readers to several personal notes. Unlike many large projects involving several disciplines, these results were produced by a team, which included agricultural engineers, environmental engineers, educators, agronomists, and others, who were extremely cooperative and friendly. The result is that *Land Application of Wastes* represents the best output that could be developed with the available skills and knowledge.

The listed order of the authors is arbitrary and is not intended to reflect the level of their contribution. R. C. Loehr, Director of the Environmental Studies Program and Professor of Agricultural and Environmental Engineering, provided the leadership in developing the support from the federal agencies, and assisted in coordinating the development of the later stages of the program. W. J. Jewell, Associate Professor of Agricultural Engineering, developed the engineering design approach as the basis of the program and was the coordinator for the development of the first draft. J. D. Novak, Professor of Science Education, provided the emphasis to search continuously for the major explanatory concepts, and to incorporate these basic concepts into a modular, self-teaching educational program. Primarily through his urging and efforts, a nonprofit agreement to publish this information was developed among Cornell University, U.S. Environmental Protection Agency, U.S. Army Corps of Engineers, other contributors, and Van Nostrand Reinhold Company. W. W. Clarkson and G. S. Friedman were the two major full-time research personnel who prepared the final written drafts of all materials and were responsible for bringing the final product together. W. W. Clarkson, Research Associate in the Department of Agricultural Engineering, is an environmental engineer and drafted much of the final text. G. S. Friedman, Research Associate in the Science Education Department, also drafted final modules, and was responsible for development of the audio-tutorial component and the Instructor's Program.

The authors would like to emphasize that this educational program comes to the practitioner as a pretested program. During the latter stages of development, the material was used in five, week-long workshops, which over 150 individuals attended. It has also been used successfully by others in a number of different formats. The requested feedback and surveys of these efforts indicate that the program is capable of transferring a significant amount of knowledge under a wide variety of conditions and applications. It was the intention of the educational format that this should be so.

The authors would like to acknowledge the high-quality, key agronomic information provided on this project. In particular, J. E. Stone developed the important concepts presented in the module on "Soil as a Treatment Medium," along with several other modules. He was assisted by members of Cornell University's Agronomy Department. In particular, Professor E. L. Stone was especially helpful in interpreting information needs and bridges required between pollution control and agricultural production interests. Other agronomy faculty and staff who provided assistance included W. H. Allaway, G. Armedee, D. R. Bouldin, A. H. Johnson, S. D. Klausner, D. J. Lathwell, D. A. Lauer, G. W. Olson, and P. J. Zwerman. S. M. Dabney was primary author of the "Crop Selection" and "Non-Crop and Forest Systems" modules.

Preparation of the final draft and production of the materials for testing throughout the country depended on having a highly efficient and cooperative Cornell print shop available, as well as many other highly skilled individuals. A. C. Plescia, the final program production coordinator, was assisted by F. Shottenfeld, who worked closely with outstanding individuals such as R. W. Gingras in the Graphic Arts Department. M. M. Bogin edited copy and drafted some material.

J. K. Krizek, A. L. Liebermann, R. H. Nagell, and S. Haeni contributed artwork and graphic design. L. A. Martin, P. M. Comfort, A. C. Plescia, B. C. Littlefair, and others provided secretarial assistance. D. P. Willmot prepared and processed audio-tutorial materials. The audio-tutorial program was narrated by K. Marash.

Technical assistance of various kinds was provided by R. Batkin, W. Messner, D. Payne, D. Way, G. MacCaskill, and R. J. Krizek. Thanks are also due to many other members of the Cornell community who shared time, ideas, and materials.

In addition to the significant effort provided by the Cornell University Agronomy Department personnel, many other individuals were responsible for various aspects of the program. Persons responsible for preliminary drafts of many modules included G. A. Garrigan, C. E. Morris, and D. F. Smith. Part-time assistance was provided by W. Pollard and M. Switzenbaum.

Outside consultants who provided assistance were E. Myers, private consultant; H. J. Ongerth, California State Health Department; R. E. Thomas, and B. L. Seabrook, U.S. Environmental Protection Agency; S. C. Reed, U.S. Army Corps of Engineers; T. D. Hinesly, University of Illinois; D. M. Whiting, National Oceanographic and Atmospheric Administration, National Weather Service. Final modules were also reviewed by N. Urban, H. L. McKim, C. Merry, H. Farquhar, and others of the U.S. Army Corps of Engineers.

The generous assistance of many equipment manufacturing companies, engineering consultants, state pollution-control agencies, and municipalities and industries using land-application systems are too numerous to mention. Nevertheless, they represent a major input.

Finally, as we prepare the final drafts of this material, we know that newer information will make some components obsolete. The focus on the fundamental concepts discussed in this work should provide a useful framework to view future developments in this rapidly advancing field.

THE AUTHORS

INTRODUCTION

STATEMENT OF PURPOSE

The purpose of this module is to acquaint the reader with the program of instruction entitled *Land Application of Wastes: An Educational Program.* This introductory module includes information on the content, structure, and alternative educational uses of the program.

CONTENTS

LAND APPLICATION OF WASTES PROGRAM—A BRIEF OVERVIEW

In the nineteenth century, it became relatively common for municipalities to operate "sewage farms." Some of those facilities were successful as measured by such standards as absence of excessive odors or standing water. Eventually, as urban expansion encroached on available land and technological interests turned to the design of sewage-treatment plants, most sewage farms were abandoned. Since 1972, as a result of the passage of PL 92-500, land application as a waste-management alternative has been reemphasized. Legislative recognition of the importance of land treatment as an alternative technology for waste treatment was further emphasized by the passage in 1977 of the amendments to this law. Critical evaluation of those factors that impose specific limitations on the land application of wastes is needed. Specifically, it is necessary to evaluate:

a. the characteristics of the wastewater and sludge
b. the impact of nitrogen, phosphorus, and potentially toxic elements on the soil system, vegetative cover, runoff water, and groundwater
c. the interactions between the soil system and wastewater constituents

d. the social and legal constraints

e. the effect of the proposed land-application system on present and future regional land-use patterns

Thought must be given to the necessity of designs employing combinations of conventional systems and land application. Such an evaluation must include the broad implications of the limiting factors with respect to both land application in general and to the specific site under consideration. Modification of specific waste characteristics and site conditions to achieve economical treatment may be possible. Examples of such modifications include underdraining certain soils so that larger hydraulic loads could be applied, wastewater pretreatment to reduce heavy metal content, or frequent cropping to achieve a higher rate of nutrient removal.

THE EDUCATIONAL PROGRAM STRUCTURE

The success of a land-application system rests on scientific, legal, and social fundamentals and practices. It is necessary to integrate these, to discuss their implications, and to provide a level of practical experience.

The objective of this educational program is to develop a better understanding of the capacity of the soil to assimilate wastes. The program is designed for engineers, scientists, planners, waste-management specialists, and other practitioners in the area of environmental protection. Land application of municipal, industrial, and agricultural wastes is addressed. Knowledge from several disciplines, including sanitary, environmental, and agricultural engineering, and agronomy, soil science, economics, and law are incorporated into the program. In order to present this diverse array of information in a meaningful way, this program is presented in *modular* format. This format is designed to be useful and understandable to individuals who have had no formal training in application of waste technology as well as persons who have been involved with the design of successful land waste-treatment systems.

The Modules

The program's basic unit of formal instruction is the module. A module is a self-contained learning packet focused on a specific concept or on a set of highly integrated concepts. Within the module, the reader will find information on what they can expect to learn from the module, how the module fits into the entire program, and a discussion of specific aspects of land application of wastes. Modules require from 0.5 to 5 hours of study time, depending in part on the reader's background and on the desired degree of mastery of the study materials.

All modules are presented in a printed format. Fifteen modules have also been adapted as audio-visual presentations known as *audio-tutorials* or *A-T units*. Scripts are provided along with the tape and slide A-T presentations, and several A-T units include supplementary booklets for further study.* The audio-tutorial units are supplementary and need not be included in a study program. They have proved to be particularly valuable in workshops and college courses using the *Land Application of Wastes* materials, where they have been well received by the participants.

Each module includes a set of *learning objectives*, which indicate what the reader can expect to learn from the module. The objectives are usually presented as a series of competencies

---

*Complete information on and cost of the audio-tutorial program are available from the Instructional Materials Service, Stone Hall, Cornell University, Ithaca, New York 14853.

that the participant will be able to demonstrate after completing the module. For example, an objective for this module might read as follows:

After completing the module, the reader will be able to:

Describe the organization and content of the program, *Land Application of Wastes*; indicate how the printed modules that follow can be used in workshops, short courses, independent study, or in college courses in environmental or sanitary engineering.

If the reader can meet the objectives without completing the module, then the module can be skipped, or simply skimmed over using italicized summaries.

A table of contents is presented at the beginning of each module. This allows the reader to see precisely what information is covered and where it is found. Readers should carefully peruse the major titles and their immediate subdivisions, and then reflect on how these topics might "fit" with respect to their existing knowledge of the topic. This is the first step in making effective use of the modular format. If the readers cannot complete all of the objectives of a module, the table of contents should allow them to identify which sections contain the material they need to learn in order to complete the remaining objectives, without having to read material already familiar.

Key ideas presented in the text are summarized in italics. This also facilitates efficient learning, review, or both. Following a summary and table of contents of most of the modules, a glossary of terms and concepts used is presented.

Since each module is a self-contained learning packet, readers must be sure they have learned its contents to a sufficient degree. They can do this by returning to the module objectives and assessing their competence in each. If some of the objectives cannot be satisfied, readers can review any or all parts of the audio-tutorial or printed modules or using italicized summaries to aid in locating pertinent sections.

While each module is considered to be an individual unit, it must be remembered that each module is designed as an integral part of the entire educational program. Thus, there is extensive cross-referencing between modules. As the participant proceeds through the program, the individual modules will form an integrated package of information.

The first 10 modules are presented in Volume I of the program, and the remaining 11 modules in Volume II. Let us now look at how the individual modules are integrated into the entire program.

The Design Procedure

In order to bridge the gap between an academic learning experience such as this program, and the real-life situations faced by personnel in the field, a framework that approximates the design procedure used by engineers has been included. The framework is described in "Design Procedures for Land Application of Wastes."

The design procedure identifies two specific levels. At the first level, general information is presented on all topics relevant to land application of wastes. However, this information provides an overview of land-treatment technology, and so many details are not included. Table 1 lists the Level I module titles.

After satisfactorily completing all Level I modules, the reader should be able to arrive at an

Table 1.   Introductory Modules Tend to Center Attention on Broad Topics and
to Stress Interrelationships Between Fundamental Concepts.

Module	Title
I-1	Soil as a Treatment Medium[a]
I-2	Design Procedures for Land Application of Wastes[a]
I-3	Waste Characteristics[a]
I-4	Treatment Systems, Effluent Qualities, and Costs[a]
I-5	The Role of Vegetative Cover[a]
I-6	Site Evaluation: General Criteria—Information Sources[a]
I-7	Costing Land-Application Systems

[a]Also available as an audio-tutorial module.

initial feasibility decision for a specific design problem. At this point, the reader should be able to state what the limiting factor to land application may be for a given waste input and application site, what social aspects need further investigation, possible alternative sites for a land-application system, and generally whether land application is a feasible waste-management alternative for that particular situation.

The reader will then be ready for Level II. The Level II modules are more detailed, and they contain the necessary information to arrive at more detailed design parameters such as specific hydraulic loads, application rate, land area needed, and so on. After completing Level II modules, a much more detailed problem evaluation is possible. Table 2 lists the titles of Level II modules.

Table 2.   Level II Modules Provide More Detailed Information for
Completion of Design Problems.

Module[a]	Title[a]
I-8	Societal Constraints
I-9	Legal Aspects
I-10	Case Studies Reviewed
II-1	Nitrogen Considerations[b]
II-2	Phosphorus Considerations[b]
II-3	Organic Matter[b]
II-4	Potentially Toxic Elements
II-5	Pathogens
II-6	Climate and Wastewater Storage[b]
II-7	Crop Selection and Management Alternatives[b]
II-8	Non-crop and Forest Systems[b]
II-9	Waste Application Systems[b]
II-10	Drainage for Land-Application Sites[b]
II-11	Monitoring at Land-Application Sites[b]

[a]Volume I of *Land Application of Wastes* contains Modules I-1 to I-10, and Volume II contains Modules II-1 through II-11.
[b]Also available as an audio-tutorial module.

MODULE AND PROGRAM SEQUENCES

The program consists of over 20 modules.* There is no formal sequence of modules because, as noted, each is self-contained. To start the program, choose one of the seven Level I modules. The modules may be completed in any order desired, although some readers may find it preferable to complete the modules in sequence. The Level I modules can be completed in 3 to 20 hours of study time.

It is suggested that the readers assume that they have been asked to advise a municipality or an industrial firm about a proposed land-application system (such as offered in the sample design problems). With this focus, the reader can ask intelligent questions and gather and relate pertinent information to the information in the modules.

When this material is presented in a workshop or other course the design problems are included only to provide a focus for the fundamental information and to place it in a real rather than abstract context. The course participant should not consider solution of the design problem to be the most important part of the program. The design problem is merely to facilitate the acquisition and use of the basic information.

THE EDUCATIONAL PROGRAM—ALTERNATIVES

Whereas the modules contain a large portion of the current knowledge of land application of wastes and can be read somewhat like a textbook or a symposium volume, they are also designed to be used in a variety of educational programs. The psychological and social factors that were considered in the design of the modules are presented in an Instructor's Program.**

Workshop Programs

Workshop programs draw together a group of participants with varying interests and backgrounds for a short, intensive period of study. Most workshop programs constitute a series of lectures by "experts," and offer some opportunity for questions and discussions. The *Land Application of Wastes* program has been designed to be used effectively in a 2- to 5-day workshop that includes *individual* study of printed and audio-tutorial modules, staff tutoring, small group problem-solving sessions focused on representative design problems, some guest lectures, and special group presentations and correlated individual and group activities. A sample schedule for a 5-day workshop is shown in Table 3.

Sufficient staff must be provided to meet each participant's need for guidance. Guest speakers— experts with various backgrounds in land application—serve as additional resource personnel. Participants are encouraged to interact with the speakers, individually or in groups. The participants represent a wide range of pertinent knowledge and experience. Although each participant moves through the program as an individual, the program format is designed to encourage interaction and support.

Participants will be given realistic design problems based on the scenario of a client approaching a consultant who has some limited information at hand and requesting advice on the feasibility of land application to solve a given problem. Each participant will be asked to select one

---

*Additional modules will be prepared in the future and will become available either through the Instructional Materials Service at Cornell University or through Van Nostrand Reinhold Company.

**The Instructor's Program consists of three modules describing the organization and conduct of "workshop" educational programs, some alternative programs, and the theoretical rationale for the program as developed. The Instructor's Program is available from the Instructional Materials Service at Cornell University.

Table 3.   Schedule for a Typical Workshop

Time	Monday	Tuesday	Wednesday	Thursday	Friday
8:30 A.M.	Registration, welcome, introduction to program	Level I design procedure—Limiting Design factors	Introduction to Level II	Group discussion if needed —alternative systems	Prepare Level II design
9:00	Written and A-T modules, design problems				Presentation of Level II designs
		X	X	X	
9:30		X	X	X	
10:00	Coffee	Coffee	Coffee	Coffee	Coffee
10:30	Level I				Discussion and evaluation
	X	X	X	X	
11:00	X	X	X	X	
11:30	X	Complete Level I topics	Discussion—Pathogens and toxic elements (or nitrogen)	X	↓
Noon	Lunch	Lunch	Lunch	Lunch	Adjournment
1:00 P.M.	Speaker	Speaker	X	Speaker	
2:00	X	Prepare Level I design	X	X	
3:00	X	Presentations of Level I designs	Field trip (optional)	X	
4:00	Design problem definition and review of format and early problems	Discussion of cost-effectiveness and pollution-control efficiency	↓	Level II modules, complete public hearing	
5:00					
7:30	Evening program				

X denotes time set aside for individualized study with tapes, slides, written material, and other prepared material. Individual course instruction and tutoring are also available at these times.

"interesting" situation for study, and the participants will be divided into study teams. Each team will meet with a staff member to consider the problem. However, the staff member will only direct the discussion if it strays too far off target, and will act as a resource person to indicate where specific information can be found. The staff member is not to supply factual answers except when necessary to avoid delays in the program. Working together, the team should develop the background information necessary to assess the general feasibility of land application for the specific problem (Level I). A more detailed analysis and feasibility will occur in the subsequent part of the program (Level II).

Each study team presents reports to the total workshop group to indicate progress on their design problem and to solicit comments and criticism. Field trips and other activities may be included in a workshop program.

Independent Study

For most professionals, independent study in the office or home is the most common form of education. *Land Application of Wastes* was designed to be an effective educational tool for use by professionals who wish to study on their own. It can be used with the printed modules alone or in combination with audio-tutorial units that can be purchased through Cornell University or loaned from regional offices of the U.S. Environmental Protection Agency. In the future, we anticipate that some colleges and universities will offer faculty assistance through home study or extension education programs to assist the independent learner. The study time needed to meet the objectives given in all modules will vary depending on an individual's background and experience, with a reasonable range of 30 to 100 hours.

Short Courses and Other College Offerings

Some colleges and universities are offering "short courses" in land-application-of-wastes technology. These courses fit into summer session or other college program offerings and usually carry undergraduate or graduate credit. Both the printed and audio-tutorial modules are used to supplement semester courses in waste-treatment technology. The materials have been designed to be used effectively in conjunction with formal college courses.

To Begin the Program

We advise the reader to begin by thumbing through all of the modules, giving a few minutes to each and stopping occasionally to read italicized summaries or to study a figure or table. Then we advise that you begin with Module I-1, "Soil as a Treatment Medium," and proceed from there. An understanding of fundamental concepts necessary for the solution of waste treatment problems is the final criterion of effective learning, and hence a major goal of this program. The authors would be pleased to learn of your success or difficulties with this program.

CONTENTS

LAND APPLICATION
OF WASTES
Volume I

Module I-1

SOIL AS A TREATMENT MEDIUM

SUMMARY

This module examines the basic properties of soil which have an influence on the success of land treatment of wastes. These relevant properties include soil texture, soil structure, permeability, infiltration, available water capacity, and cation exchange capacity.

Biological, chemical, and physical mechanisms work to remove and renovate wastes after their application to the soil. Wastes are removed physically through filtration by the soil and altered by dilution, either upon entering the groundwater or by augmentation in the soil with natural rainfall or snow-melt. Filtration is limited because of the clogging of soil pores with suspended solids. Clogging can be avoided by pretreatment and by allowing rest periods between applications.

Adsorption and precipitation are the two main processes of chemical retention of wastes in soil. Potentially toxic elements and the macronutrients nitrogen and phosphorus are partially controlled by chemical mechanisms in soil. The effectiveness of soil in the removal of waste constituents either by ion exchange or specific adsorption depends upon the contact between dissolved substances and the appropriate colloidal phases.

Biological mechanisms alter waste constituents in stages. Soil organisms decompose organic compounds. The rate at which organic matter decomposes and the exact nature of the intermediate and end products depend in part on the composition of the organic material being added in the form of wastes.

The ability of the soil to handle wastes is limited by the loading of nitrogen, phosphorus, and water, the addition of potentially toxic materials, and its sodium adsorption ratio (SAR). This module summarizes these limitations, identifying nitrogen as the major limiting factor in most situations.

CONTENTS

1

GLOSSARY

adsorption—the net effect of interactions between dissolved ions or compounds and the surfaces of clay and humus particles in soil; ion exchange is one type of adsorption process.

assimilation—the conversion of inorganic forms to organic forms within living tissue.

available water capacity (AWC)—that amount of water which is held in the soil between field capacity and permanent wilting point.

cation exchange capacity—a measure of the ability of a soil to retain positively charged ions called cations, generally serves as a rough index of all reactions occurring between charged pollutants and colloidal surfaces; CEC is a function of both the relative intensity of attraction between ions and colloidal solids and of the relative concentration of exchangeable ions present in the soil solution.

colloidal soil particles—clay and humus fraction of a soil characterized by their extremely small size (≤ 0.002 mm), very high ratio of surface area to volume, and the presence of a negative electrical charge.

field capacity—the moisture content which a soil will hold against the force of gravity after it has drained for 48 hours following saturation; the amount of water retained by the micropores.

infiltration—the rate at which water enters the soil surface, expressed in inches per hour, influenced by both permeability and moisture content of the soil.

macropores and micropores—two types of individual pore spaces which generally occur in soils. Macropores characteristically allow the ready movement of air and percolating water; micropores greatly impede air and water movement, restricting it to slow capillary movement.

mineralization—the conversion of an element from an organic form to an inorganic form as a result of microbial decomposition.

overland flow—a method of land application whereby wastewater is applied onto gently sloping, relatively impermeable soil that has been planted to vegetation. Biological oxidation occurs as the wastewater flows over the ground and contacts the biota in the vegetative litter; also known as "grass filtration" and "spray runoff."

permanent wilting point—the dividing point between the soil moisture that is extractable by plant roots and the moisture that is held too tightly for plant use.

permeability—the ease with which water and air are transmitted through the soil, determined by soil pore spaces; quantified in terms of the rate of water movement through a unit cross section of saturated soil in unit time; commonly expressed in inches per hour.

precipitation—formation of an insoluble or slowly soluble product from constituents that were originally in solution.

rapid infiltration system—a method of land application whereby large volumes of water are applied to the land, infiltrate the surface, and percolate through the soil pores; suitable for soils with high permeability.

regolith—the unconsolidated mantle of earth above the bedrock resulting from weathering of the underlying rock and/or deposition of material transported by gravity, wind, water, or ice.

sodium adsorption ratio (SAR)—a ratio of specific available cations in the soil solution which indicates if the accumulation of sodium in the soil exchange complex will lead to a degradation of soil structure and thus a sharp reduction in infiltration and permeability rates. The formula for SAR is:

$$SAR = \frac{[Na^{+1}]}{\left(\dfrac{[Ca^{+2}] + [Mg^{+2}]}{2}\right)^{0.5}}$$

soil—to a soil scientist, soil is the upper portion of the regolith which has been intensely altered by living organisms and climate, giving rise to distinct horizontal layers called horizons. In waste treatment, soil refers to the entire regolith.

soil aggregates—clumps of soil particles which form units that range from weak to stable, small to large, and simple to complex.

soil structure—the organization of individual particles into clumps or aggregates.

soil texture—the coarseness or fineness of the individual mineral particles in soil.

specific adsorption—the retention of certain cations and anions so tightly by the soil that they are not exchangeable with other cations and anions. Specific adsorption occurs between ions or compounds in solution and the solid colloidal phase.

OBJECTIVES

After completing this module, the reader should be able to:

1. Describe the basic properties of the soil including texture, structure, permeability, infiltration, available water capacity, and cation exchange capacity. Explain how each property affects the soil's ability to renovate waste constituents.
2. Name the physical mechanisms of the soil that operate in land application systems.
3. Describe the chemical mechanisms that operate in land application systems.
4. Explain the biological mechanisms that operate in land application systems including the three general stages of decomposition of newly added organic material.
5. Summarize the limitations on the waste treatment system that are imposed by adding nitrogen, organics, sodium, phosphorus, and potentially toxic materials such as zinc and cadmium to the site.

INTRODUCTION

Soil, as a physical, chemical, and biological complex, is a highly variable medium. In the absence of clearcut rules to follow for waste application, predictive judgments must be made on a site-specific basis after thorough evaluation of individual soil properties and their variability.

Land application systems are commonly classified in terms of vertical water transmission properties of soil. Soils with high transmission capabilities are considered suitable for "rapid infiltration" systems; soils with moderate transmission rates are suited for use with conventional

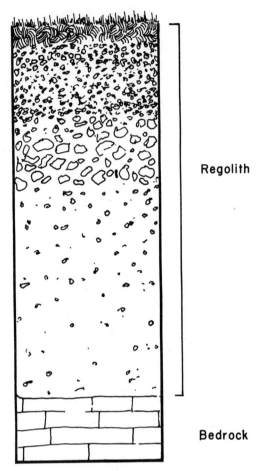

Regolith

Bedrock

Figure 1. A vertical section of a landscape showing the unconsolidated mantle (regolith) overlying bedrock. Note the presence of more or less distinct horizontal layers in the upper portion of the regolith.

"irrigation" methods; gently sloping soils with low transmission capabilities are normally suitable only for "overland flow" systems. Clearly, the behavior of water is an important consideration. Equally important is the potential for removal or alteration of other waste constituents including organics, pathogens, potentially toxic elements, dissolved salts, and major plant nutrients such as nitrogen and phosphorus. Site evaluation necessitates a basic understanding of soil components and properties, the treatment mechanisms operating in the soil, and limitations of these mechanisms in terms of pollutant loading rates.

Land application systems are generally related to the vertical water transmission of the soil. Rapid infiltration for high transmission, irrigation or slow rate for moderate transmission and overland flow for low transmission of the applied water.

In common usage, the term "soil" conveys a variety of meanings to different people and therefore requires some clarification at the outset. Figure 1 depicts a vertical section or profile

*This and other italicized summaries are intended to highlight key ideas, provide a basis for later review or to aid in skimming sections that are relatively familiar. They can be ignored in a complete reading of the text.

of a landscape extending from the surface down to bedrock. All of the material above bedrock is technically termed the regolith. This unconsolidated mantle results from weathering of the underlying rock and/or deposition of material transported by gravity, wind, water, or ice. Living organisms and climatic factors combine to alter the upper portion of the regolith, giving rise to more or less distinct horizontal layers termed horizons. To a soil scientist, soil is only this most intensely altered zone within which the nature and sequence of horizons form a basis for differentiating and mapping individual soils. In this sense, soil seldom extends deeper than 3–4 feet in temperate latitudes, although the regolith may extend hundreds of feet.

For purposes of waste treatment, however, it is convenient to use the term soil in a broader sense to include the entire regolith since much or all of the unconsolidated material can be instrumental in waste treatment. This broad interpretation of soil will be used in subsequent sections.

All material above bedrock is called the regolith; the term "soil" includes the entire regolith when speaking about waste treatment.

PROPERTIES OF SOIL MUST BE EXAMINED

Soil consists of a solid matrix interspersed with pore spaces. The solid matter consists of both mineral particles derived from rock fragments and organic matter or humus resulting from the decay of plant and animal tissue. Pore spaces are filled either with air or a solution of water and dissolved salts. In combination, these constituents provide an environment for a host of living organisms.

Soil consists of a solid matrix interspersed with pore spaces.

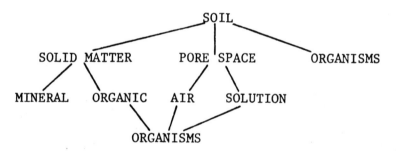

The behavior of water and other waste constituents in soil is closely related to the size and arrangement of the mineral particles and the amount of organic matter, which in turn determine the nature and amount of pore space. Figure 2 shows the approximate proportions of soil components in the surface or plow layer (6–8 inches) of a representative agricultural soil. Solid matter and pore space occupy about equal volumes. Organic matter comprises from 1 to 10% of the solid fraction with the remainder being mineral particles. Pore space is about evenly divided between air and solution unless the soil is very wet or very dry.

The behavior of wastewater in soil is influenced by the nature of the pore spaces, in turn determined by the characteristics of mineral particles and organic matter.

It must be stressed, however, that soil is highly variable both in space and time. For example, the amount of organic matter changes markedly with depth as does the size and arrangement of mineral particles. Likewise, the relative proportions of air and solution fluctuate widely in

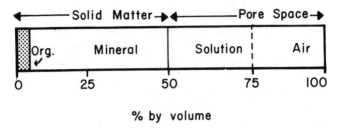

% by volume

Figure 2. Volume composition of an agricultural surface soil (6–8 inches in depth) representing favorable conditions for plant growth.

accordance with climatic events and land use. In order to evaluate soil as a medium for waste application and treatment, it is therefore necessary to further characterize soil variability.

Figure 3 depicts three different soil profiles, each to a depth of 4 feet. These profiles, from top to bottom, exhibit properties generally suitable for "rapid infiltration," "irrigation," and "overland flow" systems, respectively. Specific properties of interest in waste application are illustrated in subsequent figures. The vertical axis in each case indicates depth while the horizontal scale is percent by volume to show relative amounts of soil components. The alternately banded scale to the right of each profile delineates horizons of textural classes and structural differentiations within the soil profile. This and other information will be added in subsequent figures which will follow the same basic format of Figure 3. The heavy black line separates solid matter from pore space; within the solid fraction, the darkened area represents organic matter. Further distinctions of importance in waste application are made in the figures which follow on the basis of texture, structure, permeability, available water capacity, and cation exchange capacity.

Soil Texture Describes Mineral Particles

Soil texture refers to the coarseness or fineness of the individual mineral particles. Various systems are used to categorize mineral particle size: three systems are shown in Figure 4. Within the USDA scheme, which will be used in this module, soils are given textural class names based on the relative amounts of sand, silt, and clay in the surface layer. These basic textural classes are listed in Table 1 along with alternate terms commonly encountered in soil descriptions. By definition, sandy soils are those in which sand makes up 70% or more of the material by weight. A clayey soil must contain at least 35% clay. Between these extremes, loamy soils contain variable mixtures of sand, silt, and clay.

Textural characteristics for the three soil profiles previously introduced are shown in Figure 5. Note that the textural class name assigned on the basis of surface texture does not necessarily reflect conditions deeper in the profile. Textural variability along with structure is particularly important in determining water transmission rates.

Soils are given a textural class according to the relative amounts of sand, silt, and clay in the surface layer.

Soil Structure Describes Organization of Individual Particles

Soil structure refers to the organization of individual particles into clumps or aggregates. Sandy soils tend to be relatively structureless, particularly below the surface layer. As the percent of

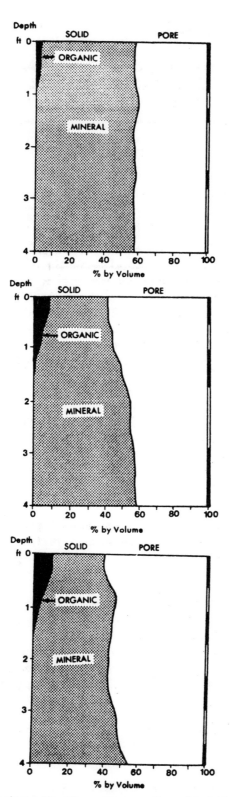

Figure 3. Profile diagrams for three soils with varying proportions of individual components. These soils, from top to bottom, represent conditions generally suitable for rapid infiltration, irrigation, and overland flow wastewater application systems, respectively.

SYSTEMS FOR CATEGORIZING MINERAL PARTICLE SIZE

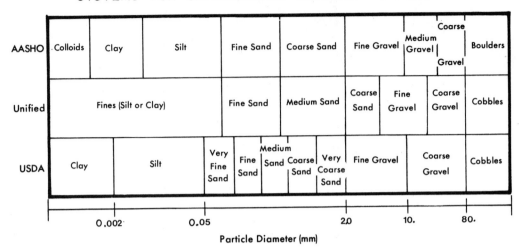

Figure 4. Three common systems for categorizing mineral particle sizes in soil according to the American Association of State Highway Officials (AASHO), the U.S. Army Corps of Engineers (Unified), and the U.S. Department of Agriculture (USDA).

silt and clay increases, however, particle aggregation occurs, forming units that range from weak to stable, small to large, and simple to complex. The formation of stable aggregates is strongly favored by increasing amounts of organic matter. Common structural types are illustrated in Figure 6.

Soil structure is determined by the degree of aggregation of individual particles.

Table 1.   Soil Textural Classes and General Terminology Used in Soil Descriptions. (After Soil Survey Staff, 1971)

General Terms		Basic Soil Textural
Common Names	Texture	Class Names
Sandy soils	Coarse	Sandy Loamy sand
Loamy soils	Moderately coarse	Sandy loam Fine sandy loam
	Medium	Very fine sandy loam Loam Silt loam Silt
	Moderately fine	Clay loam Sandy clay loam Silty clay loam
Clayey soils	Fine	Sandy clay Silty clay Clay

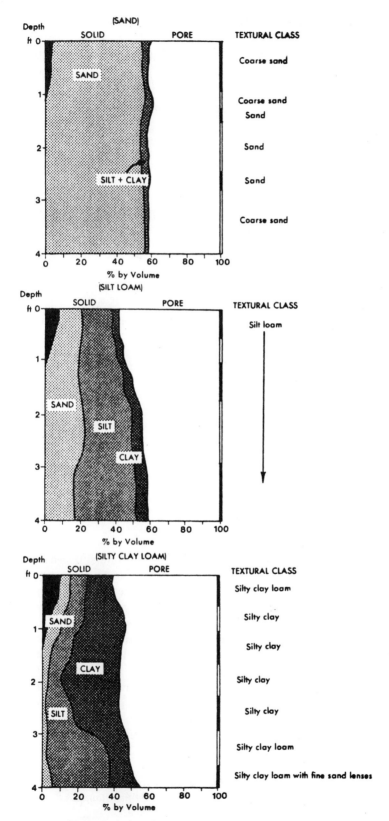

Figure 5. Soil profile diagrams showing textural variability.

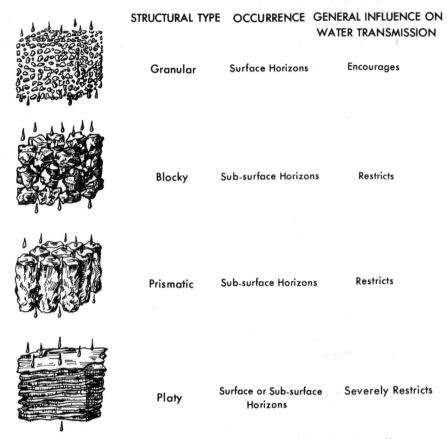

	STRUCTURAL TYPE	OCCURRENCE	GENERAL INFLUENCE ON WATER TRANSMISSION
	Granular	Surface Horizons	Encourages
	Blocky	Sub-surface Horizons	Restricts
	Prismatic	Sub-surface Horizons	Restricts
	Platy	Surface or Sub-surface Horizons	Severely Restricts

Figure 6. Common soil structural types vary in appearance, occurrence, and in their effect on water transmission through the soil. From Donahue, R. L., Shickluna, L. S., and Robertson. Soils: An Introduction to Soils and Plant Growth, 3rd ed., © 1971, p. 43. Reprinted by permission of Prentice-Hall, Inc., Englewood Cliffs, New Jersey.

A soil profile may be dominated by a single kind of structure although usually a number of different types are encountered with depth depending on texture and organic matter content. Figure 7 indicates the structural variability occurring in the three profile diagrams.

Note the occurrence of granular structure in the surface layers of all three profiles. Granular aggregates result from the presence of organic matter (humus). This kind of structure is highly desirable, particularly in loamy and clayey soils where it improves the air and water transmission capabilities. Granular structure, more than any other type, can be maintained or destroyed by management practices. Blocky and prismatic aggregates generally occur well below the surface and are less affected by management practices. However, both of these structural units are affected by moisture. Depending on the type of clay present, the aggregates may swell upon wetting, forming a tight and nearly impermeable mass. On the other hand, upon drying, shrinkage cracks between the individual aggregates may allow rapid downward movement of water.

Granular aggregates, which are desirable for waste treatment sites, result from the presence of organic matter. Granular structure can be maintained or destroyed by management of the site.

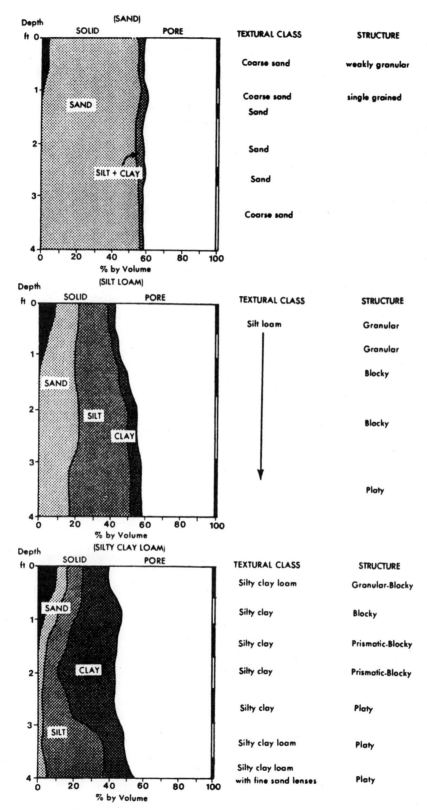

Figure 7. Soil profile diagrams indicating structural variability.

Permeability Describes Transmission of Air and Water Through Soil

Permeability, a property determined by soil pore space, refers to the ease with which water and air are transmitted through the soil. Conditions which favor the transmission of water, however, will generally also favor the movement of air unless the soil is saturated (all pores filled with water). In this section we will therefore concentrate on permeability to water.

The size of the pores in the soil determines permeability, the ease with which water and air are transmitted through the soil.

Permeability may be quantified in terms of the rate of water movement through a unit cross section of saturated soil in unit time and is commonly expressed in inches/hour. The cooperative Soil Survey of the Soil Conservation Service has defined permeability classes for use in describing and interpreting soils. These classes are listed in Table 2.

Although exceptions do exist, fine textured soils generally possess slow or very slow permeability while values for coarse textured soils range from moderately rapid to very rapid. A medium textured soil such as a loam or silt loam tends to have moderately slow permeability. Referring to Figure 7, however, we can see that the coarse sand has the least total pore space while the finer textured silty clay loam shows the greatest. The reason for this seeming paradox is that permeability is more a function of pore size than total pore space.

The finer the texture of the soil the slower the permeability tends to be. Coarse textured soils have moderately rapid to very rapid permeability.

Individual pores vary in size from a few microns to several millimeters in diameter. For convenience, pores are often simply divided into macropores, and micro- or capillary pores. Macropores, by definition, transmit water readily in saturated soils in response to gravity. In contrast, micropores retain water against gravitational force.

In saturated soil, macropores transmit water readily in response to gravity; micropores retain water against gravity.

In Figure 8, the macropore-micropore distinction has been indicated on each of the three profiles along with permeability estimates. The coarse sand showing the least total pore space is dominated by macropores and thus shows the highest overall permeability. Conversely, the silty

Table 2.   Permeability Classes for Saturated Soil.

Soil Permeability (in./hr)	Class
Less than 0.06	very slow
0.06 to 0.2	slow
0.2 to 0.6	moderately slow
0.6 to 2.0	moderate
2.0 to 6.0	moderately rapid
6.0 to 20	rapid
More than 20	very rapid

Source: USDA, Soil Conservation Service, 1971.

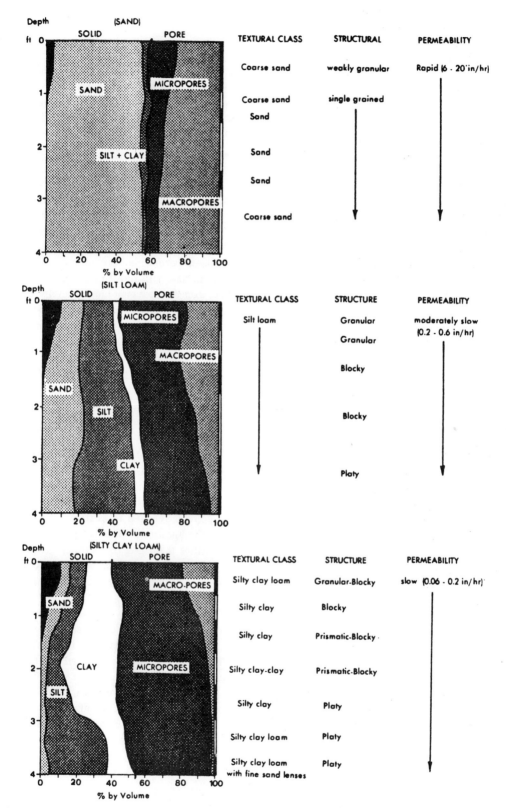

Figure 8. Soil profile diagrams depicting variability in the proportion of macropore and micropore space and overall permeability.

clay loam, with the highest total pore space, has the least amount of macropores and thus the lowest overall permeability. Note the variability in macropore space with depth. Macropore space and thus permeability are clearly related to the texture and structure of individual soil layers.

Infiltration Describes Water's Rate of Entry Into Soil

Closely related to permeability is the infiltration rate, defined as the rate at which water enters the soil surface. Infiltration rate, expressed in inches/hour, is influenced by both permeability and the moisture content of the soil. In an initially dry soil with much of the pore space filled with air, applied water enters the soil, displacing air and gradually filling the pore space. The infiltration rate, however, decreases with continued application, approaching a constant. At saturation, the constant equals the permeability of the least permeable horizon or soil layer in the profile. Continued application in excess of the limiting rate will result in surface ponding and run-off. An exception often occurs on slopes where excess water may move laterally along the face of the least permeable layer. In such cases, water will likely emerge at the slope base some distance from the original point of application. Infiltration rate thus depends on permeability within the profile, and on topography.

Infiltration rate depends on permeability, moisture content of the soil, and topography.

Available Water Capacity Affects Behavior of Applied Wastewater

Yet another property of the soil pore space, the available water capacity, affects the behavior of applied wastewater. To illustrate this property, consider a soil that is completely saturated. If no further rainfall or wastewater addition occurs, the macropore space will drain in response to gravity within approximately 48 hours. The micropores, however, will remain essentially filled with water. The moisture content of the soil at this point is referred to as field capacity. A portion of this moisture is extractable by plant roots while another portion is held too tightly for plant use. The dividing point between these two entities is termed the permanent wilting point. Available water capacity (AWC), expressed as inches of water per some unit of depth, is defined as that amount of water which is held in the soil between field capacity and the permanent wilting point.

Available water capacity varies with the amount of micropore space which in turn depends on texture, structure, and organic matter (Figure 9). The coarse sand has the smallest AWC; most of the micropore space and thus most of the available water in the profile is in the surface layer due to the organic matter content there. The silt loam profile, with a much greater micropore space, has a much higher AWC. However, a further increase in micropore space in the silty clay loam produces little increase in AWC. This is due to a concommitant increase in the amount of unavailable water. A still finer textured soil, for example, a clay, might even show a decrease in available water. Figure 10 shows the general relationship between micropore space and AWC over a wide textural range.

Available water capacity (AWC) refers to the micropore water which plant roots can extract from the soil.

The amount of available moisture in a soil is obviously important for plant growth, and it is also important in the performance of wastewater application systems. The reaction and

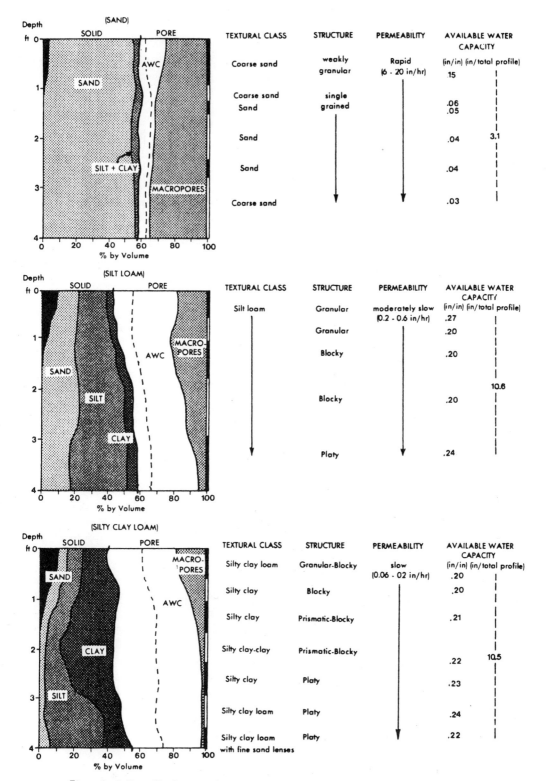

Figure 9. Soil profile diagrams showing variability in the available water capacity (AWC).

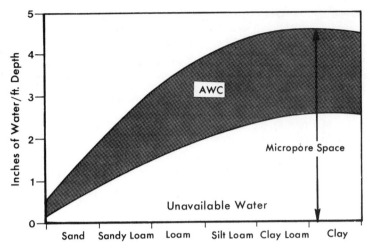

Figure 10. General relationship between micropore space, available water capacity, and textural class (adapted from Brady, 1974).

thus "treatment" of many waste constituents in the water depends on residence time in the soil. Since the available water capacity essentially measures the water storage capability of a soil, it reflects the amount of wastewater that can be applied to a dry soil without moving directly to the groundwater. Absorption of water by plants continuously depletes this store of available water during the growing season, and thus allows for the retention of subsequent additions, whether wastewater or natural rainfall. The amount of depletion varies with climate and the type of vegetation. Vegetation aspects are discussed more fully in Module I-5, "Vegetative Cover"; climatic factors are discussed in Module II-6, "Climate and Wastewater Storage," and Module I-6, "Site Evaluation."

> *Available Water Capacity of soil is essentially its water storage capability. A high AWC increases residence time of waste constituents in soil, thus promoting treatment of wastes.*

Cation Exchange Capacity Indicates Capacity for Reactions Between Charged Pollutants and Soil Particles

Up to this point our principal concern has been those properties of soil which determine water transmission and retention. Moving with the water, however, are other waste constituents, particularly dissolved ions and compounds. Somewhat like water, these constituents are alternately retained and transmitted through the soil. The clay and humus fractions of soil are primarily responsible for their retention. Both clay and humus exist in the colloidal state, characterized by an extremely small size (≤ 0.002 mm) and the presence of an electrical charge. The significance of the charge is that oppositely charged ions or compounds are attracted and held on the colloidal surfaces. The small size vastly increases the surface area available for such interaction. For example, a coarse sand has a surface area of perhaps 10–50 cm^2/g; in contrast, a clayey soil may exhibit a surface area in excess of $10,000$ cm^2/g (Cassel and Vasey, 1974).

> *Wastes in the form of dissolved ions and compounds are retained and transmitted through soil depending on the Cation Exchange Capacity (CEC).*

The net charge on colloidal particles in most soils is overwhelmingly negative. Consequently, the ions attracted are positively charged (cations) such as ammonium, calcium, magnesium, potassium, and sodium. Cation exchange capacity (CEC) is a measure of the ability of a soil to retain cations. Indirectly, however, CEC serves as a rough index of all reactions which occur between charged pollutants and colloidal surfaces. In general, the greater the CEC of a particular soil, the greater the potential for effective waste treatment.

> *CEC is a rough index of all reactions between charged pollutants and extremely small, charged soil fractions called colloids.*

Cation exchange capacity, expressed in milliequivalents per 100 grams (g) of soil or colloid (meq/100 g) varies markedly with the organic matter content and the amount and type of clay present. For a sample of pure humus, CEC averages about 200 meq/100 g, whereas for vermiculite, montmorillonite, chlorite, kaolinite, and hydrous oxide clays, average values are 150, 100, 30, 8, and 4 meq/100 g, respectively (Brady, 1974).

Because of its dependence on clay and humus content, CEC can be expected to vary both within and among soil profiles. Figure 11 indicates CEC variation in each of the three profiles. Considering all of the properties discussed thus far, we find that soils with the highest water transmission capabilities have the lowest potential for effective waste treatment as indicated by CEC. In contrast, soils most likely to remove waste constituents can accept but limited hydraulic loads. Thus "rapid infiltration" systems generally require some sacrifice, often large, in chemical removal or treatment potential. "Overland flow" systems, although usually involving soils with high CEC values, cannot make full use of this treatment potential due to limited contact with the soil mass below the immediate surface. "Irrigation" systems are intermediate with perhaps the optimum mix of water transmission and waste treatment properties.

> *Soils with a high CEC have a high potential for effective waste treatment because more reactions occur between soil and waste constituents.*

TREATMENT MECHANISMS AND LOADING LIMITATIONS CONTROL POLLUTANTS

The use of the soil as a treatment medium may be a new concept to some since historical usage has stressed land application for waste "disposal." Nothing, however, is actually disposed of. Instead, some materials pass through the soil and into the groundwater, some are utilized by growing plants, while others are retained almost indefinitely within the soil. Proper design of land application facilities must relate the fate of pollutants to the properties of soil with which they may interact and minimize the fraction of contaminants passing through to groundwater. Those people with experience in the design of wastewater treatment systems have a broad knowledge of processes which have been developed to control specific pollutants. There are several separate unit processes that can be adopted for removal of SS, TDS, BOD_5, N, P, or potentially toxic elements and an almost unlimited combination of these which ultimately comprise the treatment system. For the more common processes, the design engineer can quickly relate the quantity of a pollutant to the capacity of the process, the rate of reaction, the quantities of materials involved, and the efficiencies. An attempt has been made to summarize some of this material in Module I-3, "Waste Characteristics," and Module I-4, "Treatment Systems, Effluent Qualities and Costs." Many of the same pollutant control mechanisms are operative in soils, but few people can put them into context with conventional processes.

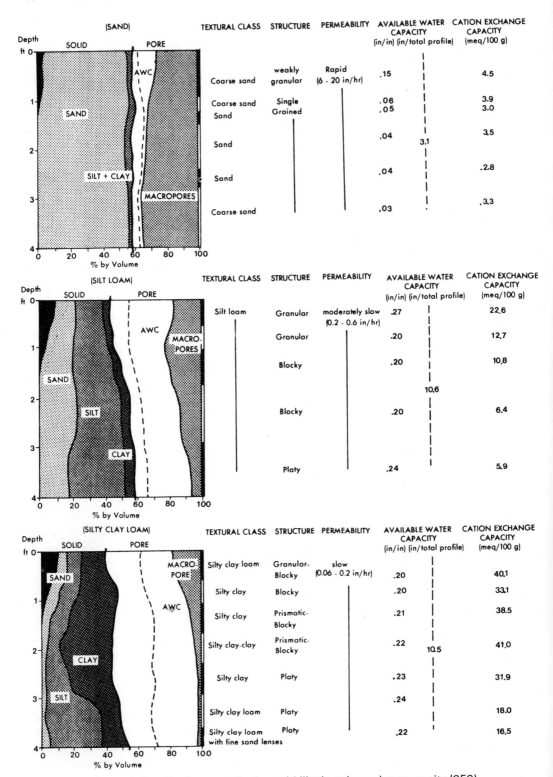

Figure 11. Soil profile diagrams indicating variability in cation exchange capacity (CEC).

Wastes are not "disposed of" in land treatment, but rather they are utilized by plants, retained in the soil, or pass through the soil to the groundwater.

Waste treatment mechanisms that occur in soils can conveniently be categorized as physical, chemical, and biological. Within each category, various processes act to remove or alter specific waste constituents.

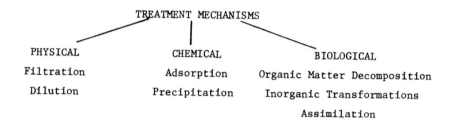

Filtration Acts as Physical Treatment Mechanism; Dilution Alters Waste Concentrations

As wastewater moves into and through soil pores, suspended solids are removed by mechanical filtration. The actual depth at which removal occurs varies with the size of suspended particles, soil texture, and the rate of application. The larger the hydraulic loading rate and the coarser the soil, the greater the distance required. However, when loading rates are such that much of the applied water is held in the soil, additional removal can occur as suspended materials settle out or adhere to the surfaces of soil particles.

> *The larger the hydraulic loading rate and the coarser the soil, the greater distance is required to filter out suspended solids from wastewater.*

Some organic particles and certain organisms such as worms and protozoa are large enough so that removal by simple blockage is likely. Both bacteria and viruses, however, are small enough so that based on size alone, movement through the pores of many soils could be expected (Burge, 1974). Nevertheless, in the limited studies reported to date, it appears that most wastewater pathogens are removed in the upper few feet of all but the very coarse textured soils. Filtration by the soil and, in some cases, by an additional organic mat formed in the top 0.2 inch of soil is the primary means of retaining bacteria in the soil (Metcalf and Eddy, 1977). Adsorption to soil particles is the basic virus retention mechanism. Module II-5, "Pathogens" covers this subject in further detail.

> • *Filtration is the primary means of retaining bacteria in the soil, preventing them from moving to the groundwater. Virus removal is by adsorption.*

Applied wastewater may also be diluted either upon entering the groundwater or by augmentation in the soil with natural rainfall or snowmelt. The dilution process is furthered by chemical and biological removal of dissolved waste constituents. The reverse of dilution—concentration—may also occur, particularly in arid or semiarid climates where evaporation losses are high.

Physical Mechanisms of Waste Removal are Limited

Suspended materials can, at times, clog soil pores and thereby severely reduce the infiltration rate. The possibility of such clogging may lead to strict requirements for pretreatment removal of suspended solids (SS). With the limited information available, however, it appears likely that other waste constituents such as nitrogen and toxic elements will limit waste applications in most cases before any significant negative effects of suspended solids are encountered.

Useful information on physical clogging of soils can be obtained from the results of sand filtration in conventional sewage treatment systems (Metcalf and Eddy, 1972). Sand filters effectively trap fine suspended solids from secondary effluents in the first few inches of filter depth. Loadings of SS may reach values equivalent to 62,500 pounds SS/acre-day (at 6 gpm/ft^2 application of 20 mg/l SS). With such loading, however, there is generally a rapid decrease in hydraulic conductivity over a period of 24 hours or less. Application periods must then be followed by a backwash (reversing flow direction) to remove the clogging particles. In contrast, land application systems can recover from clogging through natural decomposition of the suspended solids during non-application or resting periods. Furthermore, common SS loadings to land are far less than those used in conventional sand filtration processes. Two inches of effluent per week applied to the land would add less than 5,000 pounds SS/acre-yr.

/ Clogging of suspended solids at land application sites is avoided through the natural decomposition of the solids during periods of nonapplication.

A closer approximation of a design SS loading can be obtained from studies of septic tank systems (McGauhey *et al.*, 1966; Laak, 1970). A general rule of thumb is that the maximum continuous application rate for septic tank effluent on soil is about 5% of the percolation rate

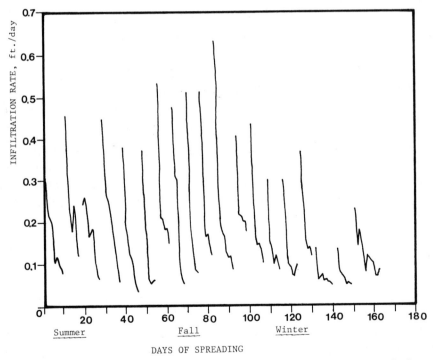

Figure 12. Recovery of infiltration rates in a Yolo loam soil after intermittent applications of primary sewage effluent (after McGauhey, *et al.*, 1966).

as measured with clean water. This may well be too conservative for systems which allow for drying and recovery. Figure 12 illustrates the recovery capability of a soil when allowed to rest in an aerobic state after successive periods of flooding with septic tank effluent. Data from Laak (1970) indicate that for a variety of soils, wastewater applications of up to 3 in./day, that is, about 200 pounds SS/acre-day, will not cause significant clogging. When resting periods of 2-5 days are allowed between applications, this value could probably be raised to about 600 pounds SS/acre-day. From these data, it appears that application scheduling and relatively simple pretreatment such as screening or primary sedimentation should be adequate to avoid excessive clogging.

Excessive clogging of the land treatment site can be avoided by simple pretreatment of wastes and alternating application with rest periods.

Wastes are Altered Through Adsorption and Precipitation

Chemical reactions among dissolved ions or compounds and interactions with the soil solid phase alter the mobility of waste constituents. Some dissolved constituents are retained within the profile indefinitely while the movement of others is only temporarily restricted or unaffected.

Two chemical processes, adsorption and precipitation, account for most of the retention. Adsorption, as a loosely applied term, refers to the net effect of interactions between dissolved ions or compounds and the surfaces of clay and humus particles. In contrast, precipitation is the formation of an insoluble or slowly soluble product from constituents that were originally in solution.

Dissolved ions or compounds in wastewater are retained in soil primarily through adsorption and chemical precipitation.

Ion exchange is one type of adsorption process. A distinction is made between anion exchange (involving negatively charged ions or compounds) and cation exchange (involving positively charged ions or compounds). Under acid conditions, that is pH less than 5, some soils have the ability to hold small amounts of anions such as nitrate, sulfate, and phosphate in an exchangeable form. The hydrous oxide clays of iron and aluminum are most responsible for anion exchange properties. Anion exchange, however, is of very minor importance in land application systems. Phosphorus is the only anion appreciably retained in soils, though the primary mechanism is not anion exchange.

The predominant ion exchange reactions in most U.S. soils involve cations. The magnitude of cation exchange properties in soil is measurable by the cation exchange capacity (CEC), a term introduced in a previous section. Cation exchange is a function of both the relative intensity of attraction between ions and colloidal solids, and of the relative concentration of exchangeable ions present in the soil solution.

Ion exchange reactions in most U.S. soils involve cations, positively charged ions or compounds.

The following series shows various cations in decreasing order of intensity of attraction between the ion and soil colloids:

$$Al^{+3} \quad > \quad H^{+1} \quad > \quad Ca^{+2} \quad > \quad Mg^{+2} \quad > \quad K^{+1} \quad > \quad NH_4^{+1} \quad > \quad Na^{+1}$$

(Aluminum)   (Hydrogen)   (Calcium)   (Magnesium)   (Potassium)   (Ammonium)   (Sodium)

As an illustration, consider a closed system consisting of a solid colloidal phase and a solution phase (Figure 13a). Within the system assume equivalent amounts of calcium and sodium, distributed between the two phases. At any given instant, some cations are released into solution from the solid phase and others move to replace them. The system is said to be in dynamic equilibrium when these random exchanges occur without altering the overall proportion of the two cations in solution or on the solid phase. Because of the greater intensity of attraction between calcium and the colloidal surfaces, Ca^{+2} will dominate the charge sites at equilibrium.

Assume now that there is an influx of sodium into the system (Figure 13b). Due to the much greater concentration of Na^{+1} in solution, random exchanges in the solid phase now favor the replacement of Ca^{+2}, despite its greater intensity of attraction. Therefore, at equilibrium, Na^{+1} will likely occupy the greater number of charge sites. Similarly, in wastewater treatment systems, the retention of dissolved cations depends largely on their concentration in the solution entering the soil.

The reaction in which sodium replaces some other cation is particularly important. A dominance of sodium on the soil colloids weakens the stability of soil aggregates causing dispersion and swelling. This in turn decreases the macropore space and thus sharply reduces permeability.

Exchange reactions involving ammonium (NH_4^{+1}) are also of special interest, since they offer one means to retain nitrogen at least temporarily. Such retention allows time for biological processes to transform ammonium to nitrate, (NO_3^{-1}), a highly mobile anion.

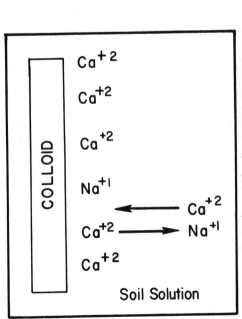
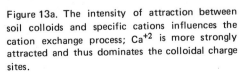
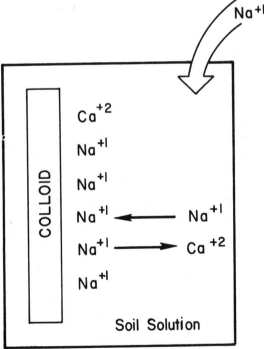

Figure 13a. The intensity of attraction between soil colloids and specific cations influences the cation exchange process; Ca^{+2} is more strongly attracted and thus dominates the colloidal charge sites.

Figure 13b. Concentration can offset the effect of intensity of attraction; the greater concentration of Na^{+1} enables it to dominate the colloidal charge sites.

In wastewater treatment systems the retention of dissolved cations depends largely on their concentration in the solution entering the soil. Large concentrations will overcome a higher degree of attraction of other cations toward the soil matrix.

It must be emphasized that by definition exchangeable cations are replaceable. Thus, when sodium, ammonium, or any other cation is removed from wastewater via cation exchange, there must be a simultaneous release of some other cations into solution. The net effect is therefore some readjustment in the composition of the exchange and solution phases, but the total soluble salt concentration does not change appreciably.

Exchangeable cations are replaceable and when any cation is removed from wastewater via cation exchange, there must be a simultaneous release of some other cations into solution.

Soils have a variable capacity to retain certain cations and anions so tightly that they are not exchangeable, a process termed specific adsorption. Like ion exchange, specific adsorption occurs between ions or compounds in solution and the solid colloidal phase. For example, orthophosphate anions ($H_2PO_4^{-1}$, HPO_4^{-2}) react on the surfaces of iron- and aluminum-containing clays. Initially, this phosphate may be exchangeable with other anions but with time it becomes more and more tightly bound. One explanation for this so-called reversion is that the phosphate becomes incorporated into the soil solid phase as an impurity (Brady, 1974).

Specific adsorption occurs when soils retain certain cations and anions so tightly that they are not exchangeable. Heavy metal cations such as zinc, copper, nickel, cadmium, and lead can be incorporated into the soil in a nonexchangeable form.

Many of the heavy metal cations such as zinc, copper, nickel, cadmium, mercury, lead, and chromium are present in wastewaters at concentrations too low to be appreciably affected by cation exchange reactions. However, these cations seem to be incorporated into the soil solid phase in a non-exchangeable form. The actual reversion mechanisms remain poorly understood. CEC is the most important soil parameter for immobilizing the metal constituents in sludge. The concentrations of these ions is much higher in sludge than wastewater, which enables interaction with soil CEC to proceed more readily.

The effectiveness of soil in the removal of waste constituents either by ion exchange or specific adsorption is dependent upon contact between dissolved substances and the appropriate colloidal phases. Contact depends largely on the degree to which a soil is uniformly wetted. Initially, only the external surfaces of aggregates are in direct contact with wastewater. Over the longer term, internal surfaces tend to equilibrate with constituents held on external surfaces. Thus, the length of time that the water remains in the soil in no small way affects the amount of waste constituents that can be removed from the water. This consideration is important in determining application rates and also the frequency of rest periods. Over extended periods, the adsorption capability may be rejuvenated through reversion processes.

The more uniformly the soil is wetted the more effective are ion exchange and specific adsorption mechanisms.

The chemical mechanisms discussed thus far have involved the interaction of dissolved constituents and the solid colloidal phase in the soil. Many ion species react within the solution phase itself, resulting in the formation of insoluble or slowly soluble precipitates. The point at which chemical precipitation occurs depends on the concentration of the participating ions as defined by their solubility product constant (K_{sp}). The solubility product constant is obtained by multiplying together the concentration of reactants (moles/1) in a saturated solution.

For example, the K_{sp} value for calcium sulfate ($CaSO_4$) is 2.4×10^{-5}. This means that whenever the concentration of the sulfate ion times the concentration of the calcium ion exceeds 2.4×10^{-5}, $CaSO_4$ will precipitate out of solution. Suppose the sulfate concentration in applied wastewater was 125 mg/1 (1.3×10^{-3} moles/1). According to the solubility product, the concentration of calcium in solution cannot exceed 750 mg/1 (1.85×10^{-2} moles/1). If, after entering the soil, evaporation caused the wastewater to become more concentrated, the product of Ca^{+2} and SO_4^{-2} would exceed the K_{sp} value and the reaction below would proceed to the right, forming insoluble $CaSO_4$.

$$Ca^{+2} + SO_4^{-2} \rightleftarrows CaSO_4 \downarrow$$

The addition of rainwater and/or removal of reactants by ion exchange, specific adsorption or other means would tend to dilute the solution driving the above reaction to the left. Under such conditions, solid phase $CaSO_4$ dissolves.

Many types of ions react within the solution phase itself, forming insoluble or slowly soluble precipitates.

In general, the concentration of dissolved constituents in the soil solution cannot exceed the concentration defined by their solubility product constant. However, two notable exceptions exist. The first occurs in cases where the formation of a precipitate proceeds very slowly. For example, although varasite [$Al(H_2PO_4) (OH)_2$] is highly insoluble in soil ($K_{sp} = 3 \times 10^{-31}$), its formation may take weeks or even months. This reaction is one of many which account for the long-term retention of phosphorus in soils. The second exception is due to formation of organic complexes (chelates). As an example, certain soluble organic compounds can incorporate heavy metal cations into their structure. The cations thus remain in solution but are not subject to chemical precipitation reactions. In effect, the formation of complexes reduces the soil's ability to retain heavy metals through precipitation reactions.

The formation of organic complexes or chelates reduces the soil's ability to retain heavy metals through precipitation reactions.

Chemical Reactions are Limited in Removal of Waste Constituents

Two general types of waste constituents, potentially toxic elements and the macronutrients phosphorus and nitrogen, are at least partially controlled by chemical mechanisms in the soil. These are discussed in detail in Module II-4, "Potentially Toxic Elements," Module II-1, "Nitrogen Considerations," and Module II-2 "Phosphorus Considerations." A brief description of soil capacities to "treat" these potential pollutants is presented here to enable approximation of soil loading limitations.

Phosphorus, nitrogen and potentially toxic elements are partially controlled by chemical mechanisms in soil.

Many of the potentially toxic elements such as zinc (Zn), and nickel (Ni) are positively charged and their retention in soil is related to the cation exchange capacity. Much research has been done in recent years with the intent of establishing application guidelines for heavy metals and other potentially toxic elements. Most attention has been focused on Zn, Cu, and Ni, which can be phytotoxic (toxic to plants) and Cd, which can accumulate in plants to levels toxic to animals consuming certain plant parts. Application levels have been proposed according to the relative toxicity of the metals, soil texture, organic matter, and CEC. Environmental Protection Agency recommendations published in 1977 include the following guidelines (Table 3) for cumulative site lifetime loadings to private agricultural land. It is felt that cropland can accept these loadings, assuming good pH and other management control, with no restrictions on its productivity in the free market. The EPA recommendations suggest that higher application rates may be acceptable on publicly-owned land application sites employing adequate monitoring safeguards.

Several years ago, the focus on phosphorus removal from wastewater caused renewed interest in land application for this purpose. Agricultural experience had already shown that efficient phosphorus retention occurred in soils, but limitations of this removal capacity were not clear. Current knowledge indicates that phosphorus removal to a concentration of 0.05 mg/1 can be achieved over site lifetimes of 20 years or more at annual loading rates of at least 150 pounds P/acre-yr, and perhaps twice this amount. Only the high-rate rapid infiltration systems exceed this rate of loading. However, efficient removal can only be achieved where intimate contact between wastewater and the soil is achieved. High efficiency P removal should therefore not be expected in overland flow systems.

Efficient removal of phosphorus can only be achieved where intimate contact between the soil and wastewater is achieved, making overland flow systems less effective.

As will be seen throughout these modules, nitrogen loading constitutes a major limiting factor for most land application systems. For this reason, it is important that the reader understand the many aspects of the nitrogen cycle presented in Module II-1, "Nitrogen Considerations." The chemical mechanism of most significance to nitrogen is the reaction of positively charged ammonium ions with the soil cation exchange complex. For a soil with a CEC of 15 meq/100 g, about 100 pounds of ammonium-nitrogen per acre can be retained in this way before saturation is reached (Lance, 1972). In comparison, a 2-inch application of unnitrified effluent would commonly add no more than about 16 lb/acre of ammonium-nitrogen. Ammonium retention is

Table 3.   Maximum Sludge Metal Applications for Privately Owned Farmland.

		Soil CEC (meq/100g)		
	Metal	<5	5–15	>15
Maximum metal addition (kg/ha)	Pb	500	1,000	2,000
	Zn	250	500	1,000
	Cu	125	250	500
	Ni	50	100	200
	Cd	5	10	20

From Dowdy, R. H., R. E. Larson and E. Epstein, © 1976. Sewage sludge and effluent use in agriculture, pp. 138–153. *In Land Application of Waste Materials.* Soil Conservation Society of America, Ankeny, Iowa; 313p.

a useful control mechanism on a short-term basis, but is of little long-term value since the ammonium ion is biologically converted to nitrate, a readily leached form of nitrogen.

> *Nitrogen loading is a major limiting factor in most land application systems; the most important chemical mechanism for nitrogen removal is the reaction of positively charged ammonium ions with the soil cation exchange complex.*

As noted earlier, the accumulation of sodium on the soil exchange complex can lead to a degradation of soil structure and thus a sharp reduction in infiltration and permeability rates. The sodium limitation of a wastewater is often expressed in terms of the sodium adsorption ratio (SAR). The SAR is defined as:

$$SAR = \frac{[Na^{+1}]}{\left(\frac{[Ca^{+2}] + [Mg^{+2}]}{2}\right)^{0.5}}$$

where the concentrations of sodium, calcium, and magnesium are expressed in milliequivalents per liter (meq/l).

[*Note*] $\left(\frac{mg\,Na^{+1}/l}{22.99}\right) = meq\,Na^{+1}/l;$ $\left(\frac{mg\,Ca^{+2}/l}{20.04}\right) = meq\,Ca^{+2}/l;$

$$\left(\frac{mg\,Mg^{+2}/l}{12.15}\right) = meq\,Mg^{+2}/l.$$

As a general rule, the SAR of applied wastewater should not exceed 10 (U.S. Salinity Laboratory Staff, 1953).

Biological Mechanisms Alter Waste Constituents in Stages

Organisms alter waste constituents through organic matter decomposition, inorganic transformations, and nutrient assimilation. Such biological "treatment" processes are largely restricted to the upper few feet of soil, sometimes termed the biologically active zone or rooting zone.

> *Biological treatment of wastewater occurs primarily in the upper few feet of soil called the rooting zone.*

The ability of soil organisms to decompose organic compounds is a function of their population complexity. Soils normally contain a wide diversity of native organisms including many kinds of bacteria, fungi, actinomycetes, protozoa, worms, and insects along with higher plants and animals. Applied wastes may contain additional organisms which are few or absent in untreated soils. The diversity of organisms enhances the capability of the soil to degrade a wide variety of organic substances.

> *The diversity of organisms in wastewater enhances the soil's ability to degrade a wide variety of organic substances.*

Decomposition of newly added organic material may be envisioned as taking place in three general steps as shown in Figure 14. In general, this is the same sequence of reactions that takes place in a biological waste treatment plant. Initially, organisms digest the more easily decomposed material, consuming oxygen and releasing carbon dioxide and water in the process. The

5-day biochemical oxygen demand (BOD_5) measures the amount of oxygen consumed in this stage. This pulse of activity can result in a rapid increase in organism numbers. In cases of extreme organic overloading, temporary clogging of the soil can result.

The five day biochemical oxygen demand measures the amount of oxygen consumed initially by organisms digesting the more easily decomposed material.

In the second stage, organism numbers decline as the easily decomposed organic fraction is exhausted. The resulting mass of dead microbial tissue along with other intermediate decay products provide substrate for new and remaining organisms. This material, along with more resistant compounds from the original addition, the so-called refractory organics, are partially degraded to a relatively stable end product, humus.

In the second stage of biological treatment, dead microbial tissue from organisms die off; intermediate decayed products and certain resistant compounds are partially degraded, forming humus.

The organism numbers ultimately decline to about the same level as before the addition of fresh organic material. This marks the final stage of organic matter breakdown during which the humus itself is slowly degraded by highly specialized organisms. In natural systems that receive localized or periodic additions of organic matter, these three stages may overlap with several processes occurring simultaneously.

In the final stage of biological treatment, humus is degraded by highly specialized organisms.

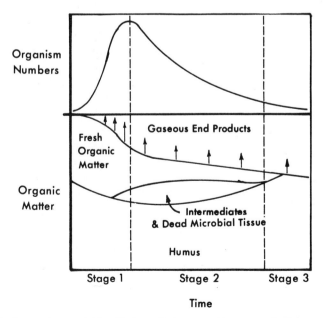

Figure 14. When fresh organic material is added to soil, decomposition occurs in three general stages (adapted from Brady, 1974).

The rate at which organic matter decomposition occurs and the exact nature of the intermediate and end products depends in part on the composition of the added organic material. Soil factors, however, exert considerable control as well. The presence or absence of oxygen, more than any other single factor, determines the rate and end products. The oxygen status of the soil is a function of soil porosity, and properties that favor rapid transmission of water also favor oxygen movement unless the soil is completely saturated. The presence of adequate oxygen gives rise to aerobic conditions while its lack results in anaerobic conditions. Decomposition proceeds in either case, but the rate and nature of products formed differ markedly (Figure 15).

The presence or absence of oxygen in soil largely determines the rate at which organic matter decomposes and the end products that are formed.

Under aerobic conditions, up to 60% of the organic carbon may be respired by organisms as carbon dioxide in the initial stage of decomposition. Much of the remaining carbon is incorporated into microbial cells and some of this is subsequently respired when the population declines. Anaerobic decomposition also produces some carbon dioxide along with methane (CH_4). However, the bulk of carbon, perhaps 70%, remains in partially decomposed intermediates such as organic acids and alcohols (Miller, 1973). Since relatively few organisms can degrade these products in the absence of oxygen, they accumulate. Methane, however, is one of the ultimate products if these intermediates are anaerobically decomposed.

Through organic matter decomposition, nitrogen, phosphorus, sulfur, and a host of other trace elements are converted from organic to inorganic forms, a process termed mineralization. The form and fate of many of these elements in the soil is determined by the oxygen status of the medium. For example, mineralized nitrogen first appears as ammonium (NH_4^{+1}). Under aerobic conditions, NH_4^{+1} is rapidly transformed by specific microbes (nitrifying organisms) into nitrate, a highly mobile anion which can easily be leached to groundwater. Under anaerobic conditions nitrate is not formed and so ammonium accumulates. By alternating aerobic and anaerobic conditions, nitrate may form and then be converted to nitrous oxide (N_2O) and/or molecular nitrogen (N_2), both gases. This latter transformation is termed denitrification. By a somewhat similar means, sulfate (SO_4^{-2}), a product of aerobic decomposition, is transformed to hydrogen sulfide gas (H_2S) under anaerobic conditions.

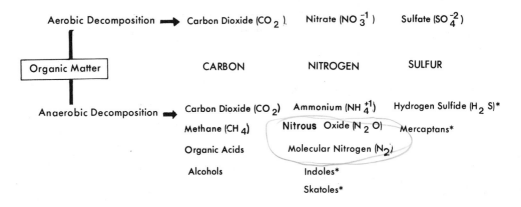

*Objectionable Odor

Figure 15. Products of aerobic and anaerobic decomposition of organic matter.

Many of the elements which are mineralized during organic matter decomposition and are then subject to inorganic transformations in the soil, may also be assimilated by plants. By definition, assimilation is the conversion of inorganic forms to organic forms within living tissue. Vegetation thus functions as a sink where waste nutrients, most notably nitrogen and phosphorus, can be effectively immobilized. When harvested, vegetation plays an integral part in the renovation or "treatment" of applied wastes. Other roles of vegetation along with specific nutrient uptake rates are discussed in Module I-5, "Vegetative Cover."

Limitations of Biological Mechanisms

Organic matter is continuously added to soils as plant residues and is continuously oxidized by organisms. As organic additions increase, soil respiration also increases until a maximum rate of oxidation is reached. Continued increases beyond this point result in the accumulation of organic materials. Although the rate of organic carbon oxidation in soils is known to be high, limitations for wastewater and sludge additions are not well established. Jewell (1976) reported that a soil system, previously acclimated to highly organic wastewater from a vegetable processing facility, could degrade organics at a rate exceeding 5,000 lb/acre-day. In light of these results, it appears likely that other factors such as soil permeability and nitrogen control will limit waste application rates long before maximum organic loading capacities are reached.

Soil permeability and nitrogen content will limit waste application rates long before the maximum loading capacity for organics has been reached.

The capability of soil organisms to manipulate nitrogen additions therefore takes on added importance. Considerable attention has been focused on the conversion of nitrate to gaseous forms under anaerobic conditions. No existing system receiving domestic sewage, however, has been shown to remove more than about 30% of the total nitrogen by this process. Specific site modifications, such as drainage and recycling high nitrate percolates, have been verified in experimental work but have yet to be proven economic or needed in full-scale application. For the present then, it appears that the most reliable method for nitrogen control is crop management and N removal by plant uptake. Reliance on cropping for nitrogen control will limit the total N application rate to about 100–500 lb/acre-yr depending on specific crops and management techniques.

No land treatment site has yet been able to remove more than 30% of the applied nitrogen by converting nitrate to gaseous forms under anaerobic conditions. The main method for nitrogen removal is still crop management and plant uptake.

Nitrogen is Major Limiting Factor in Operation of Site

Table 4 summarizes limitations for waste additions to soil. There are always exceptions to general rules, however, and these data are useful only in estimating gross land area requirements to determine the feasibility of adopting a land application alternative. Specific site conditions will often modify all of these values. For further discussion of site selection, see Module I-6, "Site Evaluation."

A representation of computed land area requirements based on various factors is shown in Figure 16. Based on the relative land areas required, nitrogen is most often the controlling design parameter. When wastes are applied over the area required for nitrogen, an added degree

Table 4.   Summary of General Limitations for Waste Application to Soils.

Constituent	Limitation
Organics	
BOD$_5$	4,000 lb/acre per application period[a]
SS	600 lb/acre per application period[a]
Nutrients	
P	150–300 lb/acre-yr
Total N	100–500 lb/acre-yr
Toxic materials:	
Zinc, copper, nickel, cadmium	Relate to soil cation exchange capacity[b]
Sodium	SAR < 10

[a]It is assumed that the waste application period is followed by a drying period of at least 3–5 days.
[b]See Table 3, page 25.

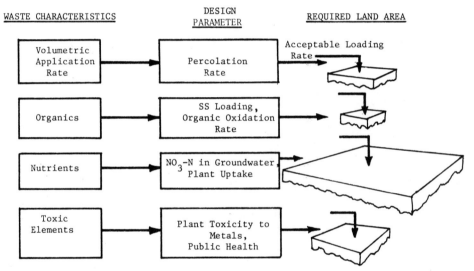

Figure 16. Example of relationships between waste constituents and limiting design parameters for land application systems.

of safety occurs in terms of the loading rates of other constituents. For example, if the nitrogen area requirement is fifteen times that for toxics, this reflects a fifteen-fold safety factor in the application area for toxics.

BIBLIOGRAPHY

Brady, N. C. 1974. The nature and properties of soils. 8th ed., Macmillan Publishing Co., Inc., New York. 639 p.

Burge, W. D. 1974. Pathogen considerations. pp. 37–50. *In* National Program Staff. Factors involved in land application of agricultural and municipal wastes. (DRAFT). ARS, USDA. Beltsville, Md. 200 p.

Cassel, D. K. and E. H. Vasey. 1974. How fertilizer moves in soils. Ext. Bull. No. 21, Coop. Ext. Serv. North Dakota State Univ., Fargo, N.D. 23 p.

Donahue, R. H., R. E. Shickluna, and L. S. Robertson. 1971. Soils, an introduction to soils and plant growth. 3rd. ed., Prentice-Hall, Inc., Englewood Cliffs, N.J. 587 p.

Dowdy, R. H., R. E. Larson, and E. Epstein. 1976. Sewage sludge and effluent use in agriculture. *In* Land application of waste materials. Soil Conservation Society of America, Ankeny, Iowa. pp. 138–153.

Jewell, W. J. 1976. Organic assimilation capacities of land treatment systems receiving vegetable processing wastewater. Presented at the 31st Annual Indus. Waste Conf., Purdue Univ., West Lafayette, Ind. May 6, 1976.

Jorling, T. C. 1977. Federal register. Vol. 42, No. 211. pp. 57420–57427. *Re.* Technical bulletin-Municipal sludge management: environmental factors. MCD-28 (EPA 430/9-77-004).

Laak, R. 1970. Influence of domestic wastewater pretreatment on soil clogging. *J. Water Pollut. Contr. Fed.*, 42:1495–1500.

Lance, J. C. 1972. Nitrogen removal by soil mechanisms. *J. Water Pollut. Contr. Fed.*, 44:1352–1361.

McGauhey, P. H., R. B. Krone, and J. H. Winneberger. 1966. Soil mantle as a wastewater treatment system. Univ. Cal., Berkeley. SERL Rep. No. 66–7. 120 p.

Metcalf and Eddy, Inc. 1972. Wastewater engineering. McGraw-Hill Book Co., New York. 782 p.

Metcalf and Eddy, Inc. 1977. Land treatment of municipal wastewater. U.S. EPA, U.S. Army Corps of Engineers, and U.S. Dept. Agric. EPA 625/1-77-008. ERIC-Technol. Transfer. Cincinnati, OH.

Miller, R. H. 1973. The soil as a biological filter. pp. 71–94. *In* Sopper, W. E. and L. T. Kardos. Recycling treated municipal wastewater and sludge through forest and cropland. Penn. State University Press, University Park, PA. 479 p.

Soil Conservation Service. Soil Survey Staff. 1971. Guide for interpreting engineering uses of soils. U.S. Dept. Agric. U.S. Govt. Print. Office, Washington, D.C. 87 p.

U.S. Salinity Laboratory Staff. 1953. Diagnosis and improvement of saline and alkali soils. USDA Handbook No. 60. U.S. Govt. Print. Office Washington, D.C. 160 p.

Module I-2

DESIGN PROCEDURES FOR LAND APPLICATION OF WASTE

SUMMARY

The purpose of this module is to develop a general procedure to evaluate the feasibility of land application as a waste management alternative, given a specific problem situation. This procedure provides a framework within which to apply the information presented in the other modules in Volumes I and II. Emphasis is placed on Level I, the intent of which is to present the subject matter and analytical techniques required for feasibility decision making. The primary function of this module is to serve as a brief introduction, or guide, to the design problems found in workshops or various courses. The same procedures may be followed by designers facing similar problems in actual practice.

An outline of the general engineering design procedure is presented, then related to the procedure to be followed here for land application. By applying the material in these modules, it is possible to carry out the initial and detailed feasibility determinations of land treatment options. This results in the recommendation of one option for detailed design and implementation.

The design procedure is divided into a two-level approach. The first, Level I, is intended to roughly approximate the initial feasibility determination for this technology. Major problems created by water management, solids and organic characteristics of the wastes, nutrients, toxic elements, and site determination are identified. This analysis indicates the factors that dictate the solution requirements, i.e., the limiting factors. The Level I analysis is illustrated in this module by the design example on land application of harbor dredge spoil.

The Level II analysis makes use of the comprehensive modules to examine the limiting factors in detail and other major concerns that will affect the final problem solution. Modifications which would significantly change the solution feasibility are identified at this point. Site evaluation, from Level I, is examined in further detail for the specific sites which are determined as feasible. The titles of the Level I and Level II modules are indicated in the Introduction.

The overall outcome of this two-level analysis is the determination whether land application of wastes is technically feasible, is the estimate whether is economically competitive with other major alternatives, and the identification of specific locations for implementation of solutions. This procedure could form the basis for detailed planning, engineering, and on-site investigations.

CONTENTS

OBJECTIVES

Upon completion of this module, the reader should be able to:

1. Define Level I and Level II design procedures and demonstrate an understanding of how these steps relate to an overall engineering design sequence.
2. Make use of the other Level I modules to identify potential limiting factors for land application systems, and estimate land area requirements for each factor.
3. Demonstrate the use of mapping techniques in site evaluation for land application systems.
4. Identify other considerations, not included in the design example in this module, which would also be part of Level I and II feasibility analyses for land application projects.

INTRODUCTION

When the alternative of placing sludge or wastewaters on land is considered, many questions arise as to the impact of specific factors. Water movement and runoff, pathogen control, nutrient utilization, and many other considerations will influence the final design. Complex engineering problems are usually solved using a rational procedure which allocates priorities to the variables, with the most limiting parameter dictating the final solution. To date, no general design procedure is in use or available which will assist in evaluating the major variables that influence the design of a land application system. The information in this module is intended to illustrate a screening procedure, combining the information in other modules, which will lead to feasibility determinations and site specific solutions for the land application of wastes.

The goal of this module is to develop a general procedure, based on an understanding of the pollutant management capabilities of soils, for evaluating the feasibility of land application of waste under various conditions. This procedure is a rational screening method which should lead to (1) the identification of specific limiting factors, (2) an idea of the safety factors involved in using land application of waste for non-limiting pollutants, and (3) site locations that combine the required characteristics for safe pollutant management. Essentially the information in this module provides a framework for the utilization of the information presented in the other modules.

DESIGN PROCEDURE

General Engineering Design Procedures

Because of the wide scope of knowledge needed in planning solutions for land application of wastes, many of the individuals involved with these designs may not be engineers. The rational problem-solving approach common to much of engineering practice may be alien to some members of the design team. Therefore, before proceeding directly to land application requirements, it is useful to consider the general design approach.

This design approach may be represented as in Figure 1, having six distinct steps (A-F) ranging from problem definition through evaluation of the implemented solution. After the problem has been defined with the assistance of the affected interest groups, the possible solutions are listed. Initial feasibility of the suggested solutions should lead to several distinct alternatives. These are then further defined, with some being eliminated. These two steps essentially represent the type of activities carried on at Level I. All information needed to complete the Level I design function for land application of wastes is included in the seven general overview Modules (Modules 1–7) of this program.

The next step is to identify, in depth, the major limitations of the design possibilities and any factors which might prohibit implementation of viable solutions. Generally, one solution will be favored or several will appear equally worthy of further consideration based on the Level I analysis. The favored solution(s) is analyzed to see if it is technically adequate to achieve the design objectives and then compared with other likely solutions for technical and cost-effectiveness. The designer includes as many factors as possible for consideration. Based on this analysis, one solution is recommended for final design and implementation. These procedures make up Level II design in the Land Application of Wastes Educational Program. Any further steps outlined in Figure 1 are outside the scope of this program.

> *The general engineering design procedure is presented as a six-step process ranging from problem definition through feasibility studies, detailed solution, implementation, and evaluation.*

---

*This and other italicized summaries are intended to highlight key ideas, provide a basis for later review or to aid in skimming sections that are relatively familiar. They can be ignored in a complete reading of the text.

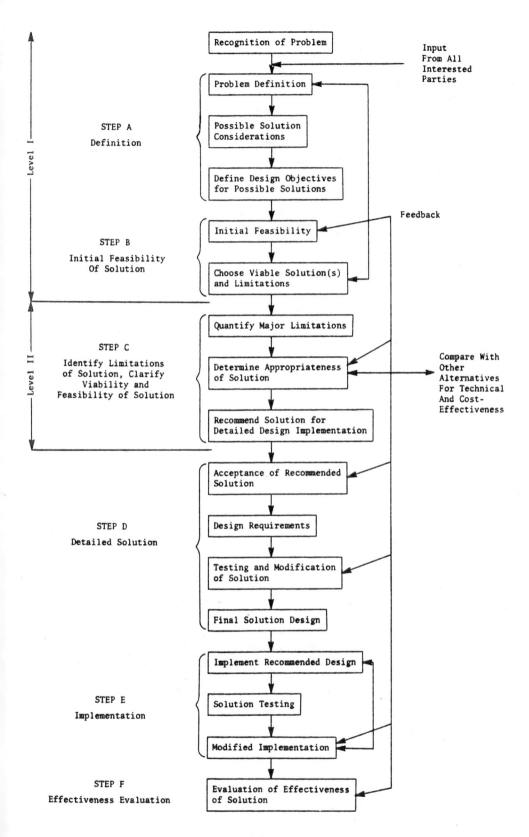

Figure 1. Illustration of the general steps involved in an engineering design procedure.

Following selection and acceptance of a solution, the detailed solution is then defined and the design work is carried out. Any pilot-plant analyses or field investigations would occur at this stage (Step D). The solution is then implemented (Step E). Under ideal conditions the implemented solution would be evaluated and its effectiveness in solving the original problem examined. This would lead to feedback which would be valuable in improving engineering practice. Unfortunately, this last step is often omitted in planning and design. However, reports are published on the performance of various engineered systems which designers attempt to adapt to their particular problems.

Relation of this Program to General Engineering Design Procedure

Obviously, the information presented here cannot provide all the skills and knowledge needed to take you through all six design phases shown in Figure 1. The information contained in all the modules in Volumes I and II should assist you in developing solutions through the stage designated as Step C in Figure 1. The Level I design procedure includes problem definition and initial solution definition and limitations, Steps A and B. The Level II procedure permits a more in-depth evaluation of this alternative (Step C).

> *Modules in this program can be used to perform initial and detailed feasibility analyses of land application vs. conventional alternatives. These functions are referred to as Level I and II analyses.*

The three important pieces of information that you should be able to develop upon completion of this design procedure are:

- Determine whether land application of sewage sludges, industrial sludges, and wastewaters represents a viable alternative to conventional discharge systems;
- Identify area-specific information that would enable one to estimate the type of land application technology that is most feasible for specific geographical locations;
- Estimate the cost effectiveness of the most viable alternatives.

The goal here is to enable you to be able to make feasibility decisions after the problem has been defined, and to provide estimates of types of systems, potential site locations, and cost-effectiveness of land application of wastes after additional investigation.

Design Procedure for Land Application of Wastes

Seldom have those involved with the development of waste management systems had to deal with as many variables as with land application of wastes. These systems require integration of physical, chemical, and biological pollutant control phenomena with climate, crop production, and uncontrollable natural phenomena. In order to make the material easier to assimilate, it has been divided into two phases—Level I and Level II as discussed above. In order to complete a Level I design, the reader should be familiar with the information presented in the first seven modules. Only the most prominent considerations are included at this level, and detailed descriptions are kept to a minimum.

> *Level I design makes use of the basic principles in Modules 1-7. Information in these modules should neither be considered complete in detail or as "rules of thumb" which may not be modified.*

It should be kept in mind that the initial feasibility determination procedure (Level I) is presented to obtain data rapidly for initial decisions. The decisions and limitations defined at this point should be considered temporary until further supporting data are developed. This procedure may be considered analogous to advice given by a consultant on initial contact by a client. Although the Level I procedure is sound and should fulfill the needs of an initial feasibility determination, more in-depth analysis is required in order to proceed with a final design.

The general Level I design procedure is illustrated in Figure 2. The waste problem is defined by a characterization study which should identify any factors which would prohibit land application of wastes. Modification of the problem by waste treatment at the source may be required for technical, legal, or social reasons. This source treatment may not be technologically- or cost-effective. Other circumstances might prohibit land application, such as the unavailability of land. At this point, only enough analysis should be conducted in regard to site evaluation to know that sufficient land area is available with the required soil properties within a certain radius. The land area to safely neutralize the various classes of pollutants would then lead to specific requirements and systems and their approximate costs. Data at Level I could be used to make initial feasibility decisions as to whether land application of wastes represents a viable management alternative.

The outcome of the initial feasibility study (Level I design) is whether land application is a viable alternative requiring further analysis.

After the decision is made to pursue land application further, Level II analyses begin. This level is characterized by a greater depth of analysis of pollutant-soil interactions, and con-

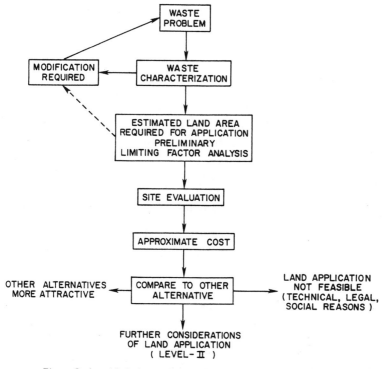

Figure 2. Level I design procedure for land application of wastes.

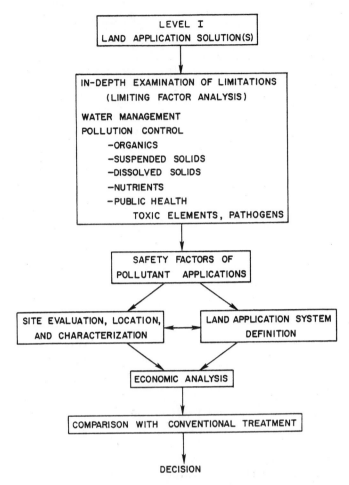

Figure 3. Generalized activities completed during Level II analysis.

siderably more attention to potential site location and evaluation. A summary of the major steps involved with this second level of analysis is presented in Figure 3. The major topics to be considered are: the limiting factors and determination of alternatives which would have the capability of eliminating particular inhibiting variables. For example, pathogen movement may be considered to be a limiting hazard from the public health viewpoint. Obvious alternatives would include disinfection of the waste prior to application, or modification of the application site or method.

> *In Level II design, potential limiting factors are examined in detail. The limiting factor determines land area requirements for a particular land treatment option. Specific site selection can then be made.*

Usually, one waste parameter will determine the largest land area required for safe application of the wastes. This is then identified as the limiting factor in the solution. This indicates that for all other parameters, the waste could be applied at a higher rate, or to a smaller area. Comparison of the land area required for safe application of each of the other pollutants to that required for the limiting factor is indicative of the safety margin involved in the application of that waste parameter. This is illustrated in the example included in this module.

The next major consideration is the availability of sufficient land area to implement the solution. Finally, site location, land area requirements, and application system definition enable a detailed cost estimate to be prepared. Then, after comparison with other technically feasible alternatives, the decision is made as to what system will be recommended for the waste treatment problem under consideration.

The outcome of Level II design is the recommendation of a specific alternative to implement.

MAJOR DESIGN CONSIDERATIONS

Topic Interactions—Level I and II Designs

The specific interactions of various parameters with waste application to land at Level I are summarized in Figure 4. This illustration represents factors that are useful in identifying the critical parameters as well as the limiting factor in the design. The reader should be able to use the other six Level I modules to examine potential land application sites and to identify safe application rates of pollutants, following the general procedure outlined in this module. After completing the modules the reader should be able to describe the major background reasons for the pollutant loading limitations.

Preliminary Site Evaluation

General Approach. The determination and choice of suitable waste treatment sites are the most difficult tasks in producing a workable system. The problem definition must be integrated with a wide range of variables such as: soil types and characteristics, topography, ground-water location and movement, crop production capability, and present and projected land use. Although it is difficult to combine all of these variables, a relatively simple procedure can be developed that is capable of identifying sites which combine the necessary properties. This method relies on the availability of detailed maps of potential application areas. Fortunately, the U.S. Geological Survey and the Soil Conservation Service provide detailed information for most parts of the U.S. Details on sources of data are given in Module I-6, "Site Evaluation." Some states, such as New York, have also developed maps showing the distribution of farmland, idle cropland, forests, and other land uses.

Three types of maps are helpful for site location and evaluation: soil survey maps, topographic maps classifying areas according to the characteristics of the terrain, and land use maps. These maps, when superimposed on each other, clearly illustrate areas where common features occur. The desirable area can then be estimated and compared to the acreage required for safe application of the limiting factor in the waste. This simplified analysis is illustrated in the following example (see Figures 6, 7, and 8, below, and the accompanying discussion).

Site selection is simplified by overlaying topographic, soil survey, and land use maps to identify areas having favorable features for land application.

DESIGN PROCEDURE EXAMPLE—FEASIBILITY OF LAND APPLICATION OF POLLUTED DREDGED HARBOR SEDIMENT

Problem Definition

It would be more common to use municipal wastewater or sludge to illustrate the principles involved with the design of land application systems. This type of problem is contained in Ap-

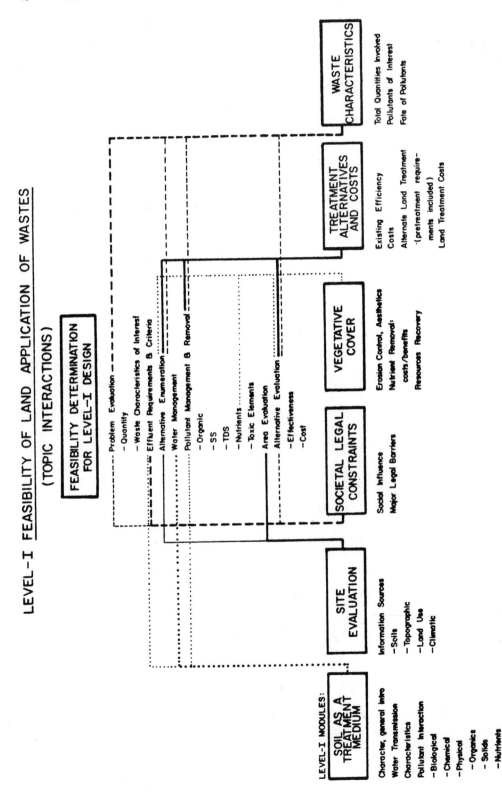

Figure 4. Interaction of introductory modules for Level I design procedure.

pendix A. Together with the suggested supporting material, this problem can be used to relate the concepts in the modules to the practical situation. To emphasize the general applicability of this procedure to complex materials, however, the rather unusual problem of land application of dredged harbor sediments will be used. The example given in this module represents actual locations and situations. All problem descriptions have been changed in some way to avoid the presentation of actual data not available to the public. This will not affect the value of the example in illustrating the viability of this technology.

A design example of land application feasibility for dredged harbor sediments is used to illustrate the general applicability of the procedure.

To maintain the nation's navigable waterways, the U.S. Army Corps of Engineers each year dredges 300 million cubic yards of channel materials (*Anon.*, 1975). This is more than 100 times the total quantity of sewage sludge generated in the United States (Dean, 1973; Fuhrman, 1973). These dredged materials often contain large quantities of toxic materials and large amounts of water. Economic disposal, without adverse environmental impact, is a major problem. Past practice has included transport of the material to open deep waters. However, increasingly strict environmental legislation has limited this option, and has resulted in the increased use of the other common alternative—storage in diked lagoons. This practice consumes 7,000 acres of new land every year.

The total cost of management of the dredging problem in the U.S. is about $170 million annually. Because of the increasing concern for protection of littoral areas and the rising costs of land, diked storage of sediment is also being reviewed as to its long-term viability as a solution to dredged material disposal.

Much of the dredged sediment is composed of valuable top soil washed from nearby agricultural land. Thus one obvious solution for deposition of the dredged material would be to use agricultural land as a disposal site. This solution has been rarely used for two reasons:

(1) it is usually costly to transport the sediment,
(2) anticipation of problems resulting from the application of sediment on the soil systems.

The problem is to define the feasibility of placing the dredged material on agricultural land. No consideration will be given to the economic feasibility of this alternative in this example.

General Waste Characteristics and Objectives of the Example

The U.S. Army Corps of Engineers, Buffalo, New York branch, estimates that the harbor at Olcott, New York, must have 30,000 m^3 of sediment removed. An aerial view of the community and marina leading into Lake Ontario is shown in Figure 5. A number of samples of this sediment indicate that it is highly contaminated with grease and oil and has up to 1,000 ppm of zinc and lead. One of the disposal alternatives for this sediment is to place it on land used in productive agriculture. Since the dredged material contains high concentrations of potentially toxic materials, many questions arise as to the desirability of this alternative. The specific objectives are to:

1. Quantify the major pollutants and their safe application rates.
2. Relate the pollutant application rate to the required land area.
3. Review the land use practices to determine the availability of agricultural land in the area.

Figure 5. Aerial view of Olcott, New York.

4. Determine the portion of the agricultural land which has characteristics which will promote the control of pollutants.

This example will not present any economic and technical comparison of land application with other treatment options. This is essential in any feasibility analysis, however, and would be carried out in an actual problem situation.

One of the first considerations with this waste is defining the constituents which must be evaluated with respect to application rates. The Environmental Protection Agency is presently cooperating with the U.S. Department of Agriculture (USDA) and the Food and Drug Administration (FDA) to determine the precise levels of various contaminants that can be placed on land used for food production. In the interim, the EPA has published (EPA, 1977) the guidelines shown in Table 1 for the application of certain potentially toxic materials on agronomic soil. These guidelines appear, along with means of approximating loadings of other waste constituents for Level I design in Module I-1, "Soil as a Treatment Medium." Additional data and

Table 1. Maximum Sludge Metal Additions to Privately Owned Farmland.

Metal	Metal Addition (kg/ha) to Soils with a Cation Exchange Capacity (meq/100g) of:		
	Less than 5	5–15	Greater than 5
Pb	500	1000	2000
Zn	250	500	1000
Cu	125	250	500
Ni	50	100	200
Cd	5	10	20

Dowdy, *et al.* (1976); Jorling (1977); EPA (1977).

other approaches limiting the application of waste sludges are given in Module II-4, "Potentially Toxic Elements."

> *Guidelines for potentially toxic element application must be used since the dredged spoil is reportedly high in some heavy metals.*

With reference to the contaminant levels and disposal standards given in Table 2, it is clear that the "open lake" dumping policy would not be applicable since the concentrations of many pollutants are higher than the maximum values suggested by EPA for this type of disposal.

Pollutant Soil Application Limitations

As the second step in the Level I analysis the factors which may limit agricultural land disposal of sludges and the risk involved with this practice will be estimated. This will be accomplished by following the pathways shown in Figure 4. It should be emphasized that little data are available on the effects of dredged materials on food crop production. If it is assumed that if the sediment is uniform, total quantities of constituents can be calculated from the values shown in Table 2. Totals are displayed in Table 3. Now that the total quantities of pollutants are estimated, the screening procedure to identify the limiting design parameter can be initiated.

Table 2. Composition of Olcott, New York, Harbor Sediments as Measured April 12, 1972. All Values on Dry Weight Basis.

Parameter	Sample Number						EPA Criteria Open Lake Disposal
	1	2	3	4	5	6	
Volatile solids, %	11.3	14.6	10.0	1.2	2.3	0.5	6
COD, %	14.0	18.6	12.5	0.5	17.3	0.5	5
Oils and grease, mg/kg	6100	9960	4220	230	490	180	1500
TKN, mg/kg	3190	4670	3220	—	485	1500	1000
Lead, mg/kg	580	770	320	68	96	20	50
Zinc, mg/kg	260	305	240	120	120	66	50
Hg, mg/kg	1.47	0.92	3.45	0.23	0.91	0.88	1
Phosphorus, mg/kg	4000	4100	3300	1100	2900	400	—

Table 3.   Estimation of Total Quantities of Materials in 30,000 m³ of Olcott Harbor Sediment Using Linear Average of All Values Shown in Table 2.

Material	In-Place Sediment Concentration, Average of Six Samples	Estimated Total Quantity For Disposal
Volatile solids	6.66%	3.2×10^6 kg
COD	10.6%	5.1×10^6 kg
Total Kjeldahl nitrogen	2610 mg/kg	1.26×10^5 kg
Oils and grease	3520 mg/kg	1.7×10^5 kg
Lead	308 mg/kg	1.48×10^4 kg
Zinc	185 mg/kg	0.89×10^4 kg
Hg	1.31 mg/kg	63 kg (140 lb)

Toxic Elements.   The most common concern with land application of sludges is the question of the effect of potentially toxic elements on the soil-crop system. This topic demands a conservative approach because of the problems that could ensue. In most soils, the metals are rapidly immobilized and accumulate in the first several centimeters of soil. Even where heavy metals accumulate, many plant systems and the human body have the inherent ability to avoid accumulation of the most of toxic elements. However, there are unknown areas and dangerous exceptions that must be considered.

Given the total quantity of lead and zinc to be applied, from Table 3, and a typical agronomic soil CEC in the 5–15 meq/100g range, land area requirements can be computed using the maximum additions of Zn and Pb from Table 1.

The computation for lead:

$$\frac{1.48 \times 10^4 \text{ kg applied}}{1.00 \times 10^3 \text{ kg/ha}} = 14.8 \text{ ha required}$$

and for zinc:

$$\frac{0.89 \times 10^4 \text{ kg applied}}{0.50 \times 10^3 \text{ kg/ha}} = 17.8 \text{ ha required}$$

The levels of Cu, Ni, and Cd should also be ascertained by laboratory analysis of the sediment, and required land areas computed in the same manner. Since Zn is limiting of the two elements for which figures are available, land area will be estimated on that basis, so 17.8 ha, or approximately 43 acres, are required for safe application of Zn. Assuming that the concentrations of Cu, Ni, and Cd are not limiting compared with lead and Zn, the adequate area for sediment application would be about 50 acres.

Land area computations are made for Zn and Pb based on guidelines presented in Table 1.

Greases and Oils.   For a specific problem such as grease and oil, it may be necessary to turn to the research literature. Large quantities of petroleum products are lost to the environment.

For this reason, a considerable amount of information is available on the fate of grease and oil in the environment. In general, the soil environment appears to be able to accept large quantities of petroleum products, since most oils and grease are eventually decomposed by microbial activity. Further, it would appear that the hydrophobic characteristics would contain these organics in the surface of the soil so that contamination of the groundwater would be a minimal problem.

On the basis of greenhouse pot experiments (Schwendinger, 1968), beans were most easily damaged by crude oil, ryegrass somewhat less, and sorghums continued to grow in soil heavily polluted with oil. For biodegradeable cooking oils, it was found that application rates as high as 112 metric tons per hectare resulted in oil decomposition rates of 8 tons/ha/week with no evidence of toxicity to the decomposition systems in the soils (Smith, 1974). The rule of thumb that has been developed is: one kilogram of oil per square meter of soil surface is considered to be the point at which damage to plant life begins (Schwendinger, 1968; Ellis and Adams, 1961). Using this as the application rate for Olcott sediment, the safe application for grease and oil application would require a land area of 1.7×10^5 square meters or 42 acres, or a land area slightly less than that needed for safe application of potentially toxic metals.

> *Grease and oil application is based on values reported in the literature from experience with other wastes.*

Organic Solids Application Rates.   The organic assimilation capacity of soils is highly variable depending on the detailed soil characteristics (see Module II-3, "Organic Matter"). In general, soils are composed of 3–5% organic matter by dry weight. Thus in the top two feet of soil, there will be more than 20×10^4 lb/acre of organic matter. Except for the oil and grease, it is likely that the organic matter in the sediments will be resistant to decomposition. In this form it may use little oxygen and application of large quantities may have little detrimental effect on the soil. Although few guidelines are available, it is likely that the addition of a total amount of organics equal to 10% of the existing soil organics would have little effect, and even doubling the organic content in the upper two feet should not cause long-term detrimental effects. If this analysis holds true, the safe application area would be less than 350 acres and could be as few as 35 acres.

> *Organic solids application is related to the amount of organic matter likely to be present in the native soil.*

Nitrogen and Phosphorus Control.   The nitrogen and phosphorus in the sediment are likely to be in the organic form. As the material enters into the decomposition cycle in the soils these nutrients will be mineralized. Phosphorus will not be a potential problem because large quantities are rapidly immobilized in most soils. However, conversion of organic nitrogen to ammonia and then to the oxidized form may result in nitrate contamination of the groundwater. Thus nitrogen will be considered as a nutrient which must be applied at a controlled rate.

The control of nitrogen in the organic form should be viewed in relation to the background concentration in the soil. The quantity of organic nitrogen in soils varies from 0.1% of the dry weight to 2.5%, depending on the character of the soil (see "Nitrogen Considerations", Module I-1, for further information). The total quantity of organic nitrogen in the plow layer of soil may vary from less than 2,500 lb/acre to more than ten times this value. Net mineralization of this soil nitrogen occurs at a rate of about 1.2% per year (Bouldin and Lathwell, 1968).

In other words, as much as several hundred pounds of nitrogen could be mineralized per acre over a few years. In most cases, the total quantity of nitrates that reach the groundwater from mineralization is minimized due to one of the following:

- low net available nitrogen as a result of a high C/N ratio,
- denitrification of the nitrified nitrogen forms,
- removal in the crop cover.

Fertilizer applications commonly add 50–150 lb/acre-year of nitrogen in the available forms of ammonia or nitrates for crop production. If it is conservatively (since the figure is probably lower) assumed that the organic nitrogen in the dredged material gives up its nitrogen at the rate of 10% per year and that no other source of nitrogen is utilized, the amount of cropland, given that 100 pounds of nitrogen per acre per year is required, can be calculated. Using these assumptions, the total land area required for safe application of nitrogen would be 276 acres.

> *Organic nitrogen addition is related to the quantity present in soil, net mineralization rates, and normal fertilizer additions.*

Although it will be shown that a significant amount of orchard land is available in the area, deposition of this material in apple orchards is not recommended. Organic nitrogen is not advised for use with productive apple orchards. It is advisable for engineers who are not familiar with farming practice to contact local agricultural extension agents to obtain such details.

This method of arriving at an acceptable nitrogen loading rate is presented as a rational analysis based on the characteristics of the waste in question. It is meant to be conservative and adequate for Level I feasibility determination. Other methods, such as that based on crop uptake found in Module I-4, Vegetative Cover, can be used with liquid waste with a high proportion of inorganic nitrogen which will be readily taken up by plants. In this example, further analysis of the nitrogen content to determine what fraction of the TKN is ammoniacal would be helpful in Level II design.

> *Other methods of estimating nitrogen loads, such as relating loading to typical crop uptake rates, may be used.*

Application of Water and Other Limitations. The quantity of water that infiltrates to the groundwater in the Olcott area probably exceeds 15 or 20 in./yr. The permeability of much of the area exceeds 2 in./hr. Thus, it can be concluded that the transmission of water from the sludge will be a minimal problem. Using only 25% of the present permeability rates, the area of application would be less than 20 acres.

One important criterion that has not been discussed is the potential odor problem. Because of the high organic solids and grease content it can be assumed that the sediments will be anaerobic and have a strong unpleasant odor. For this reason, it is suggested that the material either be placed underground by soil injection, or that it be covered with several inches of soil as soon as possible after application.

Area Requirements for Dredged Sediment Application

A summary of the application rates estimated to be acceptable and the resulting land requirements are shown in Table 4. It can be seen that the limiting factor is the nitrogen content of

Table 4. Summary of Recommended Application Rates for Various Pollutants on 300 Acres of Agricultural Land Near Olcott, New York, and the Related Estimated Safety Factor Above the Detrimental Level.

Pollutant or Substrate of Interest	Total Area Required (acres)	Safety Factor[a]
Toxic elements	50	6
Grease and oils	42	7
Organic solids	35 (350)[b]	9
Nitrogen	276	1
Water	20	14

[a]Safety factor = recommended 300 acres/required area.
[b]Application to only 35 acres would cause increase in soil organics content, but would probably have little adverse effect on the soil system.

the sediments, pending any unusual problems in organic solids application. Nitrogen is often the limiting factor for application of sludges and wastewaters in cases where the application rate is controlled by the crop needs. If this is assumed to be the required land area, it can be seen that the application rates of the other pollutants are one-third to one-tenth that which is considered to be an environmentally safe rate of application. Recommendation of the use of a 300-acre site should incorporate a safety factor large enough to account for any unforeseen events. This application is equivalent to adding the dredged sludge once to a depth of 2.25 inches.

By comparing land area requirements due to various waste constituents, the limiting factor is determined. In this case it is nitrogen, although further study of organics loading is indicated.

Site Evaluation Procedure

General Description and Land Use. It will be assumed that the distance which could be considered feasible for disposal, in view of the transportation costs, is limited to 2 miles from the sediment sites. A detailed review of the land area within a 2-mile radius from Olcott Harbor was conducted. The total estimated area included is 4,320 acres. Thus, less than 10% of the total land area is required for safe application of these dredged materials.

The area around Olcott is quite flat with an average slope of approximately 1% (elevation ranges from 280 to 330 feet). There are some steeply sloped areas along the shoreline of Lake Ontario and tributary creeks.

Orchards are an important agricultural activity in Niagara County and occupy a sizable portion of land in the Olcott area. The primary fruits are apples, tart cherries, and pears. In order to obtain a general overview of the various land uses, data from New York State's Land Use and Natural Resources (LUNR) inventory were utilized. The amount of land used in agriculture and other purposes is summarized in Table 5. These data were sketched to show the location of various land use practices in Figure 6. The total amount of the land area used in orchards and

Table 5.   Distribution of Land Use Practices in
Olcott, New York Area.

Land Use	Hectares	Acres	% Area
Residential (urban)	141	348	8.1
Cropland	320	791	18.3
Orchards	615	1520	35.1
Forest	292	722	16.7
Idle	337	823	19.3
Outdoor recreation	45	111	2.5
Total	1750	4315	100.0

other agriculture is 53.5%. Figure 6 represents one of the required maps to be used during the site selection procedure.

Land use information is available in map form, indicating cropland, forest, orchard, and residential areas within an economical transport distance from the dredging area.

In practice, the mapping procedures in this example can be accomplished by using a USGS topographic map as a base map and making clear overlays for soil types, land use, and other factors to be considered in site selection. Preferred areas can then be identified readily by combining all overlays on the base map. This is represented in Figures 6 through 8.

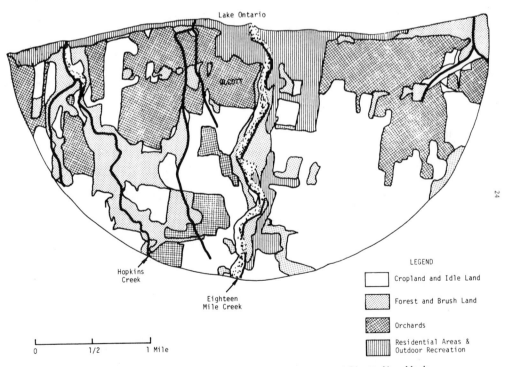

LEGEND

☐ Cropland and Idle Land

▦ Forest and Brush Land

▨ Orchards

▥ Residential Areas &
  Outdoor Recreation

Figure 6. Land use practices and their distribution around Olcott, New York.

Soil Description.   Examination of the soil survey map of Niagara County (Higgin, *et al.*, 1972) indicates that three soil associations are included in the area within a 2-mile radius of the Olcott Harbor.

1. Howard-Arkport-Phelps association. Deep, somewhat excessively to moderately well drained soils having a medium to moderately coarse textured subsoil over gravel and sand.
2. Appleton-Hilton-Sun. Deep, moderately well to very poorly drained soils having a medium textured subsoil.
3. Minoa-Galen-Elnora association. Deep, somewhat poorly and moderately well drained soils having a medium or moderately coarse texture, or coarse textured subsoil, over fine and very fine sand.

About 65% of the area belongs to the Howard-Arkport-Phelps association. This area borders Lake Ontario and is of high potential for agricultural production that is especially suited for growing fruits. More than 80% of the orchards in the area are located on the Howard-Arkport-Phelps soils.

The Appleton-Hilton-Sun association and Minoa-Galen-Elnora association occupy approximately 25% and 10% of the area within the 2-mile radius, respectively. Roughly 50% of the areas occupied by crops or left idle are located on these two soil associations. In general, these three associations form bands paralleling the lake with the Minoa-Galen-Elnora furthest inland.

Many of these soils would appear to have characteristics which should enable deposition of polluted sediments with a minimum number of problems, as long as the rates of application are controlled. The pH is of concern if it is below 6.5. However, even though the surface soils may be below this level, the lower soil horizons are calcareous and would have a higher pH. The permeability of the soils presents a different problem than in most situations, since the good drainage and percolation rates of many of the soil types in this area might cause pollutants to be washed through to the groundwater before neutralizing reactions would have a chance to occur. In order to identify the best areas for disposal of the sediment, the following characteristics of the soil are desired:

1. better drained, but slower permeability,
2. at least 1 foot depth to groundwater,
3. higher pH,
4. minimum slopes to control runoff.

Soils are grouped by their drainage and permeability, depth to groundwater, pH, and slopes and mapped for the same area used in land use mapping.

Through consultation with a soil technologist, a soil grouping was suggested. The resulting soil type grouping is shown in Figure 7. The light area of this Figure is considered to have soils with characteristics most acceptable for application of the lake sediment.

In order to more clearly relate the most desirable soil characteristics to the present land use, Figure 8 was developed by superimposing Figures 6 and 7 to illustrate the cropland and idle land that was associated with soils with the most desirable sediment disposal characteristics. This relationship indicates that there are approximately 900 acres available which combine agricultural land with the desirable soil characteristics.

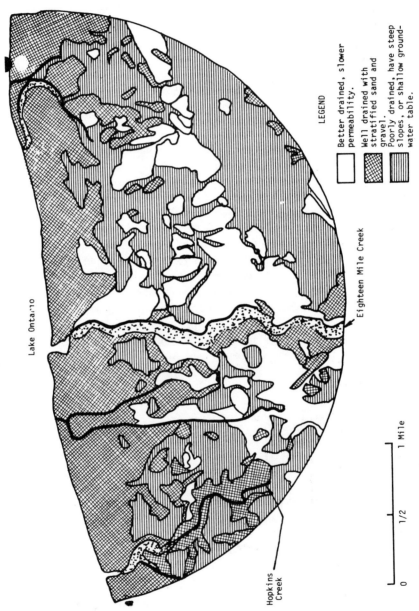

Figure 7. Distribution of soil types with characteristics of differing suitability for deposition of sediments.

Cropland and idle land on soils which are better drained and with slower permeability.

Lake Ontario

OLCOTT

Eighteen Mile Creek

Hopkins Creek

0 1/2 1 Mile

Figure 8. Identification of soil types suited to sediment disposal on agricultural land.

Land use and soil characteristics maps are superimposed, yielding a map indicating land with desirable characteristics for land application.

DISCUSSION

Comparison of the recommended application rates and area requirements to the land area that has the most desirable characteristics indicated that sediment deposition on agricultural land would appear to be feasible, and limited by the nitrogen concentration. It would require about 35% of the land meeting acceptable criteria for dredging disposal within a 2-mile radius of Olcott.

Further illustration of the relative impact of land disposal of the dredgings is illustrated in Table 6. The values are all approximations using estimated average characteristics. However, these values should serve as guides as to the potential impact of the addition of the dredged sediment to the soil. The mercury and zinc add significant amounts of material over that contained in typical soils (Page, 1974).

It had been anticipated that the toxic elements would determine the acceptable application rates. Although the addition of mercury is significant compared to typical background levels, the total additional concentration amounts to 0.47 lb/acre. Two factors would indicate that this level may not be detrimental to the soil system. First, mercury levels commonly measured in some soils may be as high as 0.6 lb/acre. Second, addition of this quantity of mercury with sewage sludge in Europe on agricultural cropland is practiced and considered to be acceptable. Although the zinc levels are also increased, common background levels in soil are also high in relation to the amount resulting from this addition.

Placement of the dredged sediment on land would not increase metal content to unacceptable levels, as may have been anticipated.

There is little doubt that the placement of Olcott sediment on agricultural land is technically acceptable and that the land area is available with suitable characteristics. Whether this practice is economically or politically feasible should be considered. Finally, the presence of chemical plants upstream from the harbor emphasizes the need to be conservative when dealing with these dredgings. It might be useful to test the recommended application rates in short plant growth tests to determine any potential unexpected impact.

Level II analyses including crops, legal aspects, climatic factors, detailed costing, application

Table 6.   Estimated Increase of Specific
Materials from the Application of Olcott,
New York, Harbor Dredgings to 300 Acres
of Agricultural Land.

Added Material	Increase in Top Soil (%)[a]
VS	8
TKN	31
Zn	65
Hg	400

[a]Estimated increase over background quantities in top 2 feet of soil.

systems, monitoring and drainage requirements are not discussed in this module. Also, in a complete design, toxicity potentials, organics, nitrogen, and phosphorus considerations would be explored in much greater depth. In particular, the limiting nitrogen application rate would be evaluated with respect to all possible uptake mechanisms so that the rough calculation of N loading and land requirement presented in Level I can be refined. This will determine application area for detailed system design. The Level II Module II-1, "Nitrogen Considerations," must be consulted to perform this analysis. Also, in the case of this waste, some uncertainty exists in the estimation of safe organic loading. Further study of this is warranted, although nitrogen should remain the limiting design factor. For this example, pathogens and wastewater storage would receive little or no attention. In more typical wastewater and sewage sludge application problems, they would.

> *Level II design includes detailed analysis of factors discussed in Level I, plus other design considerations. Nitrogen and organic loading estimates would be refined.*

One important consideration included in the Level I analysis is also not discussed in this module. Societal factors, or public acceptance, can have a great bearing on land availability and the ability of the designers to carry the project to completion. This factor, in practice, is intimately related to local and federal laws and regulations. Land application proposals must be justified within the framework of these requirements.

> *Public acceptance and legal factors must be considered in land treatment planning.*

Finally, as with any other engineering design procedure, comparison must be made with alternative treatments. This must be done in terms of economics and treatment potential in order to determine feasibility and decide which option to implement. This analysis is to be initiated in the Level I design procedure, and at this point a decision is made as to basic feasibility and cost-competitiveness of land treatment versus conventional alternatives. This decision is whether to proceed to the Level II detailed feasibility design for land treatment. Only those alternatives which are obviously not competitive are discarded at the completion of Level I, and further economic comparison is made with conventional options following Level II, at which point a system is recommended and final design will commence on the chosen system.

> *Economic comparison must be made with conventional treatment alternatives, for Level I and II feasibility analyses.*

BIBLIOGRAPHY

Anon. 1975. New method dewaters dredged material, cuts lagooning space. *Civil Engineering*, **45** (No. 4). (Apr.) pp. 90–91.

Bouldin, D. R. and D. J. Lathwell. 1968. Behavior of soil organic nitrogen. Bulletin 1023, Cornell University Agricultural Experiment Station, (Dec.). 16 p.

Dean, R. B. 1973. Disposal and reuse of sludge and sewage: What are the options? *In* Proceedings of conference on land disposal of municipal effluents and sludges, Rutgers University, New Brunswick, N.J. (March).

Dethier, B. E. 1966. Precipitation in New York State. Bulletin 1009, Cornell University Agricultural Experiment Station.

Dowdy, R. H., R. E. Larson, and E. Epstein. 1976. Sewage sludge and effluent use in agriculture. pp. 138–153. *In* Land application of waste materials. Soil Conservation Society of America. Ankeny, Iowa. 313 p.

Ellis, R. Jr. and R. S. Adams. 1961. Contamination of soils by petroleum hydrocarbons. *Advances in Agronomy*, **13**, pp. 197–216.

EPA. 1977. Technical Bulletin, Municipal sludge management: environmental factors. MCD-28. EPA 430/9-77-004. Office of Water Program Operations. Washington, D.C., 30 p. plus appendices.

Fuhrman, R. E. 1973. Memorandum, subject: Disposal of sewage sludge. Municipal Wastewater Systems Division, EPA, Washington, D.C. (Mar.).

Higgins, B. A., P. S. Puglia, R. P. Leonard, T. D. Yoakum, and W. A. Wintz. 1972. Soil survey of Niagara County, New York. USDA, Soil Conservation Service.

Jorling, T. C. 1977. Federal register. Vol. 42, No. 211. pp. 57420–57427. *Re.* Technical bulletin–Municipal sludge management: environmental factors. MCD-28. (EPA 430/9-77-004).

Leeper, G. W. 1972. Reactions of heavy metals with soils with special regard to their application in sewage wastes. U.S. Corps of Engineers. Department of the Army. Contract DACW 73-73-C-0026. 70 p.

Page, A. L. 1974. Fate and effects of trace elements in sewage sludge when applied to agricultural lands. U.S. Environmental Protection Agency Report. EPA 670/2-74-005. 108 p.

Olson, G. W. 1974. Land classifications. Search Agriculture. Agronomy, **4** (No. 7).

Schwendinger, R. B. 1968. Reclamation of soils contaminated by oil. *J. Inst. of Petroleum*, **54,** 181–197.

Smith, J. H. 1974. Decomposition in soil of waste cooking oils used in potato processing. *J. Environmental Quality*, 3 (No. 3), 279–281.

Ward, P. S. 1975. EPA warns: don't ignore land treatment. *J. Water Pollut. Contr. Fed.*, **47** (2) 232–235.

Module I-3
WASTE CHARACTERISTICS

SUMMARY

This module introduces the physical, biological, and chemical constituents of wastewaters and sludges which are of concern in land treatment systems. The characteristics of typical municipal wastewater are tabulated for strong, medium and weak sewages. Some of the factors affecting pollutant concentrations are listed.

"Waste Characteristics" is a Level I module, therefore other modules are referenced for more detailed information on organic matter content, nutrients, pathogens, and potentially toxic elements. Flow, distribution and expected removals of various waste constituents in conventional treatment systems are illustrated by flow diagrams. Since the liquid effluent or sludge from various conventional pretreatments, as well as raw wastewater, may be the influent to a land application site, this information is necessary to the design of land treatment schemes. Flow diagrams illustrating treatment of the same wastewater contaminants in land application systems are shown alongside the conventional diagrams. Raw or preliminary treated wastewater is used as the influent to both conventional and land application systems in these examples.

The characteristics of sludges from various treatment processes are discussed briefly. Sludge application to land entails some special considerations due to the concentration of settleable waste constituents in sludge.

CONTENTS

GLOSSARY

BOD$_5$—Five-day biochemical oxygen demand. A measure of the amount of dissolved oxygen required to meet the metabolic needs of aerobic microorganisms which assimilate the organic matter available to them in a water sample. Performed with microorganisms acclimated to the sample material, for 5 days at 20°C.

COD—Chemical oxygen demand. A measure of the organic matter in a sample which is subject to oxidation by a strong chemical oxidant under standard laboratory conditions.

filterable solids—That portion of the solids content of a water sample which will pass through a filter, and not be volatilized by drying of the collection vessel. Also called "filtrable residue."

MPN—Most probable number. A statistical analysis of bacterial concentration in a water sample.

PFU—Plaque-forming unit. A virus or viruses which forms a colony visible as a clear area on a plate of host cells. Used as a measure of viral concentration.

septic—Characterized by anaerobic breakdown of proteins by certain bacteria, resulting in foul-smelling end products.

suspended solids—That portion of the solids content of a water sample which will not pass through a filter. Also called "non-filtrable residue."

TOC—Total organic carbon. A measure of carbon contained in organic constituents of a water sample.

OBJECTIVES

Upon completion of this module, the reader should be able to:

1. List the major waste characteristics of concern to land treatment.
2. Name the waste constituent which usually is most limiting in land treatment design.
3. State the range of values of the following waste constituents in typical municipal sewage: total solids, total nitrogen, total phosphorus, BOD$_5$, and COD.
4. State the major constituents of concern to land treatment of sludge.

INTRODUCTION

In the evaluation and design of waste treatment alternatives, the constituents of wastes play a leading role. Some of these waste constituents present aesthetic problems while others are harmful to living organisms. This module presents a summary of data on the waste characteristics of common wastewaters and sludges, and briefly examines their fate in conventional treatment and land application systems.

The application of wastes to the land for treatment and/or disposal has received renewed emphasis in waste treatment technology. Land treatment of wastes is often an economically feasible alternative. However, this alternative requires the designer to mesh his design with an existing ecosystem. In doing this, he must be careful not to alter adversely (1) the biota within the soil/plant treatment medium, (2) the physical structure of the soil profile, or (3) the surface or groundwater quality beyond acceptable limits.

In order to determine the feasibility of land application of waste, the limiting rate of application of the controlling pollutant(s) must be correlated with the capacity for treatment of the soil/plant system. The information in this module, combined with Module 1 "Soil as a Treatment Medium," will assist in identifying the potential limiting factors and enable the comparison of pollutant conversion and removal efficiencies with those potentially available in land application systems.

WASTEWATER CHARACTERISTICS

The number of waste characteristics, each having broad variability, emphasizes the complexity found in wastes, and the flexibility demanded of treatment processes. This variability is due to the diverse sources of wastes, i.e., municipal, industrial, and agricultural sources, as well as the differing activities within each major source. Only typical municipal wastewater and sludges will be treated here.

Typical Untreated Municipal Wastewater Characteristics

A necessary preliminary step when planning for a land application system, as with any other waste treatment system, is a detailed evaluation of the waste characteristics. These waste characteristics are often divided into three major categories—physical, biological, and chemical. Table 1 displays those characteristics which are usually documented for conventional waste treatment.

Variations in Municipal Wastewaters

The variations found in municipal wastewaters are caused by many different things, some of which include (1) population size and industrial distribution, and (2) combined vs. separate storm and sanitary sewers. The figures in Table 1 do not express any of the extreme variations suggested in (1) and (2) above, but only those constituents typically found in sanitary sewer systems.

Population vs. Industrial Distribution.   In general, as population sizes increase, so do industrial facilities. Industrial loadings into municipal systems could easily project any one of the constituents in Table 1 to many times more than that shown. However, pretreatment of industrial wastes are usually required for incompatible substances prior to discharge into municipal sys-

Table 1. **Typical Municipal Wastewater Characteristics—Untreated.**
(mg/l except where noted)

	Strong	Medium	Weak	Reference[a]
Physical Characteristics				
Color (nonseptic)	Gray	Gray	Gray	1
Color (septic)	Gray–Black	Blackish	Blackish	1
Odor (nonseptic)	Musty	Musty	Musty	1
Odor (septic)	Musty–H_2S	H_2S	H_2S	1
Temperature °F (average)	55–90°	55–90°	55–90°	1
Total solids	1200	700	350	2
Suspended solids	350	200	100	2
Fixed	75	50	30	2
Volatile	275	150	70	2
Filterable solids	850	500	250	2
Fixed	525	300	145	2
Volatile	325	200	105	2
Biological Characteristics				
Total coliforms (MPN/100 ml)	100×10^6	30×10^6	1×10^6	2
Virus (PFU/l)	7000+		200	4
Chemical Characteristics				
pH	8.0	7.5	6.5	1
Total nitrogen	60	40	15	1
Organic nitrogen	19	15	5	1
Ammonia nitrogen	40	25	10	1
Nitrate nitrogen	1.0	0.5	—	1
Total phosphorus	20	10	6	1
Organic phosphorus	5	3	2	2
Inorganic phosphorus	15	7	4	2
BOD_5 (20°C)	300	200	100	2
COD	1000	500	250	2
TOC	300	200	100	2
Chlorides	100	50	30	2
Toxic elements (concentrations found in residential trunk sewers)				
Cadmium			0.007–0.019	3
Chromium			0.008–0.09	3
Copper			0.12–0.21	3
Lead			0.075–0.12	3
Nickel			0.014–0.09	3
Zinc			0.200–0.25	3

[a]1. Battelle Memorial Institute, Final Report 1974.
  2. Metcalf and Eddy, 1972.
  3. Davis and Jacknow, 1975.
  4. E. DeMichele, 1974.

tems. Discharge of potentially toxic elements from industrial sources can be an important area in which pretreatment is necessary.

Industrial discharges can affect waste characteristics greatly.

Combined vs. Separate Storm and Sanitary Sewers. Some towns and cities have a combination of storm and sanitary sewers. A summary of sewage characteristics for fifteen of these cities is shown in Table 2. The most noticeable effects that combined systems have on untreated waste-water are the increased flows (not shown in Table 2) and the increase in suspended solids. The initial surge of storm water runoff carries the greatest percentages of organic and mineral solids and creates serious problems for all waste management systems. Once this washdown has occurred, subsequent runoff is relatively clean. Often these surge flows by-pass the treatment facility because of the inability of the treatment processes to handle the excessive volumes of water. Although all recent collection system designs require the separation of storm water flows, many combined systems are still in use.

Combined storm and sanitary sewers are still in use in many older systems. Major effects are to produce shock hydraulic loads and greatly increase suspended solids.

WASTEWATER CHARACTERISTICS IN THE EVALUATION AND DESIGN OF LAND APPLICATION SYSTEMS

In evaluating waste characteristics for land application design, several stand out as having more immediate relevance than others (see Table 3). Experience has suggested that these will generally define the design limitations in land application systems.

Solids

Solids which generally pass through preliminary treatment are categorized under two major headings, suspended and filterable solids. Figure 1 outlines their relationship. Additional categories have been devised which further separate the settling characteristics and the degree of solubility. Each of these categories has a range of organic and mineral constituents. The approximate percentage of organic and mineral matter (or ash) in medium strength domestic sewage is also shown in Figure 1.

Organics. Approximately 50% of the total solids found in municipal sewage are organic. In addition to the predominant human waste organics, these include surfactants (primarily synthetic detergents) and phenols. Trace amounts of pesticides, herbicides, and other home and garden chemicals are also found. Recent legislation has required that pesticides be biodegradable within a specified time limit. It should also be noted here that a list of potentially toxic elements is published by the U.S. Environmental Protection Agency along with strict effluent concentration guidelines. Industrial sources can contribute other organic compounds not normally found in domestic wastes.

---

*This and other italicized summaries are intended to highlight key ideas, provide a basis for later review or to aid in skimming sections that are relatively familiar. They can be ignored in a complete reading of the text.

Table 2.   Comparison of Quality of Combined Sewage for Various Cities (J. A. Lager, 1974).

Type of Wastewater Location, Year	BOD$_5$ mg/l		COD mg/l		SS mg/l		Total Coliforms MPN/100 ml		Total Nitrogen mg/l as N	Total Phosphorus mg/l as P
	Avg	Range	Avg	Range	Avg	Range	Avg	Range	Avg	Avg
Typical untreated municipal (separate system)	200	100–300	500	250–750	200	100–350	5×10^7	$1 \times 10^7 – 1 \times 10^9$	40	10
Typical treated municipal (separate system)										
Primary effluent	135	70–200	330	165–500	80	40–120	2×10^7	$5 \times 10^7 – 5 \times 10^8$	35	7.5
Secondary effluent	25	15–45	55	25–80	15	10–30	1×10^3	$1 \times 10^2 – 1 \times 10^4$	30	5.0
Selected combined										
Atlanta, Ga. 1969	100	48–540	—	—	—	—	1×10^7	—	—	1.2
Berkeley, Ca. 1968–69	60	18–300	200	20–600	100	40–150	—	—	—	—
Brooklyn, NY 1972	180	86–428	—	—	1051	132–8759	—	—	—	1.2
Bucyrus, Ohio 1968–69	120	11–560	400	13–920	470	20–2440	1×10^7	$2 \times 10^5 – 5 \times 10^7$	13	3.5
Cincinnati, Ohio 1970	200	80–380	250	190–410	1100	500–1800	—	—	—	—
DesMoines, Iowa 1968–69	115	29–158	—	—	295	155–1166	—	—	12.7	11.6
Detroit, Mich. 1965	153	74–635	115	—	274	120–804	—	—	16.3	4.9
Kenosha, Wis. 1970	129	—	464	—	458	—	2×10^6	—	10	5.9
Milwaukee, Wis. 1969	55	26–182	177	118–765	244	113–848	—	$2 \times 10^5 – 3 \times 10^7$	3–24	0.8
Racine, Wis. 1971	119	—	—	—	439	—	—	—	—	—
Roanoke, Va. 1969	115	—	—	—	78	—	7×10^7	—	—	—
Sacramento, Ca. 1968–69	165	70–328	238	59–513	125	56–502	5×10^6	$7 \times 10^5 – 9 \times 10^7$	—	—
San Francisco, Ca. 1969–70	49	1.5–202	155	17–626	68	4–426	3×10^6	$2 \times 10^4 – 2 \times 10^7$	—	—
Washington, D.C. 1969	71	10–470	382	80–1760	622	35–2000	3×10^6	$4 \times 10^5 – 6 \times 10^6$	3.5	1.0

Table 3. Waste Characteristic of Concern in Land Application Systems.

Solids
  Organics
  Mineral
Nutrients
  Nitrogen
    Ammonium nitrogen
    Organic nitrogen
    Nitrate nitrogen
  Phosphorus
Hazardous substances
  Pathogens
    Virus
    Bacteria (1/100 ml to 4/100 ml coliform, testing procedure specific)[a]
    Protozoa
    Helminths
  Toxic substances—inorganic
    Arsenic (0.05 mg/l)[a]
    Barium (1 mg/l)[a]
    Boron[b]
    Cadmium (0.010 mg/l)[a, b]
    Chromium (0.05 mg/l)[a]
    Copper[b]
    Fluoride (1.4–2.4, temperature dependent)[a]
    Lead (0.05 mg/l)[a, b]
    Manganese
    Mercury (0.002 mg/l)[a]
    Nickel[b]
    Nitrate as N (10 mg/l)[a]
    Selenium (0.01 mg/1)[a, b]
    Silver (0.05 mg/l)[a]
    Vanadium
    Zinc[b]
  Toxic substances—organic
    Chlorinated hydrocarbons
      Endrin (0.0002 mg/l)[a]
      Lindane (0.004 mg/l)[a]
      Methorychlor (0.1 mg/l)[a]
      Toxaphene (0.005 mg/l)[a]
    Chlorophenoxys
      2,4-D (0.1 mg/l)[a]
      2,4,5-TP Silvex (0.01 mg/l)[a]

[a]The groundwater criteria resulting from the land application of wastewater, including the affected native groundwater (R. E. Train, 1976).
[b]Those most likely to cause toxicity to higher plants in soils where large amounts of domestic sludge are applied over a period of years (A. L. Page, 1974).

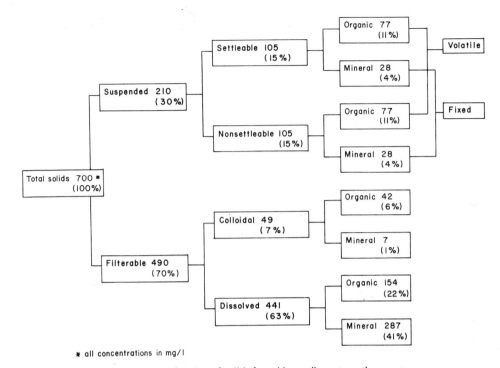

* all concentrations in mg/l

Figure 1. Classification of solids found in medium strength sewage.

Approximately 50% of municipal water total solids content is organic, including detergents, phenols and home and garden pesticides, etc.

Various methods have been devised to determine the organic content of wastewaters. A comparison of these measurements is shown in Figure 2. The 5-day biochemical oxygen demand (BOD$_5$) is one parameter often seen in wastewater analysis. It determines the oxygen

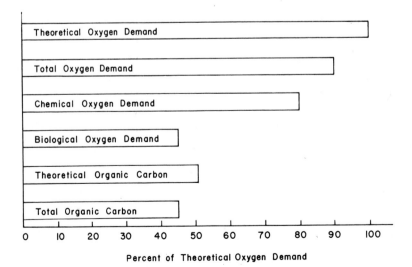

Percent of Theoretical Oxygen Demand

Figure 2. Approximate relationship among measures of the organic content of typical municipal wastewaters.

utilized by microorganisms in digesting organics over a 5-day period. It is the most widely used test for the purpose of regulatory control of wastewater treatment processes. Long-term BOD analyses provide more information about the oxygen-demanding characteristics of organic matter in a sample. These BOD analyses can be conducted for any period of time necessary to stabilize the sample, and provide useful information on the ultimate carbonaceous oxygen demand. Long-term BOD tests are used to determine the oxidation curve and exponential rate factor which must be known to compute ultimate BOD of a particular waste.

The chemical oxygen demand (COD) test measures organic matter readily oxidizable by a strong chemical oxidant. Results are available in a matter of hours rather than days, making this test generally more useful for in-plant process control decisions. The theoretical oxygen demand (ThOD), total oxygen demand (TOD), theoretical organic carbon (ThOC), and total organic carbon (TOC) are other test procedures utilized to determine total amounts of organic matter. A more detailed discussion of these testing procedures may be found in Module I-3 "Organic Matter," and in standard environmental engineering texts (Metcalf and Eddy, 1972).

Decomposition of organics in land application systems must occur within the microbial active zone in the soil profile. The microbial population is dependent upon, among other things, the available organics. The population responds quickly to organic loads on the soil system. In decomposing readily biodegradable organics, the microbes can generate an impermeable layer within the top inch of soil. This biological clogging is a function of the waste organic material added and the pore space in the receiving soil. Data linking organic loading, soil porosity, and clogging suggests that soils have a remarkably high ability to assimilate organics as long as anaerobic conditions are avoided (McGauhey, 1966). This fact emphasizes the importance of avoiding ponding in normal crop irrigation practice and providing resting periods between water applications.

Maintenance of aerobic conditions ensures that the organic assimilation capacity of microbially active soil is kept at a high level.

The total suspended solids (TSS) in the waste also has the potential to clog the soil surface. Generally, this parameter can be the cause of initial clogging, especially where the influent to the land application site consists of a high TSS wastewater applied at very high application rates such as those expected in rapid infiltration systems.

Clogging of the soil profile is a real threat in land application systems, especially in those systems receiving large amounts of organics. For this reason, the total suspended solids and the BOD_5 or COD should be two waste characteristics monitored in the influent of high rate (>5 ft/wk) land application systems.

Clogging of the soil can result from biological decomposition as well as physical blockage of soil pores by suspended solids in high rate systems.

Organics are discussed at length in Module I-1, "Soil as a Treatment Medium" and in Module II-3 "Organic Matter." Additional data on decomposition and soil clogging can be found in these modules.

Minerals. The mineral portion of total solids is largely made up of dissolved salts and is commonly called total dissolved solids (TDS). These solids are of interest because of their effect on the groundwater, and the related possibility of degrading drinking and irrigation waters. The Public Health Service has set a preferable limit of 500 mg/l on the total dissolved solids content of drinking waters, but in the most recent standards published by EPA (1976) only specific inorganic constituents are noted. Although many waters used for drinking in the United States exceed the suggested limit considerably, it is a useful goal to observe in wastewater management.

Total dissolved solids (TDS) must conform to groundwater regulations for drinking water supplies, and must be monitored to avoid salts buildup in arid areas.

Saline and alkali soils are the result of concentrating salts in the root zone. The continuous application of water containing dissolved solids could result in the buildup of salts and other dissolved solids within the soil profile in areas where the evapotranspiration rate is significant. This buildup of salts in the soil solution can deter crop growth (see Module II-7 "Crop Selection and Management Alternatives"). Salt buildup may be avoided by including a leaching factor in the irrigation water requirements. This type of management practice will avoid dissolved solids buildup in the soil solution. However, those solids will be concentrated as water is removed through evapotranspiration. This more concentrated soil solution will pass through to the groundwater. Where TDS content of the wastewater is less than that of the groundwater, a rapid infiltration/percolation system may be desired for groundwater dilution purposes.

As Table 1 indicates, the total dissolved solids content of municipal wastewater generally lies between 250 and 850 mg/l for weak and strong wastewaters, respectively. A salt (NaCl) concentration of 640 mg/l will result in an electrical conductivity of 1 mmho/cm (25°C). The electrical conductivity of weak and strong municipal wastewaters should be approximately .39 to 1.33 mmho/cm which is comparable to many irrigation waters presently used in the irrigated western United States (Table 4). As is true with these irrigation waters, management is the key to success. It must be stressed that the salt concentration in municipal wastewater is generally acceptable for crop irrigation. The buildup of salts in the soil solution is a danger, but management techniques are available to deter this buildup. The total dissolved solids content

Table 4.   Total Dissolved Solids Content of Selected Irrigation Waters and Irrigation Return Flows.

	California		Texas[c]	
	Imperial Valley[a]	San Joaquin Valley San Luis Drain[b]	High Plains	Low Plains
Electrical Conductivity at 25°C (mmho/cm)	1.4	11	1.1	2.2
pH	8.1	—	7.9	7.5
Total Dissolved Solids (mg/l)	915	7,000	627	1,360
Calcium	104	300	68	92
Magnesium	35	200	47	67
Sodium	143	1,500	36	217
Potassium	5	20	7	4
Carbonate	0	—	0	0
Bicarbonate	187	200	309	425
Sulfate	356	3,000	50	262
Chloride	143	1,200	134	244
Nitrate	1	—	2	11

[a]A. J. MacKenzie, 1972.
[b]L. A. Beck, 1972.
[c]C. W. Wendt, 1972.

of the wastewater as well as that of the soil solution (or leachate, whichever is limiting) must be known in order to use this management tool.

Nutrients

Nutrients found in wastewaters that have caused concern include nitrogen and phosphorus. These are essential nutrients for crop production. However, when the amounts available exceed the demand, leaching of these nutrients may occur to ground and surface waters. A major concept here will be on the design of systems based on the pollutant which causes the strictest limitation. Nitrogen is clearly the most common *limiting* waste constituent for land application in both wastewaters and most organic sludges. For a given waste, this means that the greatest land area will most often be required based on the nitrogen present in that waste.

Nitrogen. Nitrogen in wastewater may be present as ammonium (NH_4^+), organic nitrogen (N–org or R–NH$_2$) and nitrate nitrogen (NO_3^-) (see Table 1). These three forms should be determined when evaluating a waste for land application. Ammonium and organic nitrogen are usually the principal forms found in raw sewage. However, in a nitrified effluent such as that of secondary effluent as well as some tertiary effluents, nitrate nitrogen (NO_3^--N) increases in quantity. Nitrogen in the ammonium form (NH_4^+) will usually adsorb to the negatively charged soil, but nitrate is soluble and will move with the soil water. Movement of this nutrient-enriched soil water within the root zone is necessary to supply nutrients and water to the vegetative crop. Where excesses of nitrogen are applied, the potential of causing nitrogen accumulations in the groundwater exists. Module II-1 "Nitrogen Considerations," deals more specifically with nitrogen compounds, their distribution in the environment, and estimates for loading rates based upon nitrogen limitations.

> *For most wastewater, nitrogen places the most severe limitation on land treatment capacity.*

Phosphorus. Phosphorus in wastewater occurs mainly as inorganic compounds, primarily PO_4^{+3}, and is normally expressed as total phosphate. One of the primary reasons why land application of wastes is becoming a more viable treatment alternative is the soil's high capacity to remove and hold large quantities of phosphorus. In general, it will be shown in Module II-2 "Phosphorus Considerations," that phosphorus is seldom a limiting factor in the design of land application systems. The mean annual per capita excretion of phosphorus is approximately 1.2 pounds. Another 2.3 pounds per capita is contributed annually from synthetic detergents (Black and Veatch, 1971). Therefore, domestic sources of phosphorus contribute approximately 3.5 pounds per capita per year. Table 1 indicates typical phosphorus concentrations of 6-20 mg/l found in municipal wastewaters. However, when phosphorus concentrations exceed 10 mg/l, it can be assumed that commercial and industrial sources are present.

> *The soil has a great capacity for holding phosphorus.*

Usual forms of inorganic phosphorus found in municipal wastewaters include orthophosphate and polyphosphate. Orthophosphates (PO_4^{+3}, HPO_4^{-2}, $H_2PO_4^{-1}$, and H_3PO_4) are immediately available for biological use whereas polyphosphates must first undergo hydrolysis prior to biological use. At times, hydrolysis can be quite a slow process. Organic phosphorus is normally found in higher concentrations in industrial wastes and domestic sewage sludges.

In assessing the maximum application rate of a phosphorus-containing waste, total P is probably the most reliable index. The biological and chemical processes in the soil will tend to convert most of the phosphorus to orthophosphate by hydrolysis of the organic and condensed forms. It is the behavior of orthophosphate that determines the maximum lifetime of a site regarding its ability to retain added phosphorus.

Hazardous Substances

There are many pathogenic microorganisms and hazardous chemicals discharged through municipal sewer systems. Although these substances are relatively dilute in the untreated wastewater, treatment processes including land application systems tend to concentrate toxic materials. This initially occurs in waste sludges and finally in the soil profile. Because many hazardous materials are present and may be concentrated, they still pose a threat to society. A rational basis for their control must be developed in any waste management scheme. Data presented in Modules II-4, "Potentially Toxic Elements," and II-5 "Pathogens," show that the public health dangers due to such contaminants as pathogens and heavy metals can be minimized in land application systems.

Pathogens.   Many viruses are found in municipal sewage. More than 70 new enteric viruses have been identified in raw sewage over the past 25 years, all of which are found in human feces. The effective (infection-producing) dose rate of virus organisms was thought to be as high as a million but recent studies have shown that one virus particle may cause an infection in the host. While this individual may not develop a clinical disease, he may unknowingly become a carrier (McDermott, 1975).

Pathogenic bacteria are also discharged into domestic wastewaters through the feces of infected humans. Although most disease-causing organisms can be found, the concentrations are low, and many are therefore difficult to isolate. For this reason, an indicator organism (usually coliform bacteria) is used to determine if the environment will support pathogenic bacteria populations. Table 1 indicates the amounts of total coliform bacteria and virus expected in typical raw domestic sewage.

Pathogenic protozoa and helminths (parasitic worms) are two other common microorganisms found in domestic sewage, the eggs of the latter being very difficult to eradicate. These as well as bacteria and virus are discussed at length in Module II-5 "Pathogens."

The initial concentration of pathogens found in the influent of land application systems must be known to assess the resulting increase or decrease in populations found on the site. There is a direct relation between the health of the human population contributing wastes to a treatment system and the number of pathogenic organisms present in the system.

Potentially toxic elements found in municipal sewage include many substances which are also essential to microbial and plant life. Table 1 lists a few heavy metals found in trunk sewers collecting wastes from primarily residential areas (Davis, 1975). Commercial and industrial wastewater additions to municipal systems increase the variability in constituents by several orders of magnitude.

Municipal systems can be protected from inputs of toxic substances in high concentrations through pretreatment requirements leveled against commercial and industrial sources of wastes. Each situation is evaluated on a site-specific basis taking into account the industrial waste, the municipal treatment measures, and the receiving sink for the wastes. As industries implement these controls, it is likely that concentrations of toxics found in municipal wastewater will decrease. However, toxic substances in small amounts will always be present as long as metal pipes are used for home and commercial plumbing. Persistent organic chemicals such as PCB's enter the waste stream in substances used in the home as well as industrial point source discharges. These substances must also be classified as potentially toxic.

Wastewaters may contain many substances which can be toxic to plants or animals in sufficiently high concentrations. These potentially toxic elements may be treated by land application.

Table 3 lists two categories of toxic substances of concern in land application systems: (1) those most likely to cause toxicity to higher plants, and (2) those that have greatest potential for degrading ground water quality beneath land application systems. All of these substances are likely to be found in municipal wastes, and all respond to treatment in the soil. Various parameters affect the soil's ability to immobilize potentially toxic substances. Monitoring and documentation of these toxic substances must be initiated for the waste influent, and, eventually, their buildup in the soil profile. Module II-4 "Potentially Toxic Elements," discusses toxic elements at length. Module II-11 "Monitoring at Land Application Sites," discusses this aspect of site operation in relation to potentially toxic elements.

FLOW DISTRIBUTION AND POLLUTANT REMOVALS IN CONVENTIONAL AND LAND TREATMENT PROCESSES

The flow of wastewater and sludges as well as selected wastewater characteristics are shown in Figures 3–10. These diagrams outline the total amount of waste constituent entering each treatment process and depict how much of each is separated from the main flow of wastewater. These figures are drawn approximately to scale to enable the reader to estimate easily the efficiency of individual processes in controlling pollutants. The reader should relate the numbers given in each of the following figures to the composition of "strong, medium, and weak" wastewaters in Table 1, page 58. The percent removals and flows in the various processes are of importance in Figures 3–10, not absolute numbers.

The flow of wastewater and sludges shown in Figure 3 is based upon a wastewater design flow of 100 gallons per capita per day. Sludge removal in preliminary and primary treatment is less than 0.50% of the total waste flow, whereas approximately 1% is separated out in secondary treatment. Examination of the flows in this figure illustrate the reason that toxic elements are more of a problem in the sludges than in the wastewaters. It will be shown in Module II-4 "Potentially Toxic Elements" that a large fraction of the toxic elements are attached to the microbial mass and particulates removed during secondary treatment. The ratios of flow rates (inflow/sludge flow) are essentially concentration factors. Thus, any adsorbed material would increase its concentration 400 times in primary sludge and 100 times in secondary sludge. Further reductions in sludge volumes without the concomitant removal of the toxic elements will cause further concentration of the toxic elements. Advanced wastewater treatments can separate a substantial amount of the remaining solids, which may be contained in a relatively high portion of the waste flow, as shown in Figure 3. These solids may then be separated and returned to sludge treatment.

Sludge removal in conventional treatment concentrates potentially toxic elements in the separated solids. Sludge handling accounts for 30–40% of conventional treatment costs.

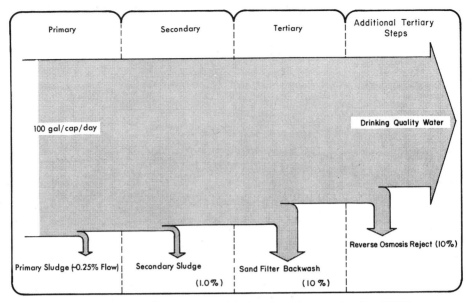

Figure 3. Flow distribution of wastewater and sludges through conventional and AWT processes.

The cost of handling sludge in conventional waste treatment is approximately 30–40% of the total system cost. This cost can be minimized in land application systems by incorporating the solids into the soil profile during the treatment process.

Organics in conventional treatment, Figure 4, are almost entirely separated in primary and secondary treatment. Aproximately 25% of the organic load in raw sewage is separated in primary sedimentation. Another 40% is utilized in microbial respiration of secondary treatment where CO_2, H_2O, and new microbial cell mass are the end products. The wasted microbial mass of secondary treatment accounts for another 20% of the total organic load. The effluent from secondary treatment carries with it approximately 15% of the original organic load. Tertiary treatment such as carbon adsorption can remove at least another 10% of the organics (based on original input quantity) leaving up to 5% of the input in tertiary effluent.

Suspended solids removal in conventional treatment, Figure 5, largely occurs during primary sedimentation. Approximately 60% of these solids are separated here. A high percentage of suspended solids are organic, as an investigation of the organics flow diagram, Figure 4, indicates. A portion of the organic solids is destroyed during microbial respiration in secondary treatment as described previously. Thirty percent of these solids are removed here, and approximately 10% are passed into receiving waters in effluents or on to tertiary treatment. Tertiary treatment may reduce this suspended solids content to as little as 2% of the original concentration.

Figure 6 indicates the level of suspended solids loading associated with a year-round (50-week) application of 2 in./wk. of raw wastewater to an irrigation system, in relation to the mass of solids in the soil. From Figure 1 approximately 75% of the suspended solids in raw wastewater can be classified as organic, or roughly 4450 lb/acre-yr organic suspended solids applied in Figure 6. This represents about 2% of the 200,000 lb/acre of native organic solids in the upper 2 feet of a typical agricultural soil. This material will be held in the aerated zone of the soil and decomposed by aerobic bacteria. The remaining 1510 lb/acre-yr of inorganic solids represents about $\frac{2}{100}$ of 1% of the inorganic soil particles per acre-2 feet.

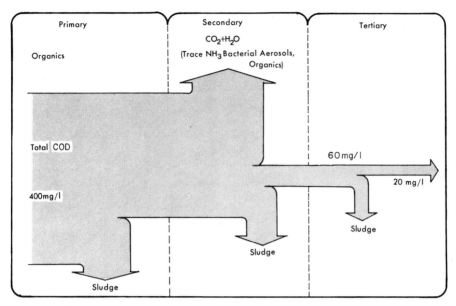

Figure 4. Fate of organics in conventional treatment and AWT processes.

A typical 5-day biological oxygen demand (BOD$_5$) of raw wastewater is approximately 250 mg/l as shown in Figure 7. Primary sedimentation removes about 35% of this through organic suspended solids removal. The microbial processes of secondary treatment are designed to remove most of the remaining BOD$_5$, therefore it is not surprising that 50–60% of influent BOD$_5$ is removed in secondary treatment. The remaining 5-15% of the BOD$_5$ is passed on to tertiary treatment as soluble organics.

Figure 8 presents a similar picture of BOD$_5$ application to a land treatment system as that

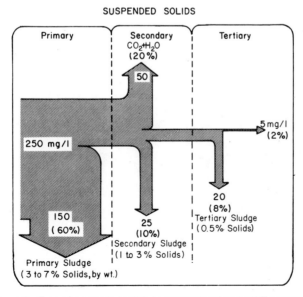

Figure 5. Fate of suspended solids in conventional and AWT processes.

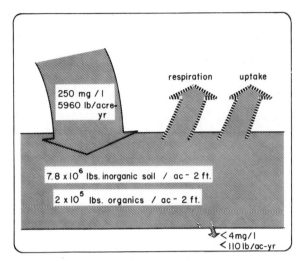

Figure 6. Fate of suspended solids in land treatment systems.

given in Figure 6 for suspended solids. Bacterial respiration will be the prime mechanism involved in reducing the BOD in percolate from the upper 2 feet of soil to a negligible level. Module II-3 "Organic Matter," examines in detail the conditions of organics removal in the soil and cites studies indicating very high removal rates at land application sites.

The total dissolved solids content of municipal wastewaters varies considerably. Figure 9 illustrates a median TDS concentration. As shown in this figure, preliminary, primary, and secondary conventional treatments do not remove these solids from the wastewater flow. Tertiary treatment processes have not attempted to remove these solids on a regular basis for to do so would be very energy intensive. However, reverse osmosis and distillation are two tertiary processes which could remove dissolved solids. The recycle and reuse of domestic wastewater must overcome the cost of TDS removal, for each time water is used, the TDS con-

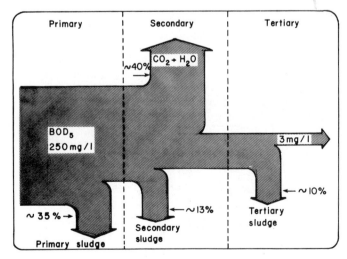

Figure 7. Fate of 5-day biochemical oxygen demand in conventional and AWT processes.

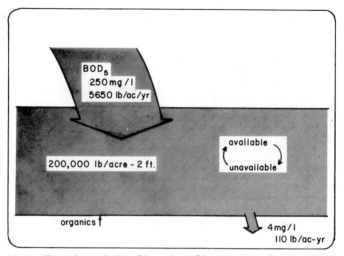

Mass Transfer of the Five-day Biochemical Oxygen Demand

Figure 8. Fate of BOD$_5$ in land treatment systems.

tent increases. Some tertiary treatment processes add chemicals which increase the TDS content of the wastewater while removing undesirable constituents, i.e., phosphorus precipitation, ion exchange.

Conventional tertiary treatment for phosphorus removal can increase dissolved solids content.

A similar picture is indicated in Figure 10 for land application systems. In fact, in arid climates, salts buildup is often a problem in irrigated agriculture. Sufficient hydraulic load is

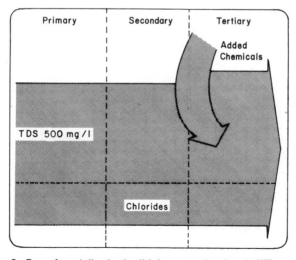

Figure 9. Fate of total dissolved solids in conventional and AWT processes.

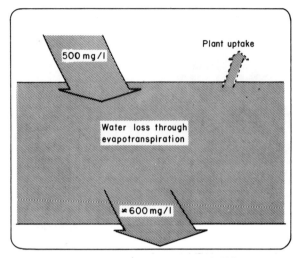

Mass Transfer of Total Dissolved Solids

Figure 10. Fate of TDS in land treatment systems.

required in these areas to leach salts from the root zone, while not accumulating too great a concentration in the groundwater if it is to be used for drinking.

The total nitrogen found in raw domestic sewage varies between 15 and 60 mg/l, where 40-50 mg/l would be a typical amount. The fate of nitrogen in wastewater treatment is shown in Figure 11. Approximately 25% of this total nitrogen is separated in primary sedimentation as organic N. The microbial assimilation of organics in secondary treatment transforms organic nitrogen to ammonia and nitrate. In this process a small amount of nitrogen is released as ammonia and nitrogen gas. Still a smaller amount of organic nitrogen is wasted with the secondary sludge. Approximately 70% of the total nitrogen found in raw wastewater passes through primary and secondary treatment to tertiary treatment where all but 2-6% can be removed

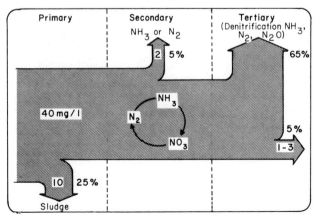

Figure 11. Fate of nitrogen in conventional and AWT processes.

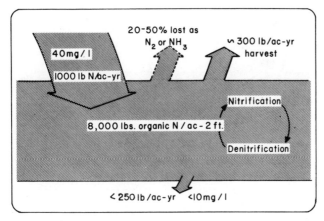

Figure 12. Fate of nitrogen in land treatment systems.

using the microbial nitrification-denitrification process. The nitrogen concentration of tertiary effluent is mostly in the nitrate form where 1–3 mg/l might be expected.

Nitrogen removal in land application systems depends mostly on volatilization and plant uptake (Figure 12). This represents application of raw or screened wastewater to an irrigation system. Twenty to 50% loss is a reliable range for ammonia volatilization, and 300 lb/acre-yr nitrogen uptake can be associated with plants having a good capacity for N utilization. Systems can be managed to produce additional removal from denitrification of NO_3^- in the soil solution. Short-term nitrogen storage is also provided in the soil by immobilization within the soil, or organic uptake of mineral nitrogen, and by ammonium adsorption on soil particles with a significant cation exchange capacity.

Phosphorus removal in conventional and AWT treatment processes is shown in Figure 13. Approximately $\frac{1}{3}$ of the total phosphorus is removed in preliminary and primary treatment through screening and sedimentation of suspended solids. Phosphorus removal in secondary treatment consists of the very small amount tied up in microbial cells which is wasted as sludge. However, tertiary treatments are available which will remove 80–95% of the total phosphorus

Mass Transfer of Phosphorus

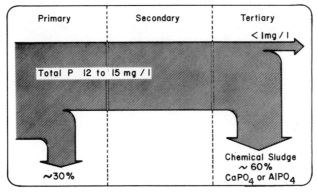

Figure 13. Fate of phosphorus in conventional and AWT processes.

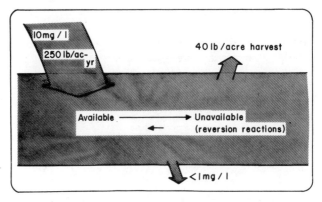

Figure 14. Fate of phosphorus in land treatment systems.

influent. This is effectively accomplished within the primary sedimentation tanks where alum addition forces the phosphorus precipitation.

Figure 14 indicates the relative input and removal of phosphorus in a land treatment system. The very low leaching loss of P is due mainly to the very large fraction of inorganic precipitates and adsorbed inorganic phosphorus found in the soil. More phosphorus will also be immobilized in organic forms. Dissolved P, which is available for plant uptake as well as leaching, comprises a small fraction of the total, including waste inputs.

The fate of *toxics* in conventional and AWT is shown in Figure 15. Potential toxics include heavy metals as well as other trace elements. Generally high concentrations of heavy metals are found in secondary and AWT sludges although the amounts are quite variable. As much as 80% of the potentially toxic substances are removed with secondary sludges whereas the remaining 20% is removed in tertiary sludges. Less than 1% of the incoming toxics are found in tertiary effluents. This illustrates the fact that potentially toxic elements are basically a sludge application problem rather than a wastewater application problem.

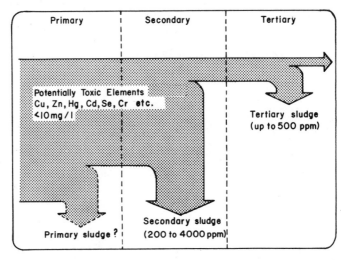

Figure 15. Fate of heavy metals and other potentially toxic elements in conventional and AWT processes.

SLUDGE CHARACTERISTICS

The properties of wastewater treatment residues which can be used in land application systems are highly variable. Sludge characteristics are a function of influent wastewater characteristics, treatment processes, and efficiency of the wastewater treatment. The form of sludge treatment, storage, and handling employed prior to land application will also affect its chemical and biological composition, and physical properties.

> *Characteristics of sludge for land application depend on influent wastewater characteristics, treatment processes and their efficiency, type of sludge treatment, storage and handling time before site delivery.*

Sludges resulting from various treatment steps have distinct physical properties depending on their constituents and level of biological stabilization. Table 5 gives a comparison of typical sludges from conventional processes.

Table 6 gives some idea of the usual range and expected values of several chemical constituents of "typical" sludge. Nitrogen, phosphorus, and potassium are important to land application sites as nutrients. The other items listed indicate the relative degree of biological stability of raw and digested sludge, and the types of inorganics and resistant organics that are normally removed only through primary treatment (cellulose and silica). The variability of sludge components is reflected in the range of values for each chemical constituent. The figures in Table 6 are useful in preliminary design, but it is important to analyze the sludge which will be applied in any given system.

Table 5.   General Physical Characteristics of Various Types of Sludge.

Sludge	Color	Other Physical Properties	Odor	Digestibility (Amenability to Further Biological Stabilization)
Primary sedimentation	Gray	Slimy	Extremely offensive	Readily digested
Chemical precipitation (primary)	Black, red surface if high in iron	Slimy, gelatinous, gives off considerable gas	Offensive	Slower rate than primary sedimentation
Activated sludge	Brown, dark if nearly septic	Flocculent	Inoffensive, earthy when fresh; putrifies rapidly	Readily digested
Trickling filter humus	Brownish	Flocculent	Relatively inoffensive, decomposes slowly	Readily digested
Digested sludge	Dark brown to black	Contains very large quantity of gas	Inoffensive if thoroughly digested; like tar or loamy soil.	Well stabilized
Septic tank sludge	Black		Offensive (H_2S) unless very long storage time	Mostly stabilized

Adapted from Metcalf and Eddy, 1972.

Table 6.   Typical Chemical Composition of Raw and Digested Sludge.

Item	Raw Primary Sludge		Digested Sludge	
	Range	Typical	Range	Typical
Total dry solids (TS), %	2.0–7.0	4.0	6.0–12.0	10.0
Volatile solids (% of TS)	60–80	65	30–60	40.0
Grease and fats				
(ether soluble, % of TS)	6.0–30.0	—	5.0–20.0	—
Protein (% of TS)	20–30	25	15–20	18
Nitrogen (N, % of TS)	1.5–4.0	2.5	1.6–6.0	3.0
Phosphorus (P_2O_5, % of TS)	0.8–2.8	1.6	1.5–4.0	2.5
Potash (K_2O, % of TS)	0–1.0	0.4	0.0–3.0	1.0
Cellulose (% of TS)	8.0–15.0	10.0	8.0–15.0	10.0
Silica (SiO_2, % of TS)	15.0–20.0	—	10.0–20.0	—
pH	5.0–8.0	6.0	6.5–7.5	7.0
Alkalinity (mg/liter as $CaCO_3$)	500–1,500	600	2,500–3,500	3,000

Metcalf and Eddy, 1972.

Table 7.   Summary of Sludge Parameters from a Widespread Sample of Sewage Treatment Plants.

Constituent		Number of Treatment Plants	Minimum	Maximum	Median	Mean	Coefficient of Variability (%)
pH		61	5.3	11.7			
Organic C	%	101	6.5	48.0	30.4	31.0	27
Total N	%	134	0.0	17.6	2.5	3.2	85
NH_4–N	%	56	0.0	6.76	0.13	0.74	171
NO_3–N	µg/g	34	9	4,880	194	646	158
Total P	%	128	0.0	6.1	1.8	1.9	61
Fe	%	104	0.0	15.3	0.8	1.4	148
Al	%	83	0.1	3.5	0.4	0.5	119
Na	%	126	0.01	2.66	0.12	0.35	146
K	%	142	0.02	1.92	0.24	0.30	99
As	µg/g	10	6.0	230.0	10.0	43.1	171
Mg	µg/g	139	300	19,700	4,600	5,414	75
B	µg/g	60	4	757	28	109	162
Zn	µg/g	134	101	27,800	1,800	2,997	134
Cu	µg/g	131	84	10,400	850	1,308	138
Ni	µg/g	109	10	3,515	190	440	162
Cr	µg/g	119	17	99,000	906	3,280	309
Mn	µg/g	82	18	7,100	200	390	209
Cd	µg/g	115	4	846	20	101	157
Pb	µg/g	116	13	19,730	652	1,656	177
Hg	µg/g	53	1.0	10,600	6.0	1,077	232
Co	µg/g	15	1.0	18	4.0	5.3	83
Mo	µg/g	29	5.0	39	30	27.7	26
Cd/Zn	%	115	0.1	46	1.7	5.7	163

McCalla, Peterson, and Lue-Hing, 1977.

Table 8.   Comparison of Metal Content of the Calumet Sewage Treatment Plant's Sludge Before and After the 1969 Metropolitan Sanitary District's Sewage and Waste Control Ordinance on Maximum Allowable Metal Concentration to the Sewer System.

Metal	Maximum Allowable Concentration In Incoming Sewage by MSDGC Ordinance	Sludge Source			Metal Reduction Ratio Before 1969:1974
		Lagoons	Anaerobic Digester		
		Before 1969[a]	1972[b]	1974[c]	
	mg/liter	——— μg/g dry-weight basis ———			
Cd	2.0	190	100	54	3.5
Cr (total)	25.0	2,100	1,100	790	2.7
Cu	3.0	1,500	900	282	5.3
Fe	50.0	53,700	36,800	24,200	2.2
Hg	0.0005	3.3	3.0	2.15	1.5
Ni	10.0	1,000	200	77	13.0
Pb	0.5	1,800	1,800	486	3.7
Zn	15.0	5,500	3,500	2,800	2.0

[a]Mean of 10 samples.
[b]Mean of 22 samples.
[c]Mean of 6 samples.

McCalla, Peterson, and Lue-Hing, 1977.

Table 7 is a summary of actual laboratory analyses of sludge from 174 treatment plants in seven midwestern and eastern states. Data on metals and salts discussed in Module II-4, "Potentially Toxic Elements," and Module II-7, "Crop Selection and Management Alternatives," are presented.

> *Wide range of characteristics for a "typical" municipal sludge shows the variability of sludge composition and emphasizes the need for analyzing sludge for each land treatment project.*

Module II-4, "Potentially Toxic Elements" points out the advantages and limitations of source control as a means of adjusting the level of metals which ultimately find their way to municipal sludge. One such program was instituted in Chicago in 1969, when the concentration of various elements which industries are allowed to discharge to the sewerage system was limited by ordinance. Table 8 compares sludge metal levels from 1969, 1972, and 1974 at a Chicago treatment plant serving a mixed industrial-municipal area. Although significant reductions in specific element levels can result from industrial source control, further reductions are difficult due to the contribution from domestic plumbing and the general urban environment.

> *Industrial source control is important in reducing metal content of sludge, but the effectiveness is limited by the amount of metals from domestic sources.*

The approximate percentage removal of sludge constituents in conventional primary sedimentation, secondary activated sludge, and tertiary processes is indicated in the mass flow diagrams (Figures 3–10 of this module). This discussion is limited to conventional treatment of municipal wastewater. Consideration of specialized industrial wastes and other treatment processes would be too involved for this section. The designer must be familiar with the waste inputs and chemicals used in sewage treatment (i.e., alum added for precipitation, resulting in high sludge aluminum content) in order to provide for proper nutrient and potentially toxic element application rates for the specific situation at hand.

BIBLIOGRAPHY

American Chemical Society. 1969. Cleaning our environment, the chemical basis for action. Report of the Committee on Chemistry and Public Affairs, Washington, D.C. p. 249.

Battelle Memorial Institute. 1974. Muncipal sewage treatment—a comparison of alternatives. Prepared for the Council on Environmental Quality, Executive Office of the President in association with the EPA, Office of Planning and Evaluation. EQC 316.

Beck, L. A. 1972. Treatment of irrigation return flows in the San Joaquin Valley. *In* EPA and Colorado State University Proceedings of the National Conference on Managing Irrigated Agriculture to Improve Water Quality.

Black and Veatch, Consulting Engineers. 1971. Process design manual for phosphorus removal. U.S.E.P.A. Technology transfer. Program #17010 GNP.

Blakeslee, P. A. 1973. Monitoring considerations for municipal wastewater effluent and sludge application to the land. pp. 183–198. *In* Proceedings of the joint conference on recycling municipal sludges and effluents on land. Champaign, Ill.

Davis, J. A. III and J. Jackson. 1975. Heavy metals in wastewater in three urban areas. *J. Water Pollut. Contr. Fed.*, 47(9):2292-2297.

Dean, R. B. and J. E. Smith, Jr. 1973. The properties of sludge pp. 39–47. *In* Proceedings of the joint conference on recycling municipal sludges and effluents on land. Champaign, Ill.

DeMichele, E. 1974. Water reuse, virus removal, and public health. Published in Virus Survival in Water and Wastewater Systems, Water Resources Symposium Number Seven pp. 45–56. Center for Research in Water Resources the University of Texas at Austin. Edited by Joseph F. Malina, Jr. and Bernard P. Sagik.

EPA. 1976. National interim primary drinking water regulations. Office of Water Supply. EPA-570/9-76-003. Washington, D.C. 159 p.

Farrell, J. B. 1974. Overview of sludge handling and disposal. pp. 5–10. *In* Proceedings of the national conference on municipal sludge management. Pittsburgh, Pa.

Lager, J. A. and W. G. Smith. 1974. Urban stormwater management and technology—an assessment. EPA-670/2-74-040 for National Environmental Research Center, Office of Research and Development, U.S. EPA, Cincinnati, Ohio.

MacKenzie, A. J. 1972. Soil, water, and cropping management for successful agriculture in the Imperial Valley. *In* EPA and Colorado State University Proceedings of the National Conference on Managing Irrigated Agriculture to Improve Water Quality.

McCalla, T. M., J. R. Peterson, and C. Lue-Hing. 1977. Properties of agricultural and municipal wastes. *In* Soils for management of organic wastes and wastewaters. SSSA, ASA, and CSSA. Madison, Wisconsin.

McDermott, J. H. 1975. Virus problems in water supplies, Part II. *Water and Sewage Works*, June 1975.

McGauhey, P. H., R. B. Krone and J. H. Winneberger. 1966. Soil mantle as a wastewater treatment system. University of California, Berkeley, California. SERL Report No. 6607, 120 p.

Metcalf and Eddy, Inc. 1972. Wastewater engineering—collection, treatment, disposal. McGraw-Hill Book Co., New York 782 p.

Page, A. L. 1974. Fate and effects of trace elements in sewage sludge when applied to agricultural lands. EPA-670/2-74-005.

Rice, R. C. 1974. Soil clogging during infiltration of secondary effluent. *J. Water Pollut. Contr. Fed.*, 46(4): 708-716.

Train, R. E. 1976. Federal Register Vol. 41, No. 29., February 1976. Alternative waste management techniques for best practicable waste treatment.

Wendt, C. W. 1972. Subirrigation studies in the high and rolling plains of Texas. *In* EPA and Colorado State University Proceedings of the National Conference on Managing Irrigated Agriculture to Improve Water Quality.

Module I-4

TREATMENT SYSTEMS, EFFLUENT QUALITIES, AND COSTS

SUMMARY

Conventional wastewater treatment in some form is often used as pretreatment to land application systems. This may vary from screening to higher levels of pretreatment for some special situations. Preliminary treatment removes items which may clog subsequent waste handling equipment. Primary and secondary treatments may be required prior to moderate and high rate rapid infiltration systems, respectively, in order to prevent possible soil clogging. The use of chlorine as a disinfectant prior to land application rarely is necessary, but may be required by state regulatory agencies.

Land application systems have been tailored after water distribution systems utilized in irrigated agriculture. This technology has been utilized for many years providing land application systems with an assortment of tried and proven application equipment.

In comparing conventional waste treatment to land application systems, it is apparent the latter may provide equal or better effluent qualities at lower costs. For a given situation, this can only be decided after a site specific evaluation of the treatment alternatives.

This module describes the following conventional treatment systems and evaluates their use as pretreatment steps for land application:

Treatment	Use as Pretreatment
Preliminary	protection of piping and spray systems
Primary	as above, plus protection of moderate rate land application from soil clogging
Secondary	protection of high rate application from soil clogging
Disinfection	following secondary treatment, reduction in numbers of pathogenic bacteria and viruses
Advanced waste treatment	not applicable; results should be comparable to land treatment

Effluent qualities are summarized, a brief discussion of application systems is given, and cost comparisons are discussed in some detail. Different approaches to sizing of conventional and land application systems are discussed, and have a significant bearing on actual cost comparisons.

CONTENTS

GLOSSARY

For the purpose of this Module, the following definitions of environmental engineering terms will apply:

advanced waste treatment—Any treatment—biological, chemical or physical—which achieves removals of nutrients and/or soluble species not adequately removed by a secondary treatment, while still attaining the suspended solids and organics removals of secondary treatment.

preliminary treatment—A subset of primary treatment. Removal of screenings and grit (readily settleable non-organic matter), without any appreciable removal of organic fraction of the wastewater.

primary treatment—Removal of screenings, grit, grease and floating solids, and readily settleable organic solids from wastewater. Treatment standards usually associate removals of about 50-60% suspended solids and 25-40% BOD with primary treatment.

secondary treatment—The application of biological treatment processes, usually an activated sludge or fixed-film microbial reactor along with secondary settling, following a primary treatment system. Removals of 85-90% BOD and suspended solids are commonly associated with secondary treatment. Thus treatment in this range of efficiency can be referred to as "equivalent to secondary treatment" if achieved by other means such as lagoons, extended aeration, or physical/chemical treatment.

treatment system—A series of treatment units arranged in a rational sequence in order to produce a desired overall effect on a wastewater. The cumulative effects of each treatment unit are taken into account in system design.

treatment unit—A single physical, chemical, or biological step used to produce a desired effect on a wastewater which has certain known or assumed characteristics.

unit operation—A treatment unit which uses chemical or physical mechanisms as the basic means of treating wastewater.

unit process—A treatment unit which uses biological mechanisms as the basic means of treating wastewater.

OBJECTIVES

Upon completion of this module, the reader should be able to:

1. Describe the level of pretreatment for irrigation, overland flow, and high rate land application systems.
2. List the bases for design flow rates of conventional and land application systems.
3. List a range of percent removal efficiencies for BOD, suspended solids, and nutrients for conventional, advanced, and land application systems.
4. Explain in terms of removal efficiencies the cost comparisons summarized in Figure 7, "Comparison of Costs."

THE PURPOSE OF CONVENTIONAL TREATMENT SYSTEMS AND THEIR VALUE AS A PRETREATMENT TO LAND APPLICATION SYSTEMS

Many different kinds of waste treatment units and systems have been developed to meet the needs of society. Each carries out certain functions, i.e., settleable solids removal, organic waste matter removal, enhancement of subsequent treatment processes, pathogen destruction, dissolved solids removal, etc. Systems are composed of some combination of physical, chemical, and biological units. Some units make use of more than one of these treatment mechanisms. The following are discussed as possible pretreatment steps to land application: (1) preliminary, (2) primary, (3) secondary, (4) disinfection, (5) advanced waste treatment (AWT).

Preliminary Treatment. The purpose of preliminary treatment is to remove large and dense objects found in raw sewage. These might include such materials as sand, gravel, wood, and rags. Figure 1 is a typical flow diagram depicting those processes that could be considered as preliminary treatment. Not all may be used at a specific plant.

> **Preliminary treatment removes large, dense objects from raw sewage. Operations employed include screening, grinding and grit removal.*

---

*This and other italicized summaries are intended to highlight key ideas, provide a basis for later review or to aid in skimming sections that are relatively familiar. They can be ignored in a complete reading of the text.

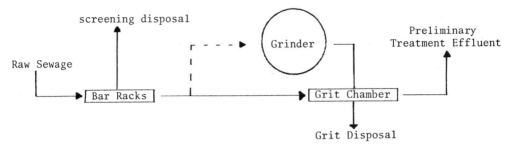

Figure 1. Typical preliminary treatment flow scheme.

The solid material separated in preliminary treatment is saturated with raw sewage, making it quite objectionable. These solids are generally disposed of in landfills or by incineration. The remaining wastewater will be comprised of less than 1% solids which may be easily pumped and conveyed by conventional water handling equipment.

At this point the only pollutants that have been removed from the wastewater stream are large objects that can be easily removed and which may damage or clog subsequent wastewater handling equipment such as pumps, pipes, valves, weirs, sprinkler nozzles, in-line filters. The land application system will benefit from low maintenance as a result of efficient preliminary pretreatment.

> *Good preliminary treatment reduces maintenance of wastewater handling equipment by removing objects that could damage or clog equipment.*

In Braunsweig, Germany, where land application of domestic sewage has been practiced since the late 1800s, this is the only pretreatment utilized. As will be shown in Module I-9, "Legal Aspects," there are few instances in the United States where pretreatment for land application systems would be acceptable at this level. However, this is an area where more research data from full-scale systems is needed. With this kind of data, pretreatment restrictions would probably be relaxed considerably. Requirements for pretreatment, where disinfection is of little concern, would be based upon system clogging potential and the maintenance program. Screening may be all that is required for smooth operation.

Primary Treatment Separates Solids.   Primary treatment is generally considered to be initial sedimentation of large particles. Many engineers think of preliminary treatment as a part of primary treatment. The distinction is made here so that evaluation of each with respect to land application systems will be clear.

The purpose of conventional primary treatment is to further separate settleable and floatable solids. Items which generally pass through preliminary treatment but are separated out in primary treatment are fats, greases, oils, soap, small pieces of rubber, cork, wood and plastics, vegetable and fruit debris, and settleable fecal matter. The floatable items are mechanically skimmed from the sedimentation tank surface while the more dense particles settle and are removed as primary sludge. This process removes 50–65% of the suspended solids and 25–40% of the 5-day biological oxygen demand (BOD_5) from the wastewater stream. Figure 2 outlines typical processes in primary treatment.

> *Floatable items are skimmed off and dense particles that have settled are removed in conventional primary treatment.*

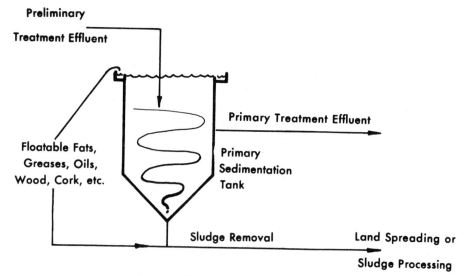

Figure 2. Primary treatment flow scheme.

Primary treatment is a valuable separation process where moderate rate land application systems receive the final effluent, i.e., rapid infiltration systems receiving between 5 and 60 in./wk. Physical and biological clogging has been known to be a problem where excessive organics are applied to the soil. Primary treatment removes a substantial amount of these organics. In systems where a crop is to be maintained, lower application rates are required, thus organic clogging may not pose a threat to the system operation. The organics that would normally be separated in primary treatment are readily assimilated within the soil/plant treatment medium. Primary treatment would not be needed as a pretreatment to land application systems where crop maintenance is part of the treatment scheme, although many crop systems operate successfully with primary pretreatment. Additional information of the fate of organics in soil systems is given in Module II-3 "Soil as a Treatment Medium," and in Module II-3 "Organic Matter."

> *Primary treatment removes settleable organics; their removal may be unnecessary if wastewater is being applied to crops which can readily assimilate them.*

Secondary Treatment Uses Microorganisms.   Secondary treatment systems include biological treatment such as aerated lagoons, trickling filters, and activated sludge, as well as subsequent solids settling. Typical systems are shown in Figure 3. These are the types of unit processes that would be considered where the pretreatment requirement included secondary treatment. These systems are designed to remove suspended solids, particulate organics, and soluble organics from the wastewater.

> *Secondary treatment removes suspended solids and soluble organics.*

These processes involve a microbial population capable of using the wastewater organics as food. In doing this, the waste organics are transformed into carbon dioxide or more stable solids which are easily separated from the waters by secondary sedimentation. The sludge resulting from these aerobic processes is separated from the wastewater stream in subsequent settling basins. The quality of the secondary effluent is directly related to the effectiveness of the sedi-

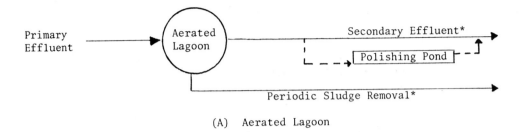

(A)   Aerated Lagoon

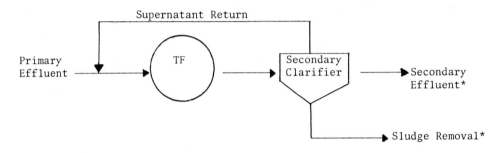

(B)   Trickling Filter

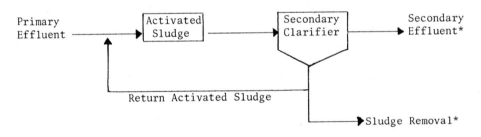

(C)   Activated Sludge

* All available for land
   application at this
   point. Sludges may go
   to digestion process.

Figure 3. Secondary treatment flow schemes.

mentation tank in removing these solids. The sludge from these types of systems may be further handled through aerobic or anaerobic digestion, chemical treatment and/or a dewatering process before final residue disposal by ocean dumping, disposal in a landfill, spreading on the land, etc.

In secondary treatment, microorganisms metabolize waste organics transforming them into CO_2 or more stable solids.

The removal of organics in secondary treatment enchances the effluent value as an influent to high rate (greater than 5 feet per week) land application systems. Although 5-10% of the suspended solids may still remain in secondary effluent, the water at this point often has a clarity approaching tap water. Of the systems reviewed by Pound and Crites (1973), all high rate land application systems received secondary treatment. Odor control is also accomplished by the aerobic biological oxidation in secondary treatment.

> *Secondary treatment effluent is suited to high rates of wastewater application to land.*

The use of secondary treatment as a pretreatment to land application systems not utilizing a high loading rate would not appear to be necessary to protect the soil from organics. The biological oxidation of organics occurs as readily in the soil system as it does in the controlled environment of secondary treatment (see Module II-3 "Organic Matter"). The reduction of BOD and suspended solids in the wastewater has been higher from land application systems than from conventional secondary treatment. Where odor control is a problem, secondary treatment or some form of aeration pretreatment will probably be required.

> *The soil can perform the breakdown of organics as readily as conventional secondary treatment systems.*

Disinfection Kills Pathogens.   Disinfection of wastewater effluents has been practiced for many years in an attempt to rid society of disease causing organisms. The organisms of greatest concern to the human are pathogenic bacteria, viruses, and amoebic cysts. These are the causes of diseases such as typhoid, cholera, dysentery, and infectious hepatitis. The use of chlorine and its compounds as a disinfectant may remove greater than 99% of the bacteria and virus population in the wastewater. (See Module II-5 "Pathogens"). Other types of disinfection have been used but have not been as cost effective. Most experience with alternate methods has been gained in Europe with ozonation. However, this pertains to potable water treatment, as wastewater disinfection is uncommon there.

> *Disinfection of wastewater kills varying numbers of bacteria, viruses, and other micro-organisms.*

Chlorination system design is based upon rapid initial mixing, adequate contact time, and the resulting chlorine residual in the effluent. In the past, emphasis has been placed on contact time, but guidelines base the effectiveness of disinfection upon the resulting chlorine residual. Chlorine residuals found in typical wastewaters vary from 0 to 3.0 mg/1. Free chlorine residuals of 0.5 mg/1 are recommended where virus inactivation is needed (Robson, 1975). Effective chlorination requires that the wastewater have low suspended solids and organic concentrations, equivalent to secondary effluent, for the reasons given below.

Since chlorine is a powerful oxidation agent, it is also consumed in many side reactions with reduced organic matter and inorganics such as ammonia. These reactions may quickly eliminate the free chlorine residual and decrease the killing action of the chlorine. This raises one of the complicated issues of land treatment systems. As was noted earlier, secondary treated effluents may not be required for organic removal, since soils have significant organic assimilation capacities. Yet in order to obtain efficient pathogen destruction at reasonable chlorine dosages, it is necessary to first remove other compounds with which chlorine will react. Where the public health problem is controlled in another manner, it might be concluded that neither secondary treatment nor chlorination is necessary. This is another area where full scale operating data is needed.

> *Because of reactions with organics and ammonia, high removals of these materials must be achieved if chlorination is to be effective.*

With respect to land application systems, crop growth has been shown to suffer under 0.5 mg/l chlorine residual in the irrigated wastewater (Reed, 1975). Trout and salmon as well as organisms on which fish feed cannot withstand a chlorine residual greater than 0.01 mg/l, whereas 0.002 mg/l should protect most aquatic organisms (Robson, 1975). Judging from the information presented above it appears that pathogen inactivation and optimum crop response cannot both be achieved utilizing chlorine as a disinfectant.

> *Chlorine has undesirable effects on crops and higher aquatic animals.*

Ozone has been used successfully as an effective wastewater disinfectant. Although it is more expensive to use than chlorine compounds, it leaves no residual to degrade the receiving sink. If disinfection is required of influents to land application systems, ozone may present a technically feasible alternative which will safeguard the application area and discharge site as well as ensure an adequate pathogen kill.

> *Ozone, although costly, may be used for disinfecting wastewater prior to land application.*

Advanced Wastewater Treatment (AWT).   Advanced wastewater treatment or tertiary treatment of wastewater refers to the treatment processes above and beyond conventional preliminary, primary, and secondary treatment with chlorination. Generally, these treatment processes are designed to remove soluble substances such as dissolved solids and organics, which normally escape secondary treatment. In some areas further SS reduction through filtration may be referred to as tertiary treatment. Some of these systems include:

1. Nitrification-denitrification   (nitrogen removal)
2. Phosphorus precipitation   (phosphorus removal)
3. Activated carbon adsorption   (soluble organics removal)
4. Ion exchange   (removal of hardness-causing cations)
5. Reverse osmosis   (dissolved solids removal)
6. Distillation   (dissolved solids removal)

The quality of effluents realized from tertiary treatments (1), (2), and (3) above can usually be exceeded by land application systems. However, systems (5) and (6) reduce the total dissolved salts concentration and can produce a high quality water suitable for drinking. It should be noted here that this represents another complex area. For example, a secondary treatment facility may prove to be slightly more cost effective than land application treatment. However, the land application system may produce a superior effluent. In comparing AWT with land application systems, the total costs must be weighed against the effluent quality required through treatment. Effluent qualities and costs are discussed in subsequent sections.

> *Land application can exceed results of tertiary treatment in producing a quality effluent except in the area of reducing dissolved salts concentration.*

LAND APPLICATION SYSTEMS AS A WASTE TREATMENT ALTERNATIVE

The application of wastes to the land for treatment and/or disposal is not a new idea. It has been happening for centuries. However, our exposure to this waste treatment alternative has been limited in the past century due to significant advances in what is now called conventional and advanced waste treatment. Present laws enacted in this country, (e.g., PL92-500, enacted in 1972) have demanded that waste treatment alternatives be investigated prior to spending federal funds for waste treatment systems. These alternatives were to include "treatment and discharge into navigable waters, land application and utilization practices, and reuse of treated waste-water" (Train, 1976). For this reason, rational design bases for land treatment systems must be used in order to gain acceptance from funding agencies as well as the people served by the system.

Federal law requires cities and towns to investigate alternatives to conventional and advanced waste treatment.

As with other waste treatment systems, land application for treatment and/or disposal has been proved to be cost effective under varying conditions of waste characteristics, water renovation capacity of the treatment medium, and the treatment medium cost. Three common land application systems—irrigation, overland flow, and rapid infiltration—are briefly discussed below.

Irrigation.   Irrigated agriculture has developed two main methods of dispersing water on the land, (1) surface application and (2) spray irrigation. Because wastewaters are generally greater than 99% water, it was only natural that these techniques would also be utilized in wastewater dispersal.

Pretreatment of wastes applied through irrigation methods will require, as a minimum, preliminary treatment. The effluent obtained from a waste management system utilizing preliminary treated influent and crop management is generally much lower in nitrogen, phosphorus, BOD_5 and SS than conventional secondary treatment effluents. Although systems designed specifically for BOD_5 and SS removal may not be required as a pretreatment to land application systems utilizing an appropriate crop management scheme, as of 1976, only one state, California, had specifically declared irrigation with wastewater without prior secondary treatment to be an acceptable practice (Module I-9, "Legal Aspects").

Surface irrigation systems have been developed around soil and topographic limitations. The rapidity with which water travels across the soil surface and through the soil profile defines the configuration of ditches and levees which make up the system. These ditches and levees are designed to provide as uniform an application as possible within the labor and water constraints at hand.

Wastewater management utilizing this application method is confronted with two unique problems. (1) Wastewaters, unlike typical irrigation waters, have a variety of pathogens that must be avoided. Therefore, hand labor should be kept at a minimum in a system which ordinarily utilizes excessive hand labor. (2) The uniformity of application of surface applied waters is generally very poor without doubling the usual labor requirement.

Workers at surface irrigation systems must follow good public health and cleanliness practices due to pathogens in wastewater. Many man-hours are required to effectively operate such a system.

Spray irrigation systems were developed with the advent of the gas and electric powered pump. Although capital costs increased through their use, labor and water could be conserved. Many configurations of permanent and portable systems have since been developed to satisfy specific design and management needs.

Although these systems seem to have minimized labor requirements while maximizing the uniformity of application, they have also created problems specific to spray irrigation. The aerosol drift associated with sprayed wastewaters may contain pathogens. Although aerosols containing pathogens are also found around conventional sewage treatment plants, the problem is contained within a relatively small area, whereas in land application systems hundreds of acres may be involved.

> *Spray application is most efficient in terms of applying wastewater evenly to the treatment site. Spray irrigation requires less labor than surface irrigation but has another problem, aerosol drift.*

In *overland flow* systems, wastewater is applied to smoothed grassed slopes and allowed to trickle over the soil surface for 100 to 300 feet. The effluent is then collected in a system of terraces and safely transported to a division point. After an evaluation of the effluent, it is either discharged to the receiving sink or recycled back through the system for further renovation. Although very little data have been published on this renovation technique, some cannery sites have been operating successfully for upwards of 25 years and the technique has the potential of becoming very popular. Both spray and surface irrigation methods are used to apply wastewater to the soil, therefore pretreatment requirements of overland flow systems are similar to application systems previously outlined. However, effluents from overland flow systems have shown lower nitrogen, phosphorus and suspended solids removal. Additional treatment may be required in the treatment scheme where more efficient removal is required. One obvious combination is to use a high loading rate overland flow system preceded by preliminary treatment and followed by high rate infiltration-percolation ponds.

Rapid infiltration/percolation: The rapid infiltration and subsequent percolation of wastewater into and through the soil profile is utilized mostly with conventionally treated effluents. Very large amounts of wastewater (up to 300 ft applied per year) are either sprayed or flooded over the infiltration basin on highly permeable soils where it readily disappears. A resting period is then provided which allows biochemical reactions such as nitrification-denitrification to occur, as well as sorption of various ions. Proper management of this wetting and drying cycle may substantially remove large amounts of nitrogen from the wastewater. The sorption capacity of the soil profile will more than likely be exhausted prematurely compared to lower rate land application systems. However, a limited amount of rejuvenation of the sorption capacity occurs over time.

Pretreatment requirements utilized in rapid infiltration have fallen into two categories, (1) those systems receiving more than 5 feet of effluent per week and (2) those systems receiving less than 5 feet per week. At least secondary treatment is recommended for land application systems passing more than 5 feet of effluent per week. Clogging of the soil surface has been the predominant management problem which generated this limitation. Systems passing less than 5 feet per week have not had a recurring clogging problem when primary effluents are applied (Pound, 1973).

> *Rapid infiltration/percolation are high-rate systems. Those passing more than 5 feet of effluent a week may need prior secondary treatment of wastewater to avoid clogging of the soil.*

Table 1.   Design Efficiencies and Effluent Qualities of Conventional and Advanced Waste Treatment Processes.

Treatment Process	Design Removal Efficiency (%)				Effluent Quality (mg/l)			
Conventional and AW treatments[c]	BOD	SS	P	N	BOD	SS	P	N
Preliminary treatment	0	0	0	0	210	230	11	30
Primary settling	20–40	50–65	–	–	140	110	–	–
Activated sludge	75–95	–	–	–	20	25	–	–
Trickling filter	75–90	–	–	–	30	35	–	–
Filtration	50	72	–	–	10	5	–	–
Activated carbon	60	60	–	–	4	2	–	–
Two stage lime treatment	–	–	50	–	–	–	0.5	–
Nitrification-denitrification	–	–	–	90	–	–	–	3
Land Application Systems[a,b]								
Irrigation	98+	98+	80–99+	85+	4	5	2	6
Overland flow	92+	92+	40–80	70–90	18	18	2–7	3–9
Infiltration/percolation	85–99	98+	60–95	0–50	30	5	4	15–30

[a]Influent from preliminary treatment.
[b]Pound, Crites, and Griffes, 1975b.
[c]Van Note, *et al.*, 1975.

ESTIMATED EFFLUENT QUALITIES FROM WASTE TREATMENT SYSTEMS

The effluent qualities expected from established conventional and advanced wastewater treatment processes are shown in Table 1. Because these systems have controlled environments and have been used for many years, their effluents may be predetermined with reasonable accuracy. However, the environments of land application systems are not as readily controlled nor have they been monitored over a long period of time. Therefore, the treatment process efficiency and expected effluent qualities are not as easily predicted. Table 1 also estimates the design efficiencies and effluent qualities of land application systems. All conventional treatment process (including tertiary) effluents have measurable pollutant contaminants.

> *Effluent quality is easier to document in conventional treatment than in land application. All predictions assume proper operation and maintenance.*

It is not unusual to measure phosphorus concentration equal to background groundwater concentration (approximately 0.05 mg P/l) and COD concentrations less than 5 mg/l from land application sites. It should be emphasized that all expected removal efficiencies depend on proper operation and maintenance.

COMPARATIVE COSTS OF TREATMENT SYSTEMS

Each decision that must be made with respect to waste treatment inevitably has an associated cost. The array of pollutants, treatment systems, and effluent limitations is such that addressing each alternative is a task beyond the scope of this module. However, to provide some indication of the relative costs of possible alternatives, we will utilize the information in "Municipal Sewage Treatment—A Comparison of Alternatives" (Battelle, 1974). These data are presented as one means of comparing various system options. Other references on costs of land application and conventional wastewater and sludge treatment can be found in Module I-7 "Costing Land Appli-

Table 2.   Possible Wastewater Treatment Strategies and Sludge Treatment Options.

Liquid treatment strategies
*1   Primary treatment with land application of liquid effluent
 2a. Waste stabilization lagoon with surface water discharge
* b. Waste stabilization lagoon with spray irrigation
 3   Trickling filter with surface water discharge
*4   Trickling filter with land application
 5   Activated sludge with surface water discharge
*6   Activated sludge with land application
 7   Biological—chemical treatment
 8   Activated sludge—coagulation—filtration
 9   Tertiary treatment
 10   Physical—chemical treatment
 11   Extended aeration

Sludge treatment and disposal options
  1   Sludge thickening, chemical conditioning, vacuum filtration, incineration, and landfill
  2   Chemical conditioning, centrifuge dewatering, incineration, and landfill
  3   Sludge thickening, conditioning by heat treatment, vacuum filtration, incineration, and landfill
  4   Sludge thickening, digestion, sand drying beds, and landfill
—▷5   Sludge thickening, digestion, and land spreading
  6   Sludge thickening, digestion, and ocean dumping by pipeline
  7   Sludge thickening, digestion, chemical conditioning, vacuum filtration, and landfill
  8   Sludge thickening, digestion, chemical conditioning, vacuum filtration, and ocean dumping by barging
  9   Chemical sludge thickening, vacuum filtration, incineration and reuse, and landfill of wasted residue
 10   Chemical sludge thickening, vacuum filtration, recalcination and reuse, and landfill of wasted residue
 11   Chemical sludge thickening, centrifuge dewatering, incineration and landfill
 12   Chemical sludge thickening, centrifuge dewatering, recalcination and reuse, and landfill of wasted residue

*Land application of treated effluent.
From Battelle Memorial Institute, 1974.

cation Systems." A concise and easily used comparison is found in the reference Pound, Crites, and Smith, 1975.

The eleven liquid treatment strategies and twelve sludge options investigated in the Battelle study are listed in Table 2. Example process profile sheets with a description of each liquid treatment strategy are presented in the following sections. These systems were chosen because of their popularity prior to 1973 and their expected continued use in the near future. The liquid treatment strategies may be followed by any one of the twelve sludge treatment and disposal options shown. This study also compared the labor, energy requirements, and costs of the eleven treatment strategies as well as the removal of BOD, suspended solids, nitrogen, phosphorus, heavy metals, and the resultant sludge volume upon completion of treatment.

Battelle Study Examines Liquid Treatment Strategies

The first example consists of preliminary and primary treatment followed by land application of the effluent as illustrated in Figure 4. Another common alternative presently adopted in

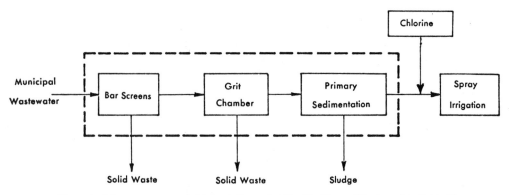

Figure 4. Primary treatment with land disposal of liquid effluent (Strategy 1 in Table 2).

many systems is the use of a waste stabilization pond followed by land application (Figure 5). This system may be incorporated in areas where long term storage is required. The third and fourth strategies listed in Table 2 consist of primary and trickling filter treatment followed by discharge of surface water or land application, respectively. The fifth and sixth strategies consist of primary and activated sludge treatment followed by discharge to surface water and land application, respectively. Activated sludge is presently the single most popular type of secondary treatment process being designed for municipalities. The complete mix activated sludge process was selected on its ability to consistently achieve high quality effluents.

Land application can follow use of a waste stabilization pond in areas where long term storage is necessary.

The seventh strategy consists of activated sludge treatment with alum addition and nitrification-denitrification followed by discharge to surface water. Land application of effluent water is not considered for this treatment sequence since nutrient removal would be superfluous if that mode of treatment were utilized. The nutrient removal capacity is presently added to protect surface waters to which intended discharges are to be made. This facility probably is representative of the better technologies currently available for organics, nitrogen and phosphorus control.

Certain liquid treatment strategies are not suited as pretreatment for land application because their level of treatment would be comparable to land treatment.

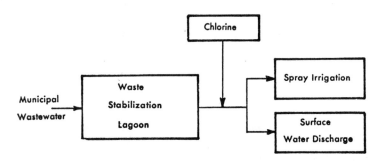

Figure 5. Waste stabilization lagoon (strategy 2 in Table 2).

The eighth strategy consists of activated sludge treatment and coagulation-filtration followed by discharge to surface waters. Once again, land application was not considered as an ultimate disposal option since its use would preclude the necessity for the high level of treatment afforded by the addition of coagulation-filtration. The ninth strategy consists of activated sludge, coagulation-filtration, carbon sorption, and zeolite ammonia removal followed by discharge to surface waters.

The tenth strategy consists of coagulation-filtration and carbon adsorption followed by discharge to surface waters. The eleventh and final strategy evaluated consists of extended aeration followed by surface water discharge of liquid effluents. Extended aeration can provide relatively high quality water if properly designed, hence effluents may be disinfected and released to surface water without further treatment. However, in practice extended aeration plants seldom perform to the theoretical capability of the process, hence their effluents should be considered for land application in the same manner as activated sludge effluents in the sixth strategy, above.

Costs are compared for the treatment strategies involving application of the treated liquid to the land (1, 2b, 4, and 6 in Table 2) and AWT processes. These include primary and secondary pretreatments prior to land application. The least cost sludge options were added to all of the treatment strategies to approximate the total cost of the waste treatment system. A comparison of these treatment and sludge handling costs is shown in Figure 6. These are average 1973 values selected from the Battelle study which gives a range of total operation and capital costs of up to ±6¢/1,000 gal. from the values in Figure 6 for some strategies.

Note that the cost of land application of primary and secondary pretreated effluents are approximately the same as AWT. The need for such a highly pretreated effluent prior to land application is questionable. In most cases, preliminary pretreatment prior to land application will result in an acceptable effluent quality, generally equal to or better than AWT. Preliminary treatment costs are estimated at 2.7¢, 0.84¢ and 0.4¢/1000 gal. for 1, 10, and 100 mgd plants respectively (Van Note, 1975). These costs did not include facilities such as offices, labs, pump stations and outfalls. The dashed horizontal line, "Land Application Costs," of Figure 6 varied from 21 to 31¢/1000 gallon as presented in the Battelle Study. It is apparent here that land treatment systems are very cost effective for small daily flows (.1, 1, 10, mgd) where high quality influents are not required.

Preliminary treatment followed by land application usually results in an acceptable effluent quality, equal or better than advanced waste treatment.

QUALITIES AND COSTS OF TREATED EFFLUENTS

The cost of obtaining an acceptable effluent quality in waste treatment varies significantly, depending upon the influent quality, the treatment process selected, and the receiving sink. The quality of effluent required to meet the 1977 goals (for "best practicable technology") established by PL 92-500 is that of secondary treatment, i.e., 30 mg/1 BOD_5 and SS, where discharge is to navigable waters. However, land application systems must meet groundwater quality requirements as set forth by PL 93-523, "Safe Drinking Water Act," for inorganic and organic chemicals, and microbial contaminants (Train, 1976).

Table 3 compares unit treatment process costs and expected effluent qualities. From this table many different wastewater schemes may be assembled. The costs may be accumulated and the effluent qualities estimated.

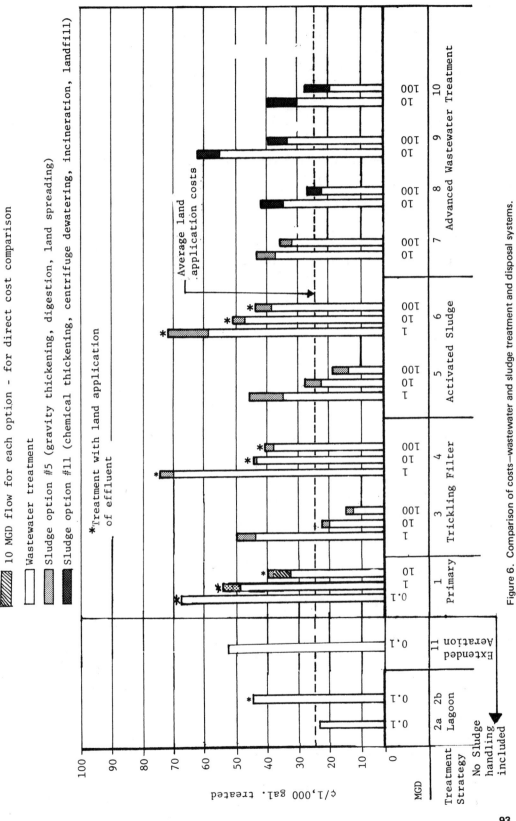

Figure 6. Comparison of costs—wastewater and sludge treatment and disposal systems.

93

Table 3.   Unit Treatment Processes—Effluent Qualities and Costs
(after Van Note, R. H., 1975 except as noted).

	Estimated Effluent						¢/1,000 gal		
	BOD	TSS	TP	TKN	TN	pH	1 mgd	10 mgd	100 mgd
Untreated Wastewater	210	230	11		30	30	7.3		
Conventional Treatment									
Preliminary treatment—bar rack, grinding, grit chamber									
	210	230	11				2.7	.84	.4
Pumping—30 ft TDH	210	230	11				6	2.6	1.3
Primary sedimentation—conventional (influent from preliminary treatment)									
	140	110	10				6.8	1.7	.8
Trickling filter—conventional (influent from primary sedimentation)									
	30	35	9				>10	4.8	3.5
Activated sludge—conventional (influent from primary sedimentation)									
	20	25	8				19	7	4
Sludge Treatment									
Anaerobic digestion (sludge from primary and secondary treatments)									
influent 5%S 70% VS							2.8	1.3	1.0
effluent 4%S 54% VS							4.2	1.0	.57
Advanced Wastewater Treatment									
Filtration									
Estimated influent	20	18	2.0						
Estimated effluent	10	5	1.0				11	5.5	2.5
Activated carbon—conventional (influent from filtration)									
	4	2	0.8				22	15	10
Two stage tertiary lime treatment—(influent from trickling filter)									
	10	10	0.5	29	30		>10.0	3.4	1.5
Biological nitrification (influent from trickling filter)									
	10	15		1	30		11	4.6	2.9
Biological denitrification (influent from biological nitrification)									
	15	16		1	3		9.5	4.4	3.6
Ion exchange (influent from filtration)									
				1	1		14	8.7	5.8
Ammonia stripping (influent from two stage tertiary lime treatment)									
				2	3		10	4.8	3.7
Disinfection (influent from any process, D.T. >15 min. ≤200 F.C./100 ml)									
							2.8	1.3	1.0
Land Application Systems[a]									
Irrigation	4	5	1		5				
Surface							25	14	
Spray—solid set							30	20	
Spray—center pivot							23	14	
Overland flow (4 ipw)	17	18	4		2		20	12	
Rapid infiltration									
(12 ipw)	2	5	3		23		13	6	

[a]Pound, Crites, and Griffes, 1975a.

Design Important in Land vs. Conventional Treatment

Although this module cannot provide a complete review of the relationships of waste characteristics to acceptable design parameters, two additional factors become apparent. These factors
may have a significant impact on the decision to use land application systems. The first issue
deals with the design flow and overall size of the treatment facility. The second issue is more of
a caution to be sure that economic comparisons are made between similar units.

Land Application Has Greater Flexibility

The commonly accepted basis for the design flow of domestic wastewater is related to the maximum variations in flow rates that can be expected for different sized populations. These flows
may vary over a wide range. For example, the peak flow for a design population of 10,000
would be $2\frac{1}{2}$ to 3 times the average daily flow. Thus a secondary treatment facility to serve this
population would be built to handle a design flow of 3 MGD even though its average present
flow is much less.

To some, this may seem to be an overly conservative approach. However, when the problems
of obtaining public approval to enlarge the bonded indebtedness of communities are considered,
along with the problems of extensive plant expansion, it is clear why the peak flow serves as a
basis for design. One attempt to change this has been to include flow equalization basins. However, operational problems have come about in some installations and they are not widely
implemented.

The design flow basis for land treatment systems is not necessarily subject to the same analysis, because the systems are often less sensitive to flow variations. This is especially true for
those facilities that include storage periods of 10 to 20 weeks. These storage units can be viewed
as extremely large equalization basins and can lend flexibility to the operation. In many cases
it will be acceptable to size the land application systems on the basis of *average daily flow* rather
than $2\frac{1}{2}$ to 3 times the average daily flow for the design population. This would result in a design flow of less than half that of conventional treatment.

> *Conventional treatment systems must be sized for peak flows of $2\frac{1}{2}$ to 3 times aver-*
> *age daily flow for the design population. Land application is more flexible; systems*
> *may be planned on average daily flow.*

Another positive aspect of land application systems is their flexibility in terms of expansion.
Although it would be wise to purchase the total quantity of land required for the design flow
and to build in major components such as pumping stations, it may not be necessary to set up
the entire system. For example, if the present average flow were half the design flow estimated
20 years hence, it might be recommended that only two thirds of the site be developed for the
system, with the remainder developed when the need arises. This type of expansion is more feasible with land treatment systems than with conventional systems because of the low capital
costs involved in the expansion of such facilities as a spray irrigation field.

> *It is generally easier to expand a land application system than a conventional treat-*
> *ment system.*

Costing Based on Cents per 1,000 Gallons Designed or Treated

The second topic to note in comparing conventional treatment to land treatment is the economic basis of the comparison. Most of the costing that has been developed expresses the treatment costs on the basis of ¢/1,000 gallons of wastewater treated. For the more capital intensive conventional systems this value is most often in terms of ¢/1,000 gallons of wastewater design flow. The cost per 1,000 gallons of wastewater treated may be considerably higher than this value. If the land application system can be gradually expanded with increasing flows, then the cost can be expressed in terms of unit volume of wastewater actually treated, rather than being based on a future design flow.

Gradual expansion of land application systems with increased flow means less cost per volume treated.

BIBLIOGRAPHY

Battelle Memorial Institute. 1974. Municipal sewage treatment—a comparison of alternatives. U.S. Government, CEQ and EPA. EQC 316. 181 p. and appendices.

Pound, C. E. and R. W. Crites. 1973. Wastewater treatment and reuse by land application. Vol. II. EPA-660/2-73-006b. Office of Research and Development, U.S. EPA. Washington, D.C. 74 p.

Pound, C. E., R. W. Crites and D. A. Griffes. 1975a. Costs of wastewater treatment by land application. EPA-430/9-75-003. 156 p.

Pound, C. E., R. W. Crites and D. A. Griffes. 1975b. Evaluation of land application systems. EPA-430/9-75-001. U.S. EPA, Washington, D.C. 182 p.

Pound, C. E., R. W. Crites and R. G. Smith. 1975. Cost-effective comparison of land application and advanced wastewater treatment. Office of Water Program Operations. EPA-430/9-75-016. Washington, D.C. 25 p.

Reed, S. C., H. McKim, H. R. Slatten, A. Palazzo. 1975. Pretreatment requirements for land application of wastewaters. Extended abstract for ASCE 2nd National Conference on Environmental Engineering Research, Development, and Design. University of Florida.

Robson, C. M., B. S. Hyatt, Jr., and S. K. Banerji. 1975. We must improve chlorination design. *Water and Wastes Engineering.* Sept. 1975. pp. 61–68.

Train, R. E. 1976. Alternative waste management techniques for best practicable waste treatment. *Fed. Reg.,* 41(29): 6190.

VanNote, R. H., P. Hebert, R. Patel, C. Chupek and L. Feldman. 1975. A guide to the selection of cost-effective wastewater treatment systems. Office of Water Program Operations. EPA-430/9-75-002. Washington, D.C.

Module I-5

ROLE OF VEGETATIVE COVER

SUMMARY

Waste treatment by land application rests on the ability of a given site to handle additions of both water and other waste constituents. A suitable vegetative cover enhances the capacity of soil to accept and renovate wastes through several means. Rooted plants protect the soil from erosion, encourage and maintain infiltration, accelerate soil drying through transpiration, absorb nutrients, produce economic benefits from crop harvest, and possess an aesthetic appeal.

This module discusses each of these objectives of incorporating vegetative cover in land treatment systems. Specific crops and forest cover are mentioned in relation to benefits associated with each, and specific treatment alternatives (irrigation, overland flow, and rapid infiltration) are included in relation to vegetative cover considerations.

"Role of Vegetative Cover" provides the Level I introductory treatment of this subject. Once this module has been completed, the modules II-7, "Crop Selection and Management Alternatives," and II-8, "Non-Crop and Forest Systems" provide more specific information relating to vegetative cover, which will be useful to the design of land treatment systems. In particular, Module II-7 discusses crop characteristics as they relate to land application, and specific topics dealing with crops, such as changes in their uptake of water and nutrients during the growth cycle.

CONTENTS

GLOSSARY

colloid—Organic and inorganic matter in the soil with very small particle size and a correspondingly large surface area per unit mass.

eutrophication—A natural aging process of lakes whereby aquatic plants become abundant and dissolved oxygen becomes deficient. Usually accelerated by introduction of nutrients such as nitrogen and phosphorus from outside sources.

evapotranspiration—Discharge of water to the atmosphere by evaporation from the soil surface and transpiration from plants.

infiltration—Movement of water through the soil surface into the ground.

macropore—Space between soil particles large enough to allow flow of water under the force of gravity.

porosity—The fraction of the total volume of soil occupied by channels and pores.

OBJECTIVES

On completion of this module, the reader should be able to:
1. Name four types of vegetative cover.
2. Give five reasons why vegetative cover is important in land application systems.
3. Describe how different ways of applying wastewater to the land alter the ability of the vegetative cover to take up nutrients.
4. Cite the effects that the different kinds of vegetative cover have on evapotranspiration and infiltration.
5. Discuss the role of vegetation in nutrient uptake.

INTRODUCTION

Success in applying waste to the land depends on the ability of that site to handle water and waste constituents. A good cover of vegetation improves the ability of the soil to accept and renovate wastes in several ways. One of the primary advantages of vegetative cover is its capacity to remove nitrogen from the soil. Since nitrogen loading per unit area is often a limiting factor in the design and operation of the site, vegetative cover takes on major importance. Rooted plants also protect the soil from erosion and reduce the amount of runoff and pollutants carried by the runoff water. Vegetation encourages and maintains infiltration by adding to the organic matter content of soil, which is the prime agent for speeding up infiltration. Through the process of evapotranspiration, vegetation accelerates the drying of the soil, which is essential in maintaining odor-free conditions on the site. Vegetation at the waste treatment site increases public acceptance and can produce economic benefits. Crops and trees are more pleasant to look at than bare ground. Furthermore, renovated wastewater can be used to benefit a community, providing irrigation for greenbelts, city parks, golf courses, and other public areas.

Care must be taken in evaluating certain types of crops for use in waste application systems if significant numbers of pathogenic organisms or concentrations of potentially toxic elements are found in the influent waste. These considerations are seldom a serious roadblock to site development, but must be explored. These topics are discussed in Module II-5, "Pathogens" and Module II-4, "Potentially Toxic Elements."

ROLES OF VEGETATIVE COVER

Plant Cover Controls Erosion

Any waste application system must contend with the problem of erosion. The loss of soil particles means an accompanying loss of incorporated waste constituents which might include phosphorus, nitrogen, persistant organics or pathogens. This is particularly harmful when the particles lost are colloidal, that is, extremely small ($\leqslant$0.002 mm) and having an electrical charge. These small particles of soil have the high surface area/volume ratio and electrical charge needed to attract charged waste constituents such as ammonium and metal ions and hold them in the soil matrix. Soil erosion is essentially the only way that fixed phosphorus is lost from a site because of the efficiency of phosphorus fixation in most soils, therefore, erosion control is very important in holding P losses to a minimum.

*The waste absorbing abilities of the soil are reduced by erosion.

The impact of water dropping on bare ground initiates soil erosion. The beating action of the water displaces and disperses soil aggregates, causing individual particles to be carried off in surface runoff. And even if the detached soil particles are not carried away, they may form a hard crust upon drying which reduces infiltration of wastewater.

When the soil is covered with vegetation and decaying plant residues, the impact of water drops is cushioned and the chances of water detaching and carrying away soil particles is reduced.

Are all forms of vegetation equally effective? No. As shown in Figure 1, sod crops are most effective among common agricultural plants followed by rotations in which a series of crops are alternately grown, such as corn, wheat, and clover. Small grains, such as wheat and oats, are the next most effective in preventing soil loss, followed by row crops like corn. Even though corn planted in rows is the least effective of common crops, it prevents soil loss much more effectively than bare earth. The leaves and residues from corn reduce the impact of water drops and the corn roots physically hold the soil in place.

Types of vegetation vary in their ability to prevent erosion.

Sod crops, such as grasses and legumes, and forage grasses allow very little erosion and when planted densely, slow water runoff. This means there is more time for waste constituents and the soil to interact. There is less chance of flowing water cutting channels in the field. Uniform movement of wastewater over the soil surface is desirable to prevent short-circuiting of the land treatment process.

Because of their greater density and more complete coverage of the earth, sod crops stop erosion at the same time they allow some surface runoff. This makes sod crops particularly suited to overland flow systems of waste application.

Sod crops are well suited to overland flow systems of waste application.

---

*This and other italicized summaries are intended to highlight key ideas, provide a basis for later review or to aid in skimming sections that are relatively familiar. They can be ignored in a complete reading of the text.

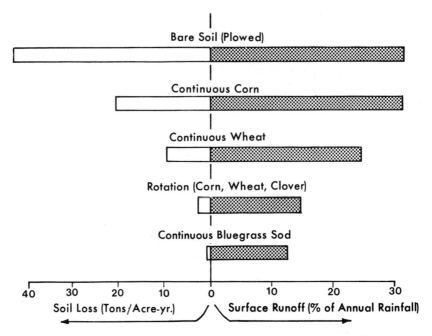

Fig. 1. Cropping systems differ in ability to control surface runoff and erosion. These data are average annual values over a 14-year period on a silt loam soil (3.7% slope, 90-feet long). Average annual rainfall was approximately 40 inches (adapted from Miller and Krusekopf 1932).

Traffic, Tillage Affect Infiltration

Vegetative cover speeds up the rate at which water enters the soil surface. The rate of entry, called infiltration, varies from one type of vegetation to another.

The way the crop is managed affects the infiltration rates. For instance, corn and small grains planted in rows require extensive tillage which compacts the soil. Because there is up to a 7-month period between harvest and replanting, these crops also leave the soil exposed to the impact of rain drops for a significant time.

The way the site is managed affects the compaction of the soil, an important factor in infiltration.

When the site is planted in hay, there is less tillage and thus less compaction. Permanent pasture lands require infrequent or no tillage and when well managed these sites have moderately high infiltration rates. However, heavy grazing of pasture land can compact the soil just as heavy machinery can compact row crops. The vegetative cover with the best infiltration is undisturbed forest land. See Figure 2 for a comparison of infiltration rates under various types of vegetation.

Another factor affecting infiltration is the presence of organic matter in the soil. In fact, its presence in the soil is the chief agent for increasing the infiltration rate. Under naturally occurring vegetation, much or all of the annual production of plant tissue is returned to the soil. Even with harvested crops, vegetative cover still adds considerable organic matter to the soil. For

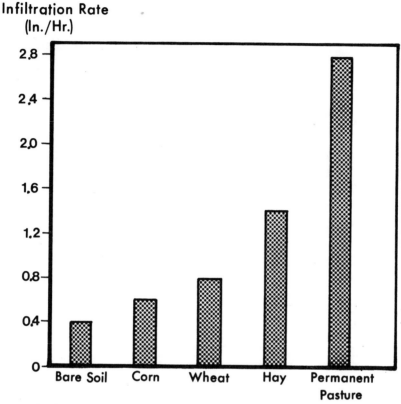

Fig. 2. The type of soil cover markedly affects water infiltration rates. Holton, H. N. and M. H. Kirkpatrick, Jr., 1950. Rainfall, infiltration, and hydraulics of flow in runoff computation, *Trans. Amer. Geophys. Union,* 31: 771–799.

instance, corn produces an average of 4 to 6 tons of above-ground dry matter per acre, some of which is left on the soil surface. In addition, corn adds 2 to 3 tons of organic material per acre to the soil annually by its roots alone.

Organic matter in the soil is the prime agent for maintaining the infiltration rate.

Organic matter encourages the granular structure of the soil by increasing the proportion of macropores, especially in clayey soils. These large pore spaces transmit water readily in response to gravity. Granular structure is highly desirable for infiltration, particularly in loamy or clayey soils. See Module I-1, "Soil as a Treatment Medium," for further discussion of soil structure.

Well aggregated soils that are high in organic matter freely accept water even when frozen. This porosity is due to the presence of roots and decaying plant residues in the soil. It may seem that frozen soils would be impermeable to water. On the contrary, some frozen soils have infiltration rates that equal or exceed rates when not frozen. But it is true that bare or compacted soils, which are low in organic matter, turn into concrete-like masses when frozen. (Trimble *et al.*, 1958).

Daily Evapotranspiration
Rate (Inches)

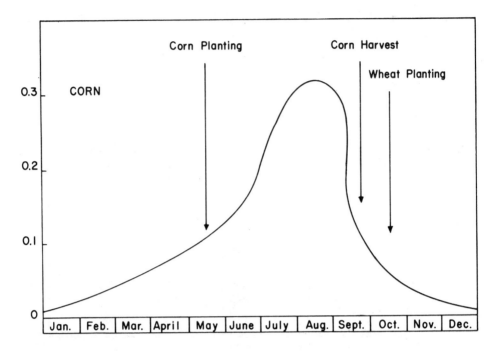

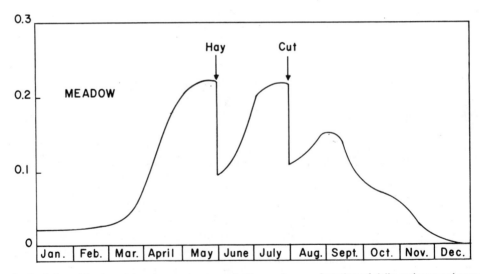

Fig. 3. On irrigated land as shown here, evapotranspiration varies as a function of daily and seasonal energy inputs as well as the stage of crop development. These results are for similar soils and climatic conditions in Ohio. (Adapted from Soil Conservation Service 1964).

Vegetative residues cause the soil to retain its porosity even when frozen.

Even though well aggregated soils may be highly permeable when frozen, it should be remembered that biological activity decreases drastically at low temperatures, and therefore, waste-loading rates often must be reduced or stopped in the winter.

Waste-loading still must be reduced in winter due to the decreases in biological activity.

One of the most common obstacles to public acceptance of land treatment is the possibility of odor emanating from the site. The difference between no smell and an offensive odor is the difference between aerobic and anaerobic conditions. Aerobic conditions are needed for organic matter to decompose rapidly. These conditions can be maintained by scheduling the application of wastewater carefully so that the soil has a chance to dry between applications. These resting periods allow the soil to drain and aerate.

Transpiration

Vegetative cover introduces another way for water to be removed from the site besides evaporation, through transpiration. Loss of water through direct evaporation is limited to water at or very near the soil surface. The plant draws water from the soil, reducing the water content of first the surface layers and then successively deeper zones depending on the depth and density of the roots.

Plant roots absorb water and nutrients from the soil. The water moves upward through the plant body and is lost to the atmosphere from the plant leaves through transpiration. In this way, vegetation accelerates the drying and aeration of soils between wastewater applications.

Vegetative cover hastens the drying of the soil, essential in maintaining odor-free conditions.

Transpiration, like evaporation, depends on climatic conditions including temperature, precipitation, solar radiation, and wind. Transpiration also depends on the availability of soil moisture, and vegetation characteristics such as rooting depth and the seasonal pattern of both root and leaf development (Figure 3).

It is not practical to separate the amount of direct evaporation and transpiration that goes on, so the combined value is called evapotranspiration (ET). This value can never exceed the maximum allowed by absorbed energy. Therefore, regional estimates of potential ET, applicable to most crops, can be calculated empirically or from heat budget studies. Evapotranspiration is discussed in Module II-6, "Climate and Wastewater Storage." Also see Module II-7, "Crop Selection and Management Alternatives" for methods of computing potential ET.

Nutrient Uptake

In irrigation systems, vegetative cover is the primary mechanism for nitrogen removal. Since nitrogen loading rates are often a limiting factor in operating the site, vegetation takes on a prime importance.

Nutrients contained in municipal wastes and sludges can cause harm when discharged to bodies of water. Nitrogen and phosphorus, in excess, are the major causes of eutrophication in surface waters. Vegetative cover on the waste treatment site uses such elements as nutrients for growth.

Wastewater and sludge contain most, if not all, of the essential nutrients for growth, although not necessarily in the right proportions. Vegetation provides a sink for these and other nutrients, and thus plays another important part in the renovation of applied wastes. For instance, reed canary grass can take up more than 350 pounds of nitrogen per acre annually. Phosphorus is not removed so readily. An acre of reed canary grass removes only 35 pounds of phosphorus per year; blue-grass removes only about 12 pounds of phosphorus. The removal of absolute quantities of nitrogen and phosphorus tend to differ by a factor of about 10, as shown in Figure 4. Figure 4 shows other types of vegetative cover and their removal rates.

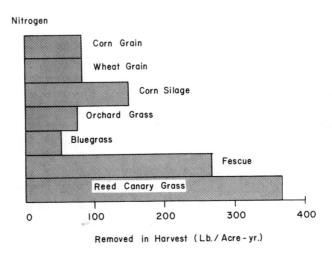

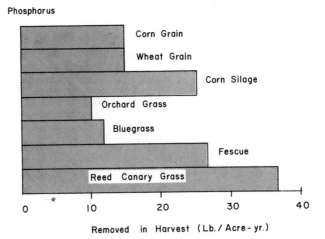

Fig. 4. The relative amounts of nitrogen and phosphorus removed in crop harvest vary with the type of crop and the proportion of the tissue removed. Note that nitrogen and phosphorus scales differ by a factor of 10. (Based on data from Hart 1974; Peterson, et al., 1973).

Vegetation acts as an effective sink for nutrients when the crop is harvested and removed.

It is important to note that nitrogen is absorbed in greatest quantities by certain species of grasses. Grasses also are most effective in preventing erosion, promoting infiltration, and allowing for long periods of interaction between waste constituents and the soil-vegetative complex. Notable examples which have widespread usage in land application sites are reed canary and coastal Bermuda grasses.

Grasses absorb the greatest amount of nitrogen, are most effective in preventing erosion, promote infiltration, and provide for a longer period of interaction between waste elements and the soil-vegetative complex.

Harvesting the entire above-ground parts of a crop removes more total nutrients from the site than harvesting only selected portions of the crop. For instance, more nutrients are removed from the site if corn silage is harvested rather than corn grain. This is because decay of natural residues of the plant releases nutrient stores back into the soil, redepositing them instead of removing them from the soil. The same is true of forest lands. In traditional harvest of forest land, only the stemwood is removed every 40 to 100 years. Trees take up as much nutrients as some agricultural crops do during a single growing season, but much of the uptake is redeposited. For example, an annual uptake of 80 pounds of nitrogen per acre by trees may result in only about 15-20 pounds of actual nitrogen retention per acre of forest. This is due to the large quantity of leaves, twigs, branches, and roots which are left and release their nutrients back to the soil. Recent work (Bormann, Likens, and Melillo, 1977) indicates the possibility of a smaller proportion of nitrogen being returned to the forest floor than shown above, due to internal movement of the N from leaves back into the stems just prior to leaf fall.

Harvesting as much of the plant as possible removes more nutrients from the soil than merely harvesting selected parts of the plant.

Nutrient uptake is influenced by loading rates. For example, as shown in Figure 5, nitrogen absorption in selected grasses increases with fertilizer application rates. The relationship, however, is not linear, and the higher application rates result in a lower percent removal. Furthermore, when much of the applied nitrogen is in organic form as in sludges, it will not be available for plant uptake until after microbial decomposition. Thus, form as well as the total amount of plant nutrients must be considered when assessing their fate in the system.

Different land treatment systems result in more or less nutrient uptake. When crops are irrigated with wastewater, harvesting of the plants removes nutrients from the site. The amount of wastewater application is dictated in part by the nitrogen requirements of plants.

Different waste application systems affect the amount of nutrients the soil will take up.

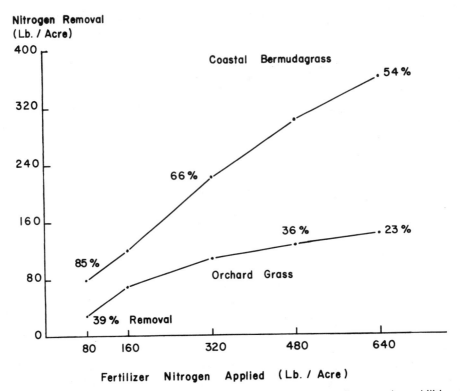

Fig. 5. Nitrogen removal by grass is in part a function of application rate as well as growth capabilities of the species. The inserted numbers indicate the percentage of applied fertilizer nitrogen removed at each level (adapted from Burton *et al.*, 1963; Dotzenko, 1961).

In overland flow systems, both crop uptake and denitrification play major roles in nitrogen removal. Phosphorus removal, however, may depend heavily on vegetative uptake because in overland flow systems wastewaters have only minimal contact with the soil.

Under the rapid infiltration system of land application, there is very little or no uptake of nutrients by vegetation because of the relatively short period of interaction between wastewater and the soil-plant complex. The amount of nutrients removed from wastewater is minor compared to the total loading rates. In this system, the main advantage of vegetative cover is that it increases infiltration rates.

As stated earlier, forest land has not been considered the best site for taking up nutrients after application of waste. This is because only the stemwood is removed at infrequent intervals with much of the plant residues returning to the soil. However, undisturbed forest land is the best vegetative cover for promoting infiltration.

New methods of harvest can increase the use of forest lands as waste application sites. If the entire above-ground crop of trees is chipped and removed at shorter intervals such as every 5–20 years, more nutrients are taken up from the soil. The potential for combining waste application with wood and pulp production using such techniques is discussed in Module II-8, "Non-Crop and Forest Systems."

Forest lands show high promise as land application sites.

Direct sales of crops and livestock or leasing of irrigated lands to local farmers produces income. In either case, prices and crop yields will vary geographically and should be determined from local sources.

The sale of annual crops such as corn grain generally produces a higher return than perennials such as hay. However, annuals usually require greater inputs of labor and equipment as well as a higher level of agronomic expertise.

The return on crops from existing land treatment systems offsets only a part of the over-all operation and maintenance expenses. Returns from the sale of hay at a food-processing plant in Paris, Texas, contributed only 8% of the operation and maintenance costs (Gilde, et al., 1971). The Werribee Farm in Australia recovers about 12% of its costs from the sale of livestock raised or fattened on irrigated pasture land (Hart, 1974). Estimated crop return for 1975 from the Muskegon, Michigan, facility is about $1,000,000. This offsets a significant portion of the annual operation and maintenance expense.

Most people find a planted area better looking than bare ground or a weed patch. The appearance of the waste application site will probably affect public acceptance of its presence in the community. Vegetative cover might be selected with an eye toward aesthetic appeal as well as utility.

For example, the problem of aerosol drift from sprinkler systems could be reduced by border strips of trees or tall shrubs. Using wastewater to irrigate existing vegetation on golf courses or highway greenbelts is another alternative. Attractive vegetation at a waste treatment site is an alternative to regarding the site as a nuisance, a place to hide from public view.

In many communities, treated wastewater is used to irrigate greenbelts, parks, golf courses, highway median strips, college and university grounds, and cemeteries. San Francisco's 800-acre Golden Gate Park is irrigated by fixed sprinklers with one-third of the water produced by one of the city's water reclamation plants. Especially in arid regions, reclaimed wastewater is cheaper to use than potable water for these purposes. For instance, in Laguna Hills, California, reclaimed wastewater is used to irrigate a golf course, fill animal water holes at a safari park, irrigate crops, and irrigate a 295-acre greenbelt. The golf course buys this reclaimed wastewater at $47 an acre-foot. This compares to the price of domestic water at $78 an acre foot (EPA, 1973).

BIBLIOGRAPHY

Bauer, W. J. 1975. Review of design parameters for Muskegon County wastewater management system no. 1 after two years of operation. Conference on the Muskegon County, Michigan Wastewater Management System. Muskegon, Mich. Sept. 17–18, 1975.

Bormann, F. H., G. E. Likens, and J. M. Melillo. 1977. Nitrogen budget for an aggrading northern hardwood forest ecosystem. *Science*, **196**, 981–993.

Burton, G. W., J. E. Jackson and R. H. Hart. 1963. Effects of cutting frequency and nitrogen on yield: *in vitro* digestibility, and protein, fiber and carotene content of Coastal bermudagrass. *Agron. J.*, **55**:500–502.

Dotzenko, A. D. 1961. Effect of different nitrogen levels on the yield, total nitrogen content, and nitrogen recovery of six grasses grown under irrigation. *Agron J.*, **53**:130–133.

EPA. 1973. Survey of facilities using land application of wastewater. EPA-430/9-73-006. Office of Water Programs Operations. Washington, D.C. 377 p.

Gilde, L. C., A. S. Kester, J. P. Law, C. H. Neely, and D. M. Parmelee. 1971. A spray irrigation system for treatment of cannery wastes. *J. Water Pollut. Contr. Fed.*, **43**:2011–2025.

Hart, R. H. 1974. Crop selection and management. *In* National Program Staff, Factors Involved in Land Application of Agricultural and Municipal Wastes. (Draft) ARS, USDA, Beltsville, Md.

Holtan, H. N. and M. H. Kirkpatrick, Jr. 1950. Rainfall, infiltration, and hydraulics of flow in runoff computation. *Trans. Amer. Geophys. Union*, **31**:771–779.

Miller, M. F. and H. H. Krusekopf. 1932. The influence of systems of croppings and methods of culture on surface runoff and soil erosion. Res. Bull. 177, Mo. Agr. Exp. Sta.

Peterson, M. (senior author) 1973. A guide to planning and designing effluent irrigation disposal systems in Missouri. Univ. Mo. Ext. Div. NP 337 3/73/1250.

Soil Conservation Service. 1964. Soil-plant-water relationships. Chap. 1. *In* Irrigation. Sec. 15, SCS Nat. Eng. Handbk. U. S. Gov. Print. Office, Washington, D.C.

Trimble, G. R., Jr., R. S. Sartz, and R. S. Pierce. 1958. How types of soil frost affect infiltration. *J. Soil Water Conserv.*, **13**:81–82.

Module I-6

SITE EVALUATION

SUMMARY

This module describes important criteria to use in evaluating land for waste treatment sites and tells where the necessary information for such evaluation can be obtained. Among the important criteria for evaluation are climate, land use of potential sites and surrounding areas, topography, drainage characteristics, soil properties, and geology. Climatic data are available for most locations in the United States in monthly and 10-year summaries. Computer programs can be obtained which identify unfavorable and favorable days for waste application in both wet climates and cold climates. Planning agencies on the local, regional, and state level have information on land use. Topographic maps, information on water levels and water quality, and local groundwater conditions are available from U.S. and state geological surveys. Modern soil surveys published since 1960 provide a wealth of data in addition to the physical properties of soil including: potential of land for farm use, potential of land for non-farm uses, dominant soil types, varying surface textures of soils, degree of slope and erosion of various soils, and engineering applications of the land. Soil surveys also give general features of the region such as population, drainage, major industries, and water supply. Aerial photos, a complementary source of information, show land use, drainage, and topography of the land.

CONTENTS

GLOSSARY

lithology—the description of the physical character of a rock as determined by eye or with a low-grade magnifier, and based on color, structure, mineralogic compounds, and grain size.

permeability—the rate at which gases or liquids penetrate or pass through a bulk mass of soil or a layer of soil.

porosity—the volume percentage of the soil bulk not occupied by solid particles.

sinkhole—a natural depression in a land surface, communicating with a subterranean passage, generally occurring in limestone regions and formed by solution or by collapse of a cavern roof.

soil association—a group of defined and named taxonomic soil units occurring together in an individual and characteristic pattern over a geographic region.

soil complex—a mapping unit used in detailed soil surveys where two or more defined taxonomic units are so intimately intermixed geographically that it is undesirable or impractical, because of the scale being used, to separate them. This is a more intimate mixing of smaller areas of individual taxonomic units than that described under soil associations.

soil phase—basic mapping unit on detailed soil surveys where soil types are further characterized by slope, erosion, or some other feature which affects their use.

soil series—the basic unit of soil classification, being a subdivision of a family and consisting of soils that are essentially alike in all major profile characteristics.

soil survey—the systematic examination, description, classification, and mapping of soils in an area. Soil surveys are classified according to the kind and intensity of field examination.

soil type—the lowest unit in the natural system of soil classification; a subdivision of a soil series consisting of or describing soils that are alike in all characteristics including texture of the A horizon.

stereoscope—an optical instrument containing two eyepieces used to impart a three-dimensional effect to two photographs of the same scene taken at slightly different angles.

transmissibility—usually called transmissibility coefficient, the number of gallons of water per day that percolates through each square mile of water-bearing bed for each foot thickness of bed.

undifferentiated units—delineations on a detailed soil survey map that consist of two or more soil types or phases that have been grouped together because of similarities of properties and management needs. The pattern and proportion of these units are not uniform. The units are named for dominant soils.

OBJECTIVES

Upon completion of this module, the reader should be able to:

1. List the general categories of information which can be found in a soil survey that relate to evaluation of a waste treatment site.
2. Describe the general climatic conditions in his zone of the United States.
3. List the sources of topographic maps and hydrogeologic studies and describe how to apply the information contained therein.
4. Summarize the criteria discussed in this module by which a potential site is judged.

INTRODUCTION

The feasibility of land application and treatment of wastes rests on no single consideration but rather on the integration of many. Among these are the kind, amount, and characteristics of the water, applicable laws and regulations, economic and socio-political factors, and characteristics of the land area itself. This module is directed to evaluating the land area.

Since this module was developed at Cornell University in upstate New York, the examples of soil surveys, soil types, and other data are taken from New York State. The examples and data could be changed to adapt to the particular region in which the module is being used, since similar information is generally available for most areas of the country.

EVALUATION CRITERIA

Climate Affects Feasibility, Design of Site

Localized areas provide little choice with respect to climatic conditions. Nevertheless, climate strongly affects the overall feasibility as well as the ultimate design of land treatment systems.

Suitable temperature and moisture conditions are necessary for organic waste decomposition and for growth and development of vegetative cover, key factors in most successful land treatment operations. Low temperatures reduce biological activity and thereby reduce the potential for waste renovation. Prolonged wet periods also impair renovation because saturation affects aeration, and the likelihood of surface runoff is increased. The net effect of unfavorable temperature and moisture conditions is that waste storage is required during a portion of the year. Broad relationships between climate and waste application systems are shown in a generalized climatic map in Figure 1 (Pound and Crites, 1973). The depicted zones are useful for preliminary planning, but, ordinarily, a detailed analysis of localized climatological data is necessary for design purposes.

Zone A, covering much of California, has a marked seasonal pattern of precipitation. Average annual precipitation is about 15 to 25 inches, confined generally to the six-month period from November through April. At low elevations, temperatures are mild in winter and hot in summer

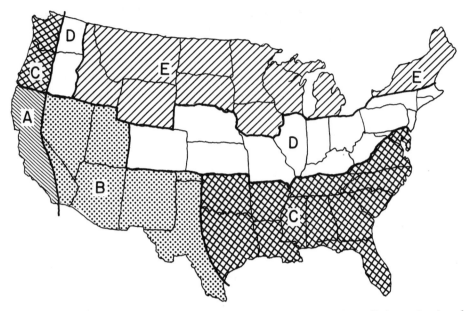

Figure 1. The United States is divided into five general climate zones useful for preliminary planning of land application. (After Pound and Crites, 1973).

so that with irrigation, plant growth can continue throughout the year. Storage of effluent during cold periods is not required, but may be desirable since crops in winter need less irrigation than in summer. Because water shortages are common in this area, wastewater application offers considerable potential for groundwater recharge and crop irrigation. Some ongoing land application systems in this region date back to 1900.

Zone B covers the southwestern region of very hot, arid climates. Winter storage of effluent is not a major concern. This may vary locally, however, according to changes in elevation. Land application of wastes will no doubt play an increasingly important role in this region.

Zone C includes the mid and deep South as well as parts of Washington and Oregon. In the South, precipitation is distributed throughout the year, with hot, humid summers and fairly mild winters. Precipitation generally varies from 40 to 60 inches during the year; average daily temperatures range from the low 40's in winter to the low 80's in summers. A twelve-month operation of land application systems is possible in many areas of the zone, although high precipitation may limit operation for short periods.

Zone D covers eastern Washington and Oregon and the central tier of states. This area has moderately cold winters, with temperatures in the 20's and 30's, and hot summers, with temperatures in the mid-70 range. Precipitation is generally well distributed throughout the year. Winter conditions are such that effluent storage may be required for up to 3 months.

Zone E covers the northernmost tier of states. Precipitation occurs in all months of the year and averages from 20 to 40 inches annually. Winter operations are usually limited due to low temperatures, ice, and snow. There are some examples of long-term sites operating year-round in this zone, but storage may be necessary for six months or more. Although this is an added concern, it is not as restrictive economically as might be expected. Data on the costs of storage can be found in Module I-7 "Costing Land Application Systems".

Figure 2. USDA Handbook Shows The Regional Pattern Of Soil Use For The U.S.

This map shows land resource regions (indicated by letter). These regions are defined mainly by similarity of soil patterns and climate and by other natural features that affect use and management of land.

Descriptions of the 20 land resource regions and CNI data for the non-federal rural land in each region are summarized in the text. Detailed descriptions of these regions are contained in the U.S. Department of Agriculture's Agriculture Handbook 296, Land Resource Regions and Major Land Resource Areas of the United States, issued in December 1965. See Table 1 for letter definitions.

Conservation Inventory Combines Climate with Other Factors

Figure 2 and Table 1 are excerpted from the USDA Soil Conservation Service booklet "$\frac{2}{3}$ of Our Land: A National Inventory" (1971). This pamphlet describes a Conservation Needs Inventory (CNI) of all privately owned rural land in the U.S., focusing on the percentage of tillable land, acreage of land use for crops, pasture, range, forest, etc.; and acreage requiring conservation measures.

The pamphlet describes how to obtain information for a county, conservation district, watershed, or other local area. The engineer can request any of the following from the local or county office of the Soil Conservation Service or from his conservation district office:

- A summary of Conservation Needs Inventory data for a county.
- County publications based on inventory data or special interpretations of the data.
- Soil survey of a county if available.
- Other soil, water, and plant information.

The pamphlet also describes how to get information on a multicounty area, a state, a group of states, a multistate region, or the mainland United States; for a river basin, a resource conservation and development project area, a planning district, or other area. This can be obtained by asking the state Soil Conservation Service Office (through the local SCS office) for any of the following:

Table 1.   SCS Describes Each of 20 Regions Shown in Fig. 2.

A. Northwest coast region

Steep mountains; gently sloping valleys; plains. Inventory area, 58 percent of region. Suitable for regular cultivation (classes I-III), 17 percent. Dominant soil limitation: erosion hazard, 72 percent; shallowness, stoniness, droughtiness, 17 percent. Land use: commercial forest, 74 percent; cropland, 11 percent. Conservation treatment needed: 60 percent of commercial forest; 66 percent of cropland.

B. Columbian region

Mostly smooth to deeply dissected plains and plateaus; few mountain ranges. Inventory area, 61 percent of region. Suitable for regular cultivation, 33 percent. Dominant soil limitation: erosion hazard, 57 percent; shallowness, stoniness, droughtiness, salinity, 31 percent. Land use: cropland, 37 percent; range, 40 percent; commercial forest, 15 percent. Conservation treatment needed: 76 percent of cropland; 72 percent of range; 66 percent of commercial forest.

C. California coast region

Low mountains; broad valleys. Inventory area, 71 percent of region Suitable for regular cultivation, 35 percent. Dominant soil limitation: erosion hazard, 47 percent; shallowness, stoniness, droughtiness, salinity, 35 percent. Land use: cropland, 30 percent; range, 26 percent; noncommercial forest, 29 percent. Conservation treatment needed: 71 percent of cropland; 54 percent of range.

D. Mountain and basin region

Plateaus, plains, basins; many isolated mountain ranges. Semidesert to desert. Inventory area, 41 percent of region. Suitable for regular cultivation, 7 percent. Dominant soil limitation: shallowness, stoniness, droughtiness, salinity, 54 percent. Land use: range, 67 percent; noncommercial forest, 13 percent; cropland, 6 percent. Conservation treatment needed: 75 percent of range; 70 percent of cropland.

E. Rocky Mountain region

Rugged mountains; some broad valleys and high plateaus. Inventory area, 39 percent of region. Suitable for regular cultivation, 15 percent. Dominant soil limitation: erosion hazard, 56 percent; shallowness, droughtiness, salinity, 33 percent. Land use: range, 43 percent; commercial forest, 25 percent; cropland, 16 percent. Conservation treatment needed: 62 percent of range; 70 percent of commercial forest; 67 percent of cropland.

F. Northern plains region

Mostly smooth topography. Inventory area, 91 percent of region. Suitable for regular cultivation, 72 percent. Dominant soil limitation: erosion hazard, 60 percent; adverse climate, 17 percent. Land use: cropland, 59 percent; range, 33 percent. Conservation treatment needed: 55 percent of cropland; 54 percent of range.

G. Western plains region

Mostly plains; sand hills and valleys; steep slopes. Inventory area, 88 percent of region. Suitable for regular cultivation, 20 percent. Dominant soil limitation: erosion hazard, 68 percent; shallowness, stoniness, droughtiness, salinity, 22 percent. Land use: range, 74 percent; cropland, 18 percent. Conservation treatment needed: 60 percent of range; 62 percent of cropland.

H. Central plains region

Plains; tableland; prairies. Inventory area, 100 percent of region. Suitable for regular cultivation, 53 percent. Dominant soil limitation: erosion hazard, 65 percent; shallowness, stoniness, droughtiness, salinity, 13 percent. Land use: cropland, 47 percent; range, 48 percent. Conservation treatment needed: 58 percent of cropland; 61 percent of range.

I. South Texas region

Plateaus and plains. Inventory area, 97 percent of region. Suitable for regular cultivation, 29 percent. Dominant soil limitation: shallowness, stoniness, droughtiness, salinity, 46 percent; erosion hazard, 37 percent. Land use: range, 76 percent; cropland, 10 percent. Conservation treatment needed: 76 percent of range, 64 percent of cropland.

J. Southern prairie region

Prairies and timbered areas; mostly gentle topography Inventory area, 90 percent of region. Suitable for regular cultivation, 57 percent. Dominant soil limitation: erosion hazard, 63 percent; shallowness, stoniness, droughtiness, 24 percent. Land use: cropland, 27 percent; pasture, 26 percent; range, 24 percent. Conservation treatment needed. 64 percent of cropland; 77 percent of pasture; 81 percent of range.

K. Northern lake region

Level to gently rolling glacial drift, till, and lake plains; many swamps, lakes, and wet lowlands. Inventory area, 83 percent of region. Suitable for regular cultivation, 48 percent. Dominant soil limitation: wetness, 41 percent; erosion hazard, 31 percent; shallowness, stoniness, droughtiness, 27 percent. Land use: commercial forest, 65 percent; cropland, 19 percent. Conservation treatment needed: 52 percent of commercial forest; 54 percent of cropland.

L. Southern lake region

Nearly level to gently sloping glacial plains. Inventory area, 85 percent of region. Suitable for regular cultivation, 79 percent. Dominant soil limitation: wetness, 48 percent; erosion hazard, 34 percent. Land use: cropland, 63 percent; commercial forest, 22 percent. Conservation treatment needed: 58 percent of cropland; 65 percent of commercial forest.

M. North-central region

Nearly level to rolling plains; sharply dissected glacial till or drift plains. Inventory area, 95 percent of region. Suitable for regular cultivation, 78 percent. Dominant soil limitation: erosion hazard, 54 percent; wetness, 29 percent. Land use: cropland, 68 percent; pasture, 12 percent; commercial forest, 11 percent. Conservation treatment needed: 67 percent of cropland; 72 percent of pasture; 79 percent of commercial forest.

N. Appalachian-Ozark region

Mountains; valleys; dissected plateaus. Inventory area, 76 percent of region. Suitable for regular cultivation, 33 percent. Dominant soil limitation: erosion hazard, 58 percent; shallowness, stoniness, droughtiness, 31 percent. Land use: commercial forest, 59 percent; cropland, 19 percent; pasture, 16 percent. Conservation treatment needed: 74 percent of commercial forest; 66 percent of cropland; 71 percent of pasture.

O. Mississippi delta region

Flood plains; terraces. Inventory area, 68 percent of region. Suitable for regular cultivation, 79 percent. Dominant soil limitation: wetness, 79 percent; erosion hazard, 10 percent. Land use: cropland, 55 percent; commercial forest, 35 percent. Conservation treatment needed: 64 percent of cropland; 77 percent of commercial forest.

P. South Atlantic slope region

Coastal plains and Piedmont plateaus; some highly dissected areas. Inventory area, 100 percent of region. Suitable for regular cultivation, 54 percent. Dominant soil limitation: erosion hazard, 53 percent; wetness, 31 percent. Land use: commercial forest, 65 percent; cropland, 20 percent. Conservation treatment needed: 74 percent of commercial forest; 68 percent of cropland.

R. Northeastern region

Plateaus; plains; mountains. Inventory area, 87 percent of region. Suitable for regular cultivation, 33 percent. Dominant soil limitation: shallowness, stoniness, droughtiness, 55 percent; excess water, 21 percent. Land use: commercial forest, 69 percent; cropland, 15 percent. Conservation treatment needed: 75 percent of commercial forest; 60 percent of cropland.

S. North Atlantic slope region

Undulating to rolling, dissected coastal plains; Piedmont plateaus; Appalachian ridges and valleys. Inventory area; 88 percent of region. Suitable for regular cultivation, 50 percent. Dominant soil limitation: erosion hazard, 56 percent; shallowness, stoniness, droughtiness. 24 percent; o wetness, 17 percent. Land use: commercial forest, 54 percent; cropland, 28 percent. Conservation treatment needed: 56 percent of commercial forest; 64 percent of cropland.

T. Atlantic coast region

Nearly level lowlands. Inventory area, 83 percent of region. Suitable for regular cultivation, 57 percent. Dominant soil limitation: wetness, 76 percent; stoniness, droughtiness, salinity, 17 percent. Land use: commercial forest, 52 percent; cropland, 22 percent. Conservation treatment needed: 76 percent of commercial forest; 72 percent of cropland.

U. Florida subtropical region

Nearly level to gently rolling coastal plain; many swamps and marshes. Inventory area, 82 percent of region. Suitable for regular cultivation, 30 percent. Dominant soil limitation: wetness, 87 percent; shallowness, stoniness, droughtiness, 13 percent. Land use: commercial forest, 47 percent; cropland, 13 percent; pasture, 11 percent; range, 11 percent. Conservation treatment needed: 81 percent of commercial forest; 63 percent of cropland.

• Summary of Conservation Needs Inventory data for your state or any number of states (contains data for each county and state totals).

• State publications based on inventory data and interpretative reports.

• Published soil surveys of counties in any state.

The state conservationist can also help the engineer obtain computer printouts of inventory data or special tabulations of the data for a land resource region or area.

Of interest to planners of land treatment systems are percentage breakdowns of land having certain agricultural limitations such as erosion hazard, wetness, or shallowness of soil. This information is summarized in Table 1 for each of the 20 regions identified on the map in Figure 2. Figure 2 also refers to the USDA Agriculture Handbook 296, available from the SCS, for more detailed treatment of this subject.

Land Use Indicates Available Sites

Knowledge of current land use in an area indicates how much land is potentially suitable and/or available for waste application. For example, agricultural land can often serve or be adapted for use in waste treatment. Abandoned farmland and forestland may also be suitable. A cursory review of land use maps can avoid consideration of areas with urban or industrial development, historical value, or unique environmental features. Occasionally, the possible site will be limited to land already owned by a municipality or industrial concern. In such cases, the uses of the land surrounding the site should be evaluated to determine if these uses are compatible with a waste application system. Projected land use plans, where they exist, may also eliminate certain areas from consideration.

A review of land uses in the area will reduce the choice of available and suitable sites.

Topography Determines Surface Water Movement

The overall configuration of the landscape determines the pathway and rate of surface water movement and often the subsurface flow. As such, topography affects how well the site will handle water and the extent of contact between waste constituents and soil particles. Except on very permeable soils, steep slopes increase the possibility of rapid surface runoff. Unchecked runoff can short-circuit the renovation process and erode the soil.

Topography affects how well a site will handle water and the extent of contact between wastes and soil.

There are no uniform regulations relating slope and waste application. The so-called Ten-States Standards for the Great Lakes Upper Mississippi River Basin (GLUMRB) however, gives generally acceptable limits for sprinkler irrigation systems. This report can be obtained by writing to Health Education Service, P.O. Box 7283, Albany, New York 12224. These guidelines state that slopes on cultivated fields should be limited to 4%. Slopes on sodded fields should not exceed 8%. Slopes of forest are limited to 8% for year-round operation although seasonal operations may be acceptable on slopes up to 14%. Slope constraints vary with other application and treatment methods. Existing overland flow systems are generally operated on slopes between 2% and 6%. Here, the length of slope must also be considered. A length of 175 feet was found to be sufficient for food processing wastes at a facility in Paris, Texas. Three hundred feet is considered to be the maximum length over which uniform distribution of wastewater can be maintained.

The degree of slope that will limit waste application varies with the type of system.

Examination of topography should not be limited to the slope of potential sites. Local variations in surrounding topography are useful in determining drainage patterns and locating areas where water is discharged or accumulates. For example, if a site is nearly level and adjacent to higher sloping terrain, it will probably receive excess water via surface runoff and/or subsurface lateral flow from the higher ground. Such conditions might preclude additional inputs of wastewater unless drainage is provided. Delivery of waste from source to site will also require the evaluation of topography.

Soils and Geology Affect Waste Application

Almost all soil properties affect or are affected by waste application. Practical considerations obviously limit investigation in the preliminary stages of decision making. Here the task is one

*This and other italicized summaries are intended to highlight key ideas, provide a basis for later review or to aid in skimming sections that are relatively familiar. They can be ignored in a complete reading of the text.

of evaluating those characteristics which are most restrictive or which best reflect the potential performance of the system. Evaluation is complicated by the fact that no well established guidelines exist. This is especially true for the overland flow and rapid infiltration methods of wastewater treatment. Nevertheless, soil properties and site characteristics in the following paragraphs are suggested for initial consideration.

Evaluate those soil characteristics that will be most restrictive to operation of site.

Texture Influences Choice of System

Soil texture, as discussed in Module I-1, "Soil as a Treatment Medium," refers to the size distribution of mineral particles, from fine clays to gravels and cobbles. Texture reflects major differences in pore size and permeability as well as the surface area available for interaction with waste constituents. Medium textured soils, ranging from sandy loams to silty clay loams, are generally suitable for effluent irrigation and sludge application. These loamy soils often exhibit the best combination of water handling capabilities and waste renovation potentials. Coarse textured soils such as sands and gravels can accept large quantities of water without runoff, but renovation capabilities are often low. Rapid infiltration systems may be considered where coarse textured subsoils are overlain by medium textured surface layers, thereby increasing the potential for renovation. Fine textured soils, unless well structured, are only suitable for overland flow systems.

Soil texture tends to dictate type of land application employed.

Effective Depth Influences Renovation Ability

The actual thickness of unconsolidated material above a permanent water table, bedrock, or some other restricting layer, constitutes the effective depth of soil useful in the renovation of applied wastes. The effective depth requirements vary for different wastes and waste application approaches. For rapid infiltration systems, at least 10 feet of permeable, unconsolidated material above a water table is generally recommended. With effluent irrigation or sludge application, I-4 to 5 feet is commonly suggested. Specific state guidelines are outlined in Module I-9 "Legal Aspects." Lesser depths may be acceptable with low application rates or where subsurface lateral flow allows additional contact between soil and waste constituents. Overland flow systems require the least effective depth since much of the actual treatment occurs at or very near the surface. Nevertheless, a foot or more of unconsolidated material overlying an impermeable layer will increase the renovation possibilities for waste constituents such as phosphorus and metals, which depend largely on adsorption reactions with soil particles. Some depth is also required for adequate root development of vegetative cover. Potential sites for solid or liquid waste application should not be subject to flooding by adjacent rivers and streams during any part of the year.

The thicker the unconsolidated layer of soil is, the greater the capacity for renovation of wastes in the soil.

Drainage Helps Determine Suitability of Site

Drainage, as a condition of the soil, refers to the frequency and duration of periods when the soil is free of saturation. Drainage classes, shown below, have been defined by the Soil Survey Division of the Soil Conservation Service (Soil Survey Staff, 1951).

Very poorly drained—water remains at or on the surface most of the year.

Poorly drained—water remains at or near the surface much of the year.

Somewhat poorly drained—soils are wet for significant portions of the year.

Moderately well drained—soils are seasonally wet (e.g., high water table in spring).

Well drained—water readily removed from the soil either by subsurface flow or percolation; optimum condition for plant growth.

Somewhat excessively drained—water is rapidly removed from the soil; characteristic of many uniform sands.

Excessively drained—very rapid removal of water with little or no retention.

Soils of the very poorly drained, poorly drained, and somewhat poorly drained classes are seldom suitable for any kind of waste application unless some form of artificial drainage is installed. Moderately well drained, well drained, and somewhat excessively drained soils are generally suitable for waste application, with the well drained soils offering the greatest potential for waste renovation. Excessively drained soils provide such rapid removal of water that they essentially preclude waste renovation.

Soils appropriate for waste application should be neither poorly drained nor excessively drained. They should statisfy the criteria for well-drained soil.

Permeability Dictates Hydraulic Loading

Water entry into the soil surface and movement through the unconsolidated material depends on permeability. The downward permeability to water of the most restricting layer in the upper few feet of soil is of particular concern since this value will largely dictate permissible hydraulic loading. Permeability values in the range of 0.6 to 6.0 in./hr, for the most restricting layer in the upper 4 to 5 feet of soil, offer the best conditions for effluent irrigation or sludge application. Values below 0.2 in./hr will generally require artificial drainage or the overland flow approach. At the other end of the scale, with permeabilities greater than 6.0 in./hr, rapid infiltration may be acceptable where adequate waste renovation can be demonstrated.

The rate of downward movement of water through the unconsolidated layer greatly determines hydraulic loading rates.

Available Water Capacity Relates to Throughput Rate and Plant Uptake

The available water capacity (AWC), as defined in Module I-1 "Soil as a Treatment Medium," refers to the maximum amount of water that can be retained in the soil against the force of gravity and yet be available to plant roots. Available water capacity depends on the texture and structure in the upper few feet of soil where most renovation occurs. AWC values greater than 6 inches are generally desirable within the upper 4 feet of soil. With lower values, the decreased retention time for wastewater in the soil will reduce the opportunity for renovation.

Available water capacity of soil should be greater than 6 in/upper 4 ft. for most successful operations.

Nature of Consolidated Material is an Important Consideration

The kind and condition of bedrock is of major importance for high-rate wastewater application systems or where overlying soils are shallow. Fractured rock allows wastes to move rapidly to groundwater with little opportunity for renovation.

Unfractured bedrock at shallow depths will act like a layer of clay, with the potential of poor drainage, groundwater mounding, and/or subsurface lateral flow depending on topography. On the other hand, fractured or fissured rock may allow unrenovated wastewater to percolate rapidly to the water table. This condition is particularly serious with high-rate systems or where wastewater or sludge application augment a high natural precipitation. Limestone (carbonate) bedrock is of particular concern since sinkholes may exist. Even when sinkholes are not initially a problem, waste additions may initiate their formation or expand those already present. Sinkholes, like fractured rock, can accelerate the movement of unrenovated wastes to groundwater.

A good site has bedrock that is neither fractured nor lies at too shallow depths.

SOURCES OF INFORMATION

Climatic Data

Climatic data for most locations in the U.S. are available from various publications of the National Oceanic and Atmospheric Administration (NOAA).

Monthly summaries of climatic data provides useful information on serveral climatic variables including total precipitation, maximum and minimum temperatures, and relative humidity values for every weather station in a given area. Evaporation data are included where available.

In the climatic summary of the U.S., climatic data for each weather station in a given area are summarized for a 10-year period. Specific information includes:

(a) Total monthly precipitation for the 10-year period.
(b) Total monthly snowfall for the period.
(c) Average number of days per month when precipitation exceeds 0.10 and 0.50 inch.
(d) Average monthly temperatures for the period.
(e) Average daily maximum and minimum temperatures for the 10-year period.
(f) Average number of freezing days per month for the period.

Climatic data are available for most locations of the U.S. in monthly summaries and 10-year summaries.

Local climatological data provides an annual summary of climatic data for only a few major weather stations.

Storage Requirement Computer Programs were recently developed at the National Climatic Center in Asheville, NC (Whiting, 1975). Three versions are now available which utilize daily climatic data from over a period of years to identify the number of favorable and unfavorable days for waste application. From this analysis, storage requirements can be calculated. Module II-6, "Climate and Wastewater Storage," provides detailed information on this source of design data.

Computer programs are available which identify favorable and unfavorable days for waste application.

Planning Agencies Provide Land Use Information

Planning agencies at local, state, and/or regional levels can usually supply pertinent information on land use. Both current and projected land use patterns are helpful in evaluating the area. Available information, however, varies widely in terms of specificity.

Planning agencies at local, regional, and state levels have information on land use.

One example of a very detailed informational source is the New York State Land Use and Natural Resource (LUNR) Inventory which includes statewide land use data derived from the interpretation of recent aerial photographs. Relatively few states have developed such a detailed analysis for existing land use. The LUNR Inventory provides information on 130 categories of land use for all areas of the state. Data are available in three forms:

- Transparent map overlays for use with 7.5 minute USGS topographic maps or New York State Department of Transportation planimetric maps.
- Computer-tabular forms.
- Computer-graphic forms.

The computerized format allows for the addition of supplemental information. For example, the computerized portion of the LUNR Inventory currently includes a map of New York's geology, a generalized state soil map, and a map of economic viability of farm areas in the state. Further information on LUNR maps and data are available from:

> New York State Office of Planning Services
> Data and Systems Bureau
> 488 Broadway
> Albany, New York 12207

Topographic Maps Serve Many Uses

The United States Geological Survey (USGS) publishes topographic maps for many areas in 7.5- and/or 15-minute series. These maps are usually at scales of 1:62,500 or 1:24,000. (A guide to the interpretation of map scales is given in Appendix A.) Standard topographic maps are useful in describing the location of potential sites and in determining topographic variations, distance from waste sources, proximity to surface waters and to population centers, and in some cases current land-use and groundwater discharge areas.

> *Topographic maps help to locate available sites. Maps are available from U.S. Geological Survey.*

Indexes to published maps are available for each state. These indexes and individual topographic maps may be obtained from:

Branch of Distribution   for Eastern States
U.S. Geological Survey   (east of the Mississippi)
1200 South Eads Street
Arlington, Virginia 22202

Branch of Distribution   for Central and Western States
U.S. Geological Survey   (west of the Mississippi)
Federal Center
Denver, Colorado 80225

Hydrogeologic Studies Report Water Levels, Quality

The Geological Survey also maintains a network of observation wells to monitor water levels and water quality. The observation well network consists of nearly 16,000 privately and publicly owned wells. Records of water level in about 3,500 of these observation wells are published in the USGS Water-Supply Paper series, "Groundwater Levels in the United States (name of geographic region)." This data will be useful in establishing the general groundwater quality of a region.

> *Information on groundwater levels and quality are available from U.S. Geological Survey.*

The Geological Survey undertakes project investigations for area groundwater studies, generally in cooperation with local, state, or other federal agencies. These studies include: reconnaissance studies which describe the general geological features, the principal wells, springs, and aquifers, and appraise water quality; generalized studies which involve surface and subsurface geologic mapping, test drilling, geophysical work, systematic well inventories, programs for water level measurement, mapping of water level contours, depth to water, saturated thickness, transmissibility, storage capacity, and water quality zones; intensive studies which are detailed investigations of lithology, porosity, horizontal and vertical permeability, storage coefficients, and water quality, as well as all types of mapping performed in the generalized studies. Results of these studies are published either by the USGS in its various publication series or in state reports in cooperation with local agenices. Further information on these sources can be obtained from the previous addresses, from State Geological Survey Offices, or State Divisions of Water Resources. An example of the use of such information in delineating waste application areas is provided by Bond, *et al.* (1972).

> *Extensive information on local groundwater conditions is available from state geological survey offices.*

SOIL SURVEYS

Soil surveys have been made and published since 1899 by various government agencies. In 1952 all survey activity was consolidated in the Soil Conservation Service and designated the National Cooperative Soil Survey. Soil Survey Reports include maps, showing the distribution of different soils and interpretations for the use of such soils. Most reports issued prior to 1960 include interpretive information limited to farming operations. The more recent reports, however, provide ratings and interpretations for many other uses including engineering applications, wildlife, recreation and community planning. As such, Soil Survey Reports constitute a valuable source of information in planning and designing land treatment systems. Specific kinds of information are discussed in the following sections.

> *Soil surveys since 1960 rate soils on their suitability for various uses as well as examine the basic soil properties.*

Soil Maps Cover Entire County or More

Modern soil survey reports contain a general soil map covering an entire county or more, and several detailed soil maps covering individual portions of the larger area. Detailed maps are published on an air photo base. The soil delineations shown on either type of map are called mapping units. General maps show soil associations and are generally published at a scale of 1:126,720 (0.5 inch to the mile) or smaller. Detailed maps which delineate types of phases of soil series, soil complexes, and undifferentiated units, are usually published at a scale of 1:15,840 (4 inches to the mile) or 1:20,000 (3.17 inches to the mile). In order to use soil survey reports effectively, it is necessary to understand the various mapping units employed and the limitations involved.

Dominant soil types are delineated on soil maps.

A soil association is a group of geographically associated soil units occurring in a defined proportional pattern over the landscape. Associations are named for the dominant soil or soils present, such as Madrid-Massena or Ontario-Hilton. The basis for grouping soils into associations, however, varies with the purpose and scale of the map. The colored map provided on the back cover of the most recent soil survey is a general soil map.

General Maps Are Limited

A map showing only soil associations is used to get a general idea of the soils in a county or to locate large tracts which are suitable for a certain land use such as waste application.

An association map, however, is limited in that the different soils in any association ordinarily differ greatly in slope, depth, stoniness, drainage, and other characteristics that strongly affect their management. In addition, information reflects soil conditions only to a depth of 4 to 5 feet.

Detailed Maps Indicate Soil Types

Groups of soils with similar profile characteristics are designated as a soil series. Each series is named for a town or other geographic feature located near the place where a soil of that series was first observed and mapped. Examples are the Cayuga Soil Series named for Cayuga Lake, New York, and the Ovid Soil Series named for Ovid, New York.

Soil series maps include soils which differ in the texture of their surface layer. Within a series, all soils having a surface layer of the same texture belong to one soil type, such as Hilton loam. Soil types may vary in slope, degree of erosion, or some other feature which affects their use. Therefore, soil types are further divided into soil phases which form a basic mapping unit on detailed soil maps. An example is Cayuga silt loam, 0 to 2% slopes. When different soils are so intricately mixed or occur in individual tracts too small to show them separately on the maps, they are shown as one mapping unit called a soil complex. The soils in a complex may be similar or sharply contrasting. A complex is ordinarily named for the major soils within it. An example is Hilton-Cazenovia stony silt loams, 0 to 3% slopes. Some delineations shown on detailed maps are undifferentiated units. These consist of two or more soil types or phases that have been grouped together because of similarities of properties and management needs. The pattern and proportion of the included soils are not uniform. Undifferentiated units are named for dominant soils joined by "and" (as opposed to soil complexes where names are joined by a hyphen), for example, Ovid and Appleton silt loams, limestone substratum.

More detailed maps are needed to determine individual soil types which differ in their surface texture. Soil phases describe the slope and degree of erosion as well as the texture of individual soils.

Detailed Maps Have Limitations

Detailed soil maps offer more information than general maps since the mapping units are more refined. Nevertheless, individually named units, as designated on detailed maps, always contain

DETAILED MAPS HAVE LIMITATIONS

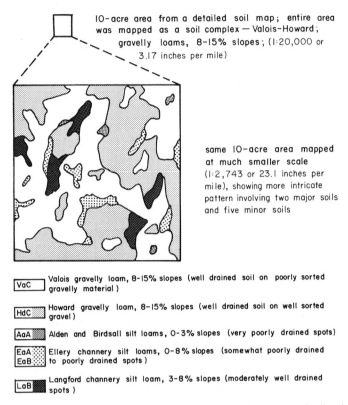

10-acre area from a detailed soil map; entire area was mapped as a soil complex — Valois-Howard; gravelly loams, 8-15% slopes; (1:20,000 or 3.17 inches per mile)

same 10-acre area mapped at much smaller scale (1:2,743 or 23.1 inches per mile), showing more intricate pattern involving two major soils and five minor soils

VaC   Valois gravelly loam, 8-15% slopes (well drained soil on poorly sorted gravelly material)

HdC   Howard gravelly loam, 8-15% slopes (well drained soil on well sorted gravel)

AaA   Alden and Birdsall silt loams, 0-3% slopes (very poorly drained spots)

EaA   Ellery channery silt loams, 0-8% slopes (somewhat poorly drained
EaB   to poorly drained spots)

LaB   Langford channery silt loam, 3-8% slopes (moderately well drained spots)

Figure 3. At the normal scale for detailed soil maps, there is a limit to the amount of soil variability that can be shown. Therefore, areas designated by a particular mapping unit will almost always contain inclusions of unidentified soils. These inclusions may be in sharp contrast to the characteristics of the named soil(s) (adapted from Olson, 1964).

variable amounts of different soils due to limitations of the mapping scale. For purposes of management interpretations such inclusions of unidentified soils seldom exceed 15% of the area designated by a particular mapping unit. This means that approximately 85% or more of an area shown on the map as Ontario loam, will in fact consist of Ontario loam or other soil units which respond similarly to management. The remaining 15%, however, may consist of quite different soils in terms of management interpretations. For example, Figure 3 shows an area mapped at the customary 1:20,000 scale and at a much larger scale of approximately 1:2,750. At the normal scale for published detailed maps, this area was named as a complex, Valois-Howard gravelly loams, 8 to 15% slopes. On the small scale map, however, it can be seen that the area actually consists of the two major soils as well as five minor soils.

The major soils, designated by the symbols VaC and HdC, are well drained; the minor soil inclusions range from moderately well drained to very poorly drained. The minor areas were not indicated on the detailed soil map as published, but could markedly affect the performance of a site used for waste application. Thus there is the need for an on-site visit by an experienced soil scientist before any final design decisions are made. Detailed soil maps, like general maps, are also limited by the depth of the soil conditions they reflect, which is a maximum of about 4 to 5 feet.

Detailed maps do not precisely describe each soil type at the site. Rather they describe the major soil types comprising at least 85% of the area. Because minor soil types at the site may affect its operation, an experienced soil scientist should be consulted before final design decisions are made.

Soil Surveys Describe Soils

Description of mapping units for both general and detailed maps are provided in the text of the soil survey report. The approximate acreage and proportional extent of each unit is given. Each series has a short description of a representative profile, and a much more detailed description of the same profile from which highly technical interpretations can be made. For example, one recent soil survey contains a description of the Palmyra Series of soils. This includes an indication of where this type of soil is generally found such as in "glacial outwash desposits of stratified sand and gravel with a high limestone content. Areas are throughout the county on kames, eskers, and terraces. . ." (Heffner and Goodman, 1973, p. 150). A very brief description of a representative site is then included. This is followed by a detailed description of a representative profile and the location of the area from which the representative profile was obtained. This is followed by descriptions of the various mapping units in the series. In the case of the Palmyra Series these include:

Palmyra gravelly fine sandy loam, 0–3 percent slopes (PaA)
Palmyra gravelly fine sandy loam 3–8 percent slopes (PaB)
Palmyra gravelly fine sandy loam, 8–15 percent slopes (PaC)
Palmyra gravelly fine sandy loam, 15–25 percent slopes (PaD)
Palmyra gravelly fine sandy loam, 25–60 slopes (PaF)
Palmyra gravelly loam, 3–8 percent slopes (PgB)

The descriptions of these mapping units include differences between the particular mapping unit profile and the general profile, the suitability of the mapping unit for various agricultural uses, and management and conservation practices recommended.

Soil Survey Indicates Land Use, Management

In addition to maps and descriptions of soils, soil survey reports contain considerable information on the use and management of soils. In the most recent reports, such information includes:

1. General management of soils for farming.
2. Capability groupings of soils according to suitability.
3. Estimates of yields for various crops on different soils.
4. Groupings of soils for use as woodland.
5. Groupings of soils for use as wildlife habitat.
6. Interpretations and ratings for engineering applications.
7. Interpretations and ratings for non-farm (urban) areas.

Use of Soil Surveys

To illustrate the use of a soil survey for land application site evaluation, we will examine the information that can be obtained for a hypothetical land treatment investigation at Penfield, New York. Maps of the Penfield area are from Soil Survey of Monroe County, New York.

Using these maps, charts of engineering and agricultural properties in the reports, and the advice of soil specialists, the consulting engineer can make judgments about the ability of the site to absorb the volume of water to be applied; the potential groundwater movement problem; constraints in the use of the soil for irrigation, drainage, and ponds; and depth of the soil to bedrock.

Recent soil surveys give extensive information on how land is farmed and the potential of the land for other uses. An examination of potential waste treatment sites in Penfield, New York, illustrates how to use a soil survey.

Soil surveys also give available water capacity and expected yields for various crops—useful in evaluating treatment alternatives. Land use is shown on the aerial photos in the soil mapping.

For the Penfield example, a site consisting of five blocks of land divided by roads or natural physical boundaries has been marked on the soil map (Figure 4). Information is obtained from the tables in the Survey.

Acreages for each plot are shown. Total area = 1460 acres.

For the purpose of illustration, one block will be examined:

Block D: Predominant soil type Madrid (Md).
- Permeability: 2.0 inch/hour at all depths.
- Irrigation use: High intake rate; moderate to high available water capacity.
- Agricultural drainage: Drainage not needed; naturally well drained.
- Depth to bedrock: 6 feet.
- Seasonal highwater table: 4 feet deep.

Based on these factors, this section of Penfield would not be suitable for land treatment by rapid infiltration due to its depth to bedrock and depth to high water table, although permeability values are acceptable. It would be well suited to crop irrigation due to its high available water capacity in addition to the other factors listed.

The other soils in the block are now examined for potential constraints:

- Massena (Mf) has high seasonal water table of 0.5 to 1.5 feet depth. Can be poorly drained. Could be some influence on groundwater movement, but depth to bedrock is more than 6 feet. Not a large area of Mf.
- Ontario (On) has slightly higher seasonal water table (2.5 to 4 feet) and lower permeability range (0.63 to 2.0 in./hr in topsoil and less than 0.63 in./hr below 39 inches deep). No restrictions.
- Sun (Ss) has prolonged high water table (0 to 0.5 feet depth) and widely varying permeability 0.63 to 6.3 inch/hour) and would affect groundwater movement.

From this information, the engineer can draw these conclusions:

- The site has the Sun soil as a limiting factor. Because of the prolonged high water table, wastewater probably should not be applied directly to this portion of the site.
- There is no high bedrock to impede groundwater movement laterally from the site.
- The predominant soil has excellent wastewater-accepting characteristics.

A similar analysis would be carried out for each of the other blocks of land (A, B, C, and E) shown in Figure 4.

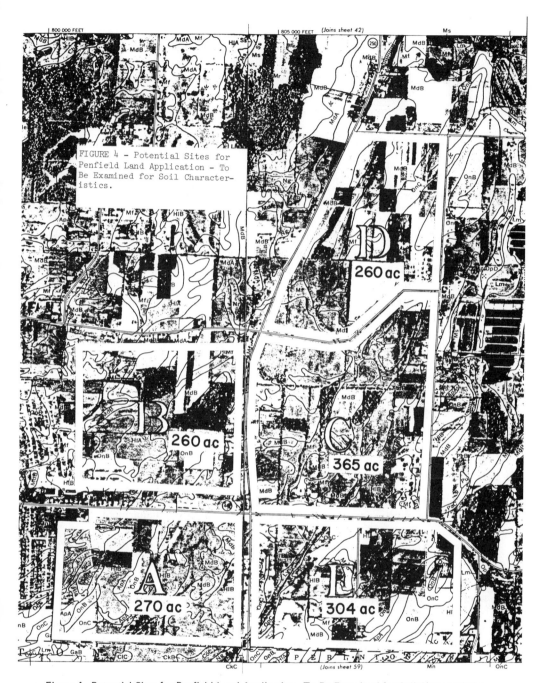

FIGURE 4 - Potential Sites for Penfield Land Application - To Be Examined for Soil Characteristics.

Figure 4. Potential Sites for Penfield Land Application—To Be Examined for Soil Characteristics.

Growth Potential

Much of the information provided in soil surveys is designed to help farmers, or those who advise farmers, in choosing suitable combinations of soil, water, and crop management practices. Individual soil characteristics that affect general management in the county are discussed; often included are acidity (pH), the effect of subsoil properties on root growth, nitrogen, phosphorus, and potassium relationships in area soils, and crop adaptation details.

> *Much information in Soil Surveys is devoted to how suitable the land is for growing field crops.*

Suitability of Soils for Crops

Capability groupings indicate the general suitability of soils in the area for most kinds of field crops. These groupings do not take into account major earthmoving that would have changed the slope, depth, or other characteristics of the soil in place.

Soils are grouped at three levels: the capability class, subclass, and unit. Eight classes indicate the degree of limitation of a particular soil; they range from Class I, including soils which have few limitations to restrict their use, to Class VIII, for soils which have such severe limitations so as to preclude their use for any kind of cropping. Subclasses designate the type of limitation; the small letter *e* indicates erosion, *w* is for wetness, *s* denotes shallowness, and *c* indicates climatic limitations. Capability units, designated by arabic numerals represent further delineations within subclasses. Soils in the same unit are enough alike to require similar management and show similar responses to management.

> *Soils are classified according to how limitations restrict their use for crops; specific limitations are noted.*

Estimated average yields are given for principal crops on each soil in the area which is suitable for cultivation. Yield estimates are generally provided for two levels of management:

- Yields obtained by farmers for a period of years preceding the published survey report.
- Yields which can be expected under highly skilled or improved managment schemes.

> *Estimates for average crop yields are given including yields actually obtained and yields expected under improved management.*

Soils Rated for Woodland and Wildlife Suitability

Area soils are rated in terms of their suitability to support various tree species. The number of suitability groups and their specific meanings are not standardized and thus vary with the county or area involved.

Soils are also rated according to various elements of wildlife habitat including plant cover and/or open water, and also in terms of different classes of wildlife such as openland wildlife, woodland wildlife, and wetland wildlife.

Engineering Properties

Specific information on the engineering uses of soils is generally absent from soil survey reports published prior to about 1960. In more recent reports, however, considerable data and inter-

Table 2. An example of Estimated Soil Properties and Engineering Test Data from a Recent Soil Survey. (Heffner and Goodman, 1973)

Soil Series and Map Symbols	Depth to		Depth from Surface (Typical Profile)	Classification
	Bedrock	Seasonal High Water Table		Dominant USDA Texture
	Feet	Feet	Inches	
Palmyra: PaA, PaB, PaC, PaD, PaF, PgB	6+	6+	0-15	Gravelly loam and gravelly fine sandy loam.
			15-22	Gravelly loam and gravelly sandy clay loam.
			22-30	Gravelly fine sandy loam and gravelly loam.
			30-60	Sand and gravel, stratified.

Classification—Continued		Coarse Fraction Larger than 3 Inches	Percentage passing sieve—				Permeability	Available Water Capacity[1]	Reaction[2]
Unified	AASHO		No. 4 (4.7 mm.)	No. 10 (2.0 mm.)	No. 40 (0.42 mm.)	No. 200 (0.074 mm.)	Inches per hour	Inches per inch of soil	pH range
		Percent	Percent						
ML or SM	A-4 or A-2	<5	70-80	65-75	50-65	30-55	2.0-6.3	0.10-0.13	6.1-7.3
SM, SC, GM, or GC	A-4 or A-2	<5	65-75	60-70	50-65	25-50	0.63-2.0	0.08-0.12	6.1-7.3
GM or GC	A-2 or A-4	<10	60-70	55-65	40-60	25-45	2.0-6.3+	0.08-0.11	6.1-7.6+

[1] Estimates generally are given to a depth of 30 inches, or to the depth of rooting if less than 30 inches.
[2] A single pH value of 7.6+ indicates that free carbonates are present and that the layer is calcareous; pH 7.6+ in range of values indicates that as the depth from surface increases, the lower part of the layer may be calcareous.

pretative information are provided. Soils are classified according to three systems: the U.S. Department of Agriculture system (USDA) based on the texture of the mineral soil particles, the American Association of State Highway Officials system (AASHO) based on load-carrying capacities, and the Unified System, used by the Corps of Engineers, based on textural and plasticity qualities. Engineering test data are given for selected soils. Various parameters are defined and discussed in the text, and tabulated in the soil survey.

> *Recent Soil Surveys give engineering classifications of soils according to USDA, AASHO, and Unified systems.*

Estimated soil properties are given for each detailed mapping unit, including:

depth to bedrock
depth to seasonal high water table
dominant textural changes with depth
permeability (inches/hour)
available water capacity
reaction (pH)

An example of these soil properties from a recent soil survey appears in Table 2. Also, engineering interpretations are given for each detailed mapping unit, including:

Suitability as a source of topsoil: granular material (sand, gravel), fill material.
Soil features affecting:
    embankment foundations
    foundations for low buildings
    ponds
    agricultural drainage
    irrigation
    diversions
    waterways

An example of this type information is shown in Table 3 which is taken from a recent soil survey. A discussion is also provided on the engineering properties of geologic deposits and bedrock.

Non-Farm Uses

Interpretive information on non-farm uses is generally limited to only the most recent soil survey reports. In such cases, soil ratings are provided for:

- sanitary landfills
- disposal of septic tank effluent
- homesites
- streets and parking lots
- recreational areas (picnic grounds, athletic field, hiking and riding trails, lawns and fairways, campsites)

An example of this type of information is shown in Table 4.

> *Recent soil surveys rate how well land is suited for sanitary landfills, recreation, homesites, and other non-farm uses.*

Table 3.   An Example of Engineering Interpretations for a Mapping Unit from a Recent Soil Survey. (Heffner and Goodman, 1973)

Soil Series and Map Symbols	Suitability as a Source of—			Soils Features Affecting—	
	Topsoil	Sand and Gravel	Fill Material	Highway Location	Embankment Foundations
Palmyra: PaA, PaB, PaC, PaD, PaF, PgB.	Poor: gravelly.	Good	Good: erodible in sandy material.	Moderately steep to very steep in units PaD and PaF; cut slopes generally stable above water table; subgrade subject to differential frost heaving.	Generally adequate strength for moderately high embankments; units PaD and PaF are moderately steep to steep.

Soil Features Affecting—Continued

Foundations for Low Buildings[1]	Farm Ponds		Agricultural Drainage	Irrigation	Diversions	Waterways
	Reservoir Areas	Embankments				
Moderately high bearing capacity; differential settling possible under vibratory loads; units PaD and PaF are moderately steep to very steep.	Rapid permeability at a depth below 30 inches; units PaC, PaD and PaF are moderately sloping to very steep.	Good stability and shear strength for outside shell; rapid permeability in places.	Drainage not needed; well drained to excessively drained.	High intake rate; moderate available water capacity; units PaD and PaF are moderately steep to steep.	Rapid permeability; units PaD and PaF are moderately steep to very steep.	Rapid permeability; erodible where steep; units PaD and PaF are moderately steep to very steep.

[1] Engineers and others should not apply specific values to the estimates given for bearing capacity of soils.

Table 4.   An Example of Estimated Degree and Kind of Limitations of a
Mapping Unit for Selected Non-Farm Uses Indicated in a
Recent Soil Survey. (Heffner and Goodman, 1973)

Series Name and Map Symbols	Sanitary Land Fill	Underground Public Utilities	Disposal of Septic Tank Effluent	Homesites
Palmyra: PaA.	Severe: rapidly permeable below a depth of 30 inches; pollution hazard.	Moderate: loose sand and gravel below a depth of about 30 inches subject to sloughing.	Slight: severe pollution hazard.	Slight

Streets and Parking Lots	Picnic and Extensive Areas	Athletic Fields and Intensive Play Areas	Campsites	Hiking and Riding Trails	Lawns and Fairway
Slight	Slight	Severe: gravelly surface layer.	Moderate: gravelly surface layer.	Slight	Moderate: gravelly surface layer.

Some soil survey reports also provide data on selected chemical properties of soils such as cation exchange capacity. When available, such data are often limited to only a few soil series. Additional information is given on general features of the county or area such as population, major industrial or manufacturing facilities, climate, geology, gross relief, drainage and physiography, and water supply.

Soil surveys describe general features of the area such as water supply, drainage, major industries.

By now it should be apparent that soil survey reports, particularly the most recent ones, can provide an enormous amount of pertinent information for feasibility evaluations and designs of land treatment systems. Note, however, that this information does not preclude the need for on-site inspections nor small-scale pilot runs to verify the predicted performance of specific wastes in the soil.

Information on how to obtain soil surveys is given in Appendix A. If only older reports or no reports are published for an area, unpublished materials are often available from county Soil Conservation Service personnel. Furthermore, soil series names are more or less standardized all over the country. Therefore, a soil of the Ovid series may occur in several counties or even several states. When no recent survey is available for the area of interest, older reports may be augmented with recent materials from adjacent counties.

If only older surveys are available, they should be augmented by recent Surveys from nearby regions, unpublished SCS materials, or consultation with SCS personnel.

Aerial Photos Serve as Additional or Alternative Resource

The amount of information obtainable from aerial photos is directly related to the experience of the personnel using them. Nevertheless, those without experience can still obtain useful information.

For evaluating waste application areas, air photos may be of greatest use when other sources such as soil survey reports or topographic maps are not available. Land use patterns are easily recognized from air photos. Tonal differences and photographic textural changes can serve to delineate forestlands, grasses, various cultivated crops, and bare soil. The value of this information will depend on how recently the photographs were made, and the date (time of year) they were taken. In addition, subtle drainage differences that might be quite difficult to detect on the ground often can be detected on air photos. Other features of the landscape such as old river channels or intermittent drainageways may also be discerned. In general, however, air photos are best used to complement rather than replace other information sources and serve to reduce field work rather than take its place.

Land use, drainage, topography can be detected in aerial photos.

Air photos commonly occur as oblique photographs, vertical photographs, and/or composite photographs. Oblique photos are taken with the axis of the camera at various angles between the horizon and the ground. They usually cover a larger area than verticals but their usefulness is limited to fairly level terrain where the view is not obstructed by ridges or highlands. Vertical photographs are taken with the aerial camera pointed straight down. Overlapping exposures in each flight line permit the interpreter to study vertical photos three-dimensionally, using a stereoscope. Unless otherwise specified, aerial photos are understood to be verticals. Mosaics are composite pictures assembled from individual vertical photos, matched to give the appearance of a single large print. Such mosaics form the base on which detailed soil maps are published. Aerial photographs range in scale from about 1:12,000 to 1:20,000. A scale of 1:20,000 is about the smallest that nonprofessional interpreters can use efficiently. Enlargements can be made, but in general they offer no additional detail and cannot be viewed with simple stereoscopes. Enlargements, however, may present definite advantages in the transfer of photo details to base maps.

Most of the United States has been photographed in recent years for various federal agencies. A key to this photography is available in map form as the "Status of Aerial Photography in the U.S." Copies may be obtained from:

> Map Information Office
> U.S. Department of the Interior
> Geological Survey
> Washington, D.C. 20240

This map shows all areas of the U.S., by counties, that have been photographed by or for the Agricultural Stabilization and Conservation Service, Soil Conservation Service, Forest Service, Geological Survey, Corps of Engineers, Air Force, Coast and Geodetic Survey, and commercial firms. Names and addresses of agencies holding the negatives for the photographs are printed on the back of the map, and inquiries should be sent directly to the appropriate organization. There is no central laboratory that can furnish all prints of all government photography. Photo index sheets or index mosaics showing the relative positions of all individual photographs within a given county can usually be examined at local offices of the Agricultural Stabilization and Conservation Service or the Soil Conservation Service.

A map indicating all areas of the United States, by counties that have been photographed by particular Federal agencies can be obtained from the Geological Survey.

In summary, there is a variety of information available to help the operator and designer of the land application system. Persons involved in land treatment should be aware of the sources in order to use this information to their advantage.

BIBLIOGRAPHY

Austin, Morris E. 1965. Land resource regions and major land resource areas of the United States exclusive of Alaska and Hawaii. USDA Agriculture Handbook No. 296. U.S. Govt. Print Office. Washington, D.C. 82 p.

Bond, J. G., R. E. Williams, and O. Shadid. 1972. Delineation of areas for terrestrial disposal of wastewater. *Water Resources Res.*, 8:1560–1573.

Great Lakes-Upper Mississippi River Board of State Sanitary Engineers. 1970. Standards for waste treatment works; municipal sewerage facilities. Addendum no. 2.

Heffner, R. L. and S. D. Goodman. 1973. Soil survey of Monroe County, New York. USDA, Soil Conservation Service. U.S. Govt. Print. Office, Washington, D.C.

Olson, G. W. 1964. Using soil surveys for problems of the expanding population in New York State. Cornell Ext. Bulletin 1123. NYS College of Agriculture, Ithaca, N.Y. 31 p.

Olson, G. W. and F. B. Warner. 1974. Engineering soil survey interpretations. Cornell Ext. Bulletin IB 77. NYS College of Agriculture, Ithaca, N.Y.

Pound, C. E. and R. W. Crites. 1973. Wastewater treatment and reuse by land application, Vol. II. EPA-660/2-73-006b. U.S. Govt. Print. Office, Washington, D.C. 249 p.

Soil Conservation Service Staff. 1971. 2/3's of our land, a national inventory. USDA Soil Conservation Service. Program Aid No. 984. 0-437-990. U.S. Govt. Print. Office, Washington, D.C. 19 p.

Soil Survey Staff. 1951. Soil survey manual. USDA Handbook. No. 18. U.S. Govt. Print. Office, Washington, D.C. 503 p.

Whiting, D. M. 1975. Use of climatic data in design of soil treatment systems. Environmental Protection Technol. Ser. EPA-660/2-75-018. U.S. Govt. Print. Office, Washington, D.C. 67 p.

Whiting, D. M. 1976. Use of climatic data in estimating storage days for soil treatment systems. Environmental Protection Technol. Ser. EPA-660/2-76-250. U.S. Govt. Print. Office, Washington, D.C. 90 p.

APPENDIX

Information on Obtaining Soil Survey Reports
and
List of Published Soil Surveys
USDA, Soil Conservation Service—January, 1976 and updates as of May, 1977

A soil survey published by the U.S. Department of Agriculture that is not out of print can be obtained in one of the following ways:

Land users in the area surveyed and professional workers who have use for the survey can obtain a free copy from the local office of the Soil Conservation Service, from their county agent, or from their congressman. Many libraries keep published soil surveys on file for reference. Also, soil conservation district officers and county agricultural extension offices have copies of local soil surveys that can be used for reference.

Most published soil surveys cover one or more counties and are so named. Where the survey covers only a part of one or more counties, the word "area" is a part of the name. The date in the list that follows is the year the field work was completed for surveys made from 1899 to 1936; from 1937 on, it is the year the publication was issued.

Soil surveys are being completed and published at a rapid rate, so this list is always somewhat out of date. For information on the current status of a soil survey not listed herein, inquiry should be made at the Soil Conservation Service field office in that county or at the office of the *Director of Soil Survey Operations, Soil Conservation Service U.S. Department of Agricul-*

ture, Washington, D.C. 20250. In some cases it is possible to obtain drafts of forthcoming surveys, if they are sufficiently close to completion.

PUBLISHED SOIL SURVEYS

January 1976

ALABAMA

*1908 AUTAUGA
*1909 BALDWIN
 1964 BALDWIN
*1914 BARBOUR
*1908 BIBB
*1905 BLOUNT
*1913 BULLOCK
*1907 BUTLER
*1908 CALHOUN
 1961 CALHOUN
*1909 CHAMBERS
 1959 CHAMBERS
 1924 CHEROKEE
*1911 CHILTON
 1972 CHILTON
 1921 CHOCTAW
*1912 CLARKE
*1915 CLAY
 1974 CLAY
*1913 CLEBURNE
*1909 COFFEE
*1908 COLBERT
 1939 COLBERT
*1912 CONECUH
*1929 COOSA
*1912 COVINGTON
 1921 CRENSHAW
*1908 CULLMAN
 1962 CULLMAN
*1910 DALE
 1960 DALE
*1905 DALLAS
 1938 DALLAS
 1958 DEKALB
*1911 ELMORE
 1955 ELMORE
*1913 ESCAMBIA
 1975 ESCAMBIA
*1908 ETOWAH
*1917 FAYETTE
 1965 FAYETTE
*1903 FORT PAYNE AREA
 1927 FRANKLIN
 1965 FRANKLIN
 1920 GENEVA
*1923 GREENE
 1971 GREENE
*1909 HALE
 1939 HALE
*1908 HENRY
*1920 HOUSTON
 1968 HOUSTON
*1903 HUNTSVILLE AREA
*1911 JACKSON
 1954 JACKSON
*1908 JEFFERSON
*1908 LAMAR
*1905 LAUDERDALE
 1931 LAUDERDALE
*1914 LAWRENCE
 1959 LAWRENCE
*1906 LEE
 1950 LEE
*1914 LIMESTONE

 1953 LIMESTONE
*1916 LOWNDES
*1904 MACON
 1944 MACON
*1911 MADISON
 1958 MADISON
*1920 MARENGO
*1907 MARION
*1911 MARSHALL
 1959 MARSHALL
*1911 MOBILE
 1930 MOBILE
*1903 MOBILE AREA
*1916 MONROE
*1905 MONTGOMERY
*1926 MONTGOMERY
 1960 MONTGOMERY
*1918 MORGAN
 1944 MORGAN
*1902 PERRY
 1930 PERRY
*1917 PICKENS
*1910 PIKE
*1911 RANDOLPH
 1967 RANDOLPH
*1913 RUSSELL
*1917 SAINT CLAIR
*1917 SHELBY
*1904 SUMTER
 1941 SUMTER
*1907 TALLADEGA
 1974 TALLADEGA
*1909 TALLAPOOSA
*1911 TUSCALOOSA
*1915 WALKER
*1915 WASHINGTON
*1916 WILCOX
 1938 WILCOX
 1937 WINSTON

ALASKA

*1914 ALASKAN RECONNAISSANCE
 1963 FAIRBANKS AREA
 1971 HOMER-NINILCHIK AREA
*1916 KENAI PENINSULA
 1962 KENAI-KASILOF AREA
 1968 MATANUSKA VALLEY AREA
 1960 NORTHEASTERN KODIAK
      ISLAND AREA
 1973 SALCHA-BIG DELTA AREA
 1973 SUSITNA VALLEY

ARIZONA

 1975 APACHE (CENTRAL PART)
 1967 BEAVER CREEK AREA
*1921 BENSON AREA
*1927 BUCKEYE-BEARDSLEY AREA
*1941 CASA GRANDE AREA
 1974 EAST MARICOPA AND
      NORTHERN PINAL
*1928 GILA BEND AREA
 1964 HOLBROOK SHOW-LOW AREA
 1974 LONG VALLEY AREA
*1917 MIDDLE GILA VALLEY AREA
*1930 NOGALES AREA

 1973 ORGAN PIPE CACTUS
      NATIONAL MONUMENT
*1928 PARADISE-VERDE AREA
 1970 SAFFORD AREA
*1900 SALT RIVER VALLEY AREA
*1926 SALT RIVER VALLEY AREA
*1921 SAN SIMON AREA
*1903 SOLMONSVILLE AREA
*1954 SULPHUR SPRINGS VALLEY
      AREA
 1950 THE DUNCAN AREA
*1931 TUCSON AREA
 1972 TUCSON-AVRA VALLEY AREA
 1938 UPPER GILA VALLEY AREA
*1942 VIRGIN RIVER VALLEY AREA
*1921 WINSLOW AREA
*1902 YUMA AREA
*1904 YUMA AREA
 1941 YUMA DESERT AREA
*1929 YUMA WELTON AREA

ARKANSAS

 1972 ARKANSAS
*1913 ASHLEY
*1925 BRADLEY
 1961 BRADLEY
 1967 CHICOT
 1968 CLEVELAND
*1914 COLUMBIA
*1907 CONWAY
*1916 CRAIGHEAD
 1974 CRITTENDEN
 1968 CROSS
 1972 DESHA
*1917 DREW
*1917 FAULKNER
*1906 FAYETTEVILLE AREA
 1971 FRANKLIN
 1969 GREENE
*1916 HEMPSTEAD
*1917 HOWARD
 1975 HOWARD
 1974 JACKSON
*1915 JEFFERSON
*1921 LONOKE
*1903 MILLER
*1914 MISSISSIPPI
 1971 MISSISSIPPI
*1925 NEVADA
 1973 OUACHITA
*1920 PERRY
 1974 PHILLIPS
*1913 POPE
*1906 PRAIRIE
*1922 PULASKI
 1975 PULASKI
*1911 RECONNAISSANCE OZARK
      REGION
 1975 SEBASTIAN
 1966 ST. FRANCIS
*1902 STUTTGART AREA
 1969 WASHINGTON
 1968 WOODRUFF
*1915 YELL

---

* OUT OF PRINT ; NOT AVAILABLE FOR DISTRIBUTION

CALIFORNIA

1966 ALAMEDA AREA
*1931 ALTURAS AREA
*1965 AMADOR AREA
*1916 ANAHEIM AREA
1969 ANTELOPE VALLEY AREA
*1924 AUBURN AREA
*1904 BAKERSFIELD AREA
*1945 BAKERSFIELB AREA
*1937 BARSTOW AREA
*1920 BIG VALLEY AREA
1924 BISHOP AREA
*1920 BRAWLEY AREA
*1907 BUTTE VALLEY AREA
*1929 CAPISTRANO AREA
1971 CARSON VALLEY AREA
*1917 CENTRAL SOUTHERN AREA
*1925 CHICO AREA
*1927 CLEAR LAKE AREA
*1923 COACHELLA VALLEY AREA
*1952 COALINGA AREA
*1907 COLUSA AREA
*1939 CONTRA COSTA
*1931 DIXON AREA
1971 EASTERN FRESNO AREA
1974 EASTERN SANTA CLARA
     AREA
1964 EASTERN STANISLAUS AREA
*1930 EL CAJON AREA
*1918 EL CENTRO AREA
1974 EL DORADO AREA
*1921 EUREKA AREA
*1900 FRESNO AREA
*1912 FRESNO AREA
*1923 GILROY AREA
1968 GLENN
*1918 GRASS VALLEY AREA
*1901 HANFORD AREA
*1915 HEALDSBURY AREA
*1923 HOLLISTER AREA
*1915 HONEY LAKE AREA
*1901 IMPERIAL AREA
*1903 IMPERIAL AREA
*1903 INDIO AREA
*1924 KING CITY AREA
*1946 KINGS
*1922 LANCASTER AREA
*1910 LIVERMORE AREA
*1937 LODI AREA
*1903 LOS ANGELES AREA
*1916 LOS ANGELES AREA
1952 LOS BANOS AREA
*1901 LOWER SALINAS VALLEY
     AREA
*1915 LOWER SAN JOAQUIN VALLEY
*1910 MADERA AREA
*1962 MADERA AREA
1974 MARIPOSA AREA
*1909 MARYSVILLE AREA
1956 MENDOTA AREA
*1914 MERCED AREA
1962 MERCED AREA
*1916 MIDDLE SAN JOAQUIN
     VALLEY AREA
*1908 MODESTO-TURLOCK AREA
*1938 NAPA AREA
1975 NEVADA AREA
1948 NEWMAN AREA
*1929 OCEANSIDE AREA
*1926 OROVILLE AREA
*1908 PAJARO VALLEY AREA
*1922 PALO VERDE AREA
1974 PALO VERDE AREA
*1915 PASADENA AREA
*1928 PASO ROBLEA AREA
*1942 PIXLEY AREA

*1927 PLACERVILLE AREA
*1908 PORTERSVILLE AREA
*1910 RED BLUFF AREA
*1907 REDDING AREA
*1915 RIVERSIDE AREA
*1904 SACRAMENTO AREA
*1941 SACRAMENTO AREA
*1954 SACRAMENTO AREA
*1941 SACRAMENTO SAN JOAQUIN
     DELTA AREA
*1913 SACRAMENTO VALLEY AREA
*1925 SALINAS AREA
1969 SAN BENITO
*1904 SAN BERNARDINO AREA
*1915 SAN DIEGO AREA
1973 SAN DIEGO AREA
*1915 SAN FERNANDO VALLEY AREA
*1914 SAN FRANCISCO BAY AREA
*1901 SAN GABRIEL AREA
*1903 SAN JOSE AREA
*1928 SAN LUIS OBISPO AREA
1961 SAN MATEO AREA
*1900 SANTA ANNA AREA
*1958 SANTA BARBARA AREA
1972 SANTA BARBARA AREA
     (NORTHERN)
1958 SANTA CLARA AREA
*1944 SANTA CRUZ AREA
*1916 SANTA MARIA AREA
*1927 SANTA YNEZ AREA
1974 SHASTA AREA
*1919 SHASTA VALLEY AREA
1975 SIERRA VALLEY AREA
1972 SONOMA
*1905 STOCKTON AREA
1951 STOCKTON AREA
*1930 SUISAN AREA
1974 SURPRISE VALLEY-
     HOME CAMP AREA
1974 TAHOE BASIN AREA
1967 TEHAMA
*1943 TRACY AREA
*1914 UKIAH AREA
*1917 UPPER SAN JOAQUIN
     VALLEY AREA
*1901 VENTURA AREA
*1917 VENTURA AREA
1970 VENTURA AREA
*1921 VICTORVILLE AREA
*1940 VISALIA AREA
1942 WASCO AREA
1971 WESTERN RIVERSIDE AREA
*1918 WILLITS AREA
*1909 WOODLAND AREA
1972 YOLO
*1904 YUMA AREA
*1929 YUMA-WELTON AREA

COLORADO

1974 ADAMS
1947 AKRON AREA
1973 ALAMOSA AREA
1971 ARAPAHOE
*1926 ARKANSAS VALLEY AREA
1973 BACA
1971 BENT
1975 BOULDER
*1932 BRIGHTON AREA
*1899 CACHE LA POUDRE VALLEY
     AREA
1974 CASTLE ROCK AREA
1975 CHAFFEE LAKE AREA
1968 CROWLEY
*1967 DELTA-MONTROSE AREA
1966 ELBERT(EASTERN PART)
*1927 FORT COLLINS AREA
*1962 FRASER-ALPINE AREA

*1905 GRAND JUNCTION AREA
1955 GRAND JUNCTION AREA
*1904 GREELEY AREA
*1929 GREELEY AREA
1975 GUNNISON AREA
*1930 LONGMONT AREA
*1902 LOWER ARKANSAS VALLEY
     AREA
1968 MORGAN
1972 OTERO
1971 PHILLIPS
1966 PROWERS
*1903 SAN LUIS VALLEY AREA
1970 SEDGWICH
1961 TROUT CREEK WATERSHED
*1910 UNCOMPAHGRE VALLEY AREA

CONNECTICUT

*1899 CONNECTICUT VALLEY AREA
*1903 CONNECTICUT VALLEY AREA
1962 HARTFORD
1970 LITCHFIELD
*1912 NEW LONDON
1966 TOLLAND
*1911 WINDHAM

DELAWARE

*1903 DOVER AREA
*1918 KENT
1971 KENT
*1915 NEW CASTLE
1970 NEW CASTLE
*1920 SUSSEX
1974 SUSSEX

FLORIDA

*1954 ALACHUA
*1913 BRADFORD
1974 BREVARD
1954 COLLIER
1958 DADE
*1921 DUVAL
*1906 ESCAMBIA
1960 ESCAMBIA
*1918 FLAGLER
*1915 FORT LAUDERDALE AREA
*1915 FRANKLIN
*1903 GADSDEN
1962 GADSDEN
*1904 GAINESVILLE AREA
*1914 HERNANDO
*1916 HILLSBOROUGH
1958 HILLSBOROUGH
1975 HOLMES
*1913 INDIAN RIVER AREA
*1910 JACKSONVILLE AREA
*1907 JEFFERSON
*1923 LAKE
1975 LAKE AREA
*1905 LEON
1958 MANATEE
*1909 MARIANNA AREA
*1912 OCALA AREA
1975 OCALA NATIONAL FOREST
     AREA
1971 OKEECHOBEE
*1919 ORANGE
1960 ORANGE
*1913 PINELLAS
1972 PINELLAS
*1927 POLK
*1914 PUTNAM
1959 SARASOTA
1966 SEMINOLE
*1917 ST. JOHNS

---

* OUT OF PRINT ; NOT AVAILABLE FOR DISTRIBUTION

1965 SUWANNEE
1965 WASHINGTON

GEORGIA

1975 APPLING AND JEFF DAVIS
*1904 BAINBRIDGE AREA
1971 BANKS AND STEPHENS
*1941 BARTOW
*1912 BEN HILL
1969 BEN HILL-IRWIN
1973 BERRIEN AND LANIER
*1922 BIBB
*1916 BROOKS
1974 BRYAN AND CHATHAM
*1910 BULLOCH
1968 BULLOCH
*1917 BURKE
*1919 BUTTS AND HENRY
*1925 CALHOUN
*1948 CANDLER
*1921 CARROLL
1971 CARROLL AND HARALSON
*1941 CATOOSA
*1911 CHATHAM
*1924 CHATTAHOOCHEE
*1912 CHATTOOGA
1973 CHEROKEE, GILMER AND
     PICKENS
*1927 CLARKE
1968 CLARKE-OCONEE
*1914 CLAY
*1901 COBB
1973 COBB
*1914 COLQUITT
1975 COLQUITT & COOK
*1911 COLUMBIA
*1928 COOK
*1901 COVINGTON AREA
*1919 COWETA AND FAYETTE
*1916 CRISP
*1942 DADE
1972 DAWSON, LUMPKIN, AND
     WHITE
*1939 DECATUR
*1914 DEKALB
*1904 DODGE
1923 DOOLY
*1912 DOUGHERTY
1968 DOUGHERTY
1961 DOUGLAS
*1918 EARLY
*1928 ELBERT
*1923 FANNIN
*1917 FLOYD
1960 FORSYTH
*1903 FORT VALLEY AREA
*1909 FRANKLIN
1958 FULTON
*1911 GLYNN
*1923 GORDON
1965 GORDON
*1908 GRADY
1967 GWINNETT
*1923 HABERSHAM
1963 HABERSHAM
*1941 HALL
*1909 HANCOCK
*1929 HART
1963 HART
1967 HOUSTON AND PEACH
*1914 JACKSON
*1916 JASPER
*1913 JEFF DAVIS
*1930 JEFFERSON
*1923 JENKINS
1968 JENKINS
*1913 JONES

*1925 LAMAR
1972 LAMAR, PIKE, AND UPSON
*1915 LAURENS
*1927 LEE
*1917 LOWNDES
*1918 MADISON
*1937 MCDUFFIE
*1929 MCINTOSH
1961 MCINTOSH
*1916 MERIWETHER
1965 MERIWETHER
*1913 MILLER
*1920 MITCHELL
*1920 MONROE
1973 MONTGOMERY, TOOMBS AND
     WHEELER
1965 MORGAN
*1922 MUSCOGEE
*1919 OCONEE, MORGAN, AND
     PUTNAM
*1918 PIERCE
1968 PIERCE
*1909 PIKE
*1914 POLK
*1918 PULASKI
*1926 QUITMAN
*1920 RABUN
*1924 RANDOLPH
*1912 RECONNAISSANCE TATTNALL
*1916 RICHMOND
*1920 ROCKDALE
1974 SCHLEY AND SUMTER
*1920 SCREVEN
*1905 SPALDING
1964 SPALDING
*1913 STEWART
*1910 SUMTER
*1913 TALBOT
*1914 TATTNALL
1914 TERRELL
*1908 THOMAS
*1909 TIFT
1959 TIFT
*1939 TOOMBS
*1954 TOWNS
1964 TREUTLEN
*1912 TROUP
*1915 TURNER
1963 TWIGGS
1950 UNION
*1910 WALKER
1964 WALTON
*1915 WASHINGTON
*1906 WAYCROSS AREA
*1926 WAYNE
1965 WAYNE
*1915 WILKES
*1929 WORTH

HAWAII

1973 ISLAND OF HAWAII
1972 KAUAI, OAHU, MAUI,
     MOLOKAI, AND LANAI
1955 THE TERRITORY OF HAWAII

IDAHO

*1926 BEAR LAKE VALLEY AREA
*1930 BENEWAH
1973 BINGHAM
*1903 BLACKFOOT AREA
1943 BLACKFOOT-ABERDEEN AREA
*1901 BOISE AREA
*1939 BONNER
1972 CANYON AREA
1965 GEM COUNTY AREA
*1929 GOODING AREA

1950 IDAHO FALLS AREA
*1927 JEROME AREA
1971 KOOSKIA
*1919 KOOTENAI
*1915 LATAH
*1902 LEWISTON AREA
*1907 MINIDOKA AREA
*1923 MINIDOKA AREA
1975 MINIDOKA AREA
*1917 NEZ PERCE AND LEWIS
*1918 PORTNEUF AREA
*1925 SODA SPRINGS BANCROFF
     AREA
1969 TETON AREA IDAHO-WYOMING
*1921 TWIN FALLS AREA

ILLINOIS

*1902 CLAY
*1902 CLINTON
1971 DOUGLAS
1972 EDWARDS AND RICHLAND
1969 GALLATIN
1974 GREENE
1956 HENDERSON(STATE)
1966 JERSEY(STATE)
*1903 JOHNSON
1964 JOHNSON(STATE)
*1903 KNOX
1970 LAKE
1972 LASALLE(STATE)
1956 LAWRENCE(STATE)
1974 LOGAN
1965 MCHENRY(STATE)
*1903 MCLEAN
1953 MENARD(STATE)
1969 MONTGOMERY
*1904 O'FALLON AREA
1975 POPE, HARDIN & MASSAC
1968 PULASKI AND ALEXANDER
*1903 SANGAMON
*1902 ST. CLAIR
*1902 TAZEWELL
1964 WABASH
*1912 WILL
1962 WILL(STATE)
1959 WILLIAMSON(STATE)
*1903 WINNEBAGO

INDIANA

1921 ADAMS
*1908 ALLEN
1969 ALLEN
1947 BARTHOLOMEW
1916 BENTON
*1928 BLACKFORD
*1912 BOONE
1975 BOONE
*1904 BOONEVILLE AREA
1946 BROWN
1958 CARROLL
*1955 CASS
1974 CLARK AND FLOYD
1922 CLAY
*1914 CLINTON
1975 CRAWFORD
1974 DAVIESS
1910 DECATUR
*1913 DELAWARE
1972 DELAWARE
1937 DUBOIS
*1914 ELKHART
1974 ELKHART
1960 FAYETTE AND UNION
1966 FOUNTAIN
1950 FRANKLIN
1946 FULTON

_____
* OUT OF PRINT : NOT AVAILABLE FOR DISTRIBUTION

1922 GIBSON
*1915 GRANT
*1906 GREENE
*1912 HAMILTON
1925 HANCOCK
1975 HARRISON
1913 HENDRICKS
1974 HENDRICKS
1971 HOWARD
1940 JENNINGS
1948 JOHNSON
1943 KNOX
1922 KOSCIUSKO
1944 LA PORTE
*1917 LAKE
1972 LAKE
*1922 LAWRENCE
*1903 MADISON
1967 MADISON
*1907 MARION
*1904 MARSHALL
1946 MARTIN
1927 MIAMI
*1922 MONROE
*1912 MONTGOMERY
1950 MORGAN
*1905 NEWTON
1955 NEWTON
*1953 NOBLE
1930 OHIO AND SWITZERLAND
1964 OWEN
1967 PARKE
1969 PERRY
1938 PIKE
*1916 PORTER
*1902 POSEY
1968 PULASKI
1925 PUTNAM
1931 RANDOLPH
*1937 RUSH
*1904 SCOTT
1962 SCOTT
1974 SHELBY
1973 SPENCER
1950 ST. JOSEPH
*1915 STARKE
1940 STEUBEN
1971 SULLIVAN
*1905 TIPPECANOE
1959 TIPPECANOE
*1912 TIPTON
1944 VANDERBURGH
1930 VERMILLION
1974 VIGO
*1914 WARREN
1939 WASHINGTON
1925 WAYNE
*1915 WELLS
*1915 WHITE

IOWA

*1919 ADAIR
1963 ADAMS
1958 ALLAMAKEE
*1923 APPANOOSE
1940 AUDUBON
*1921 BENTON
*1917 BLACK HAWK
*1920 BOONE
*1913 BREMER
1967 BREMER
*1926 BUCHANAN
*1917 BUENA VISTA
*1928 BUTLER
1930 CALHOUN
*1926 CARROLL
1969 CASS

1919 CEDAR
*1903 CERRO GORDO
1940 CERRO GORDO
*1924 CHEROKEE
*1927 CHICKASAW
1923 CLARKE
*1916 CLAY
1969 CLAY
*1925 CLAYTON
*1915 CLINTON
*1928 CRAWFORD
1973 CRAWFORD
*1920 DALLAS
1940 DAVIS
1939 DECATUR
*1922 DELAWARE
*1921 DES MOINES
*1920 DICKINSON
*1921 DUBUQUE
*1902 DUBUQUE AREA
*1920 EMMET
*1919 FAYETTE
*1922 FLOYD
*1938 FRANKLIN
*1924 FREMONT
1975 FREMONT
*1921 GREENE
*1921 GRUNDY
*1929 GUTHRIE
1974 GUTHRIE
*1917 HAMILTON
1930 HANCOCK
*1920 HARDIN
*1923 HARRISON
*1917 HENRY
1935 HOWARD
1974 HOWARD
1961 HUMBOLDT
1939 IDA
1967 IOWA
1941 JACKSON
*1921 JASPER
*1922 JEFFERSON
1960 JEFFERSON
*1919 JOHNSON
*1924 JONES
1971 KEOKUK
*1925 KOSSUTH
*1914 LEE
1917 LINN
1975 LINN
*1918 LOUISA
1960 LUCAS
1927 LYON
*1918 MADISON
1975 MADISON
*1919 MAHASKA
1939 MARION
*1919 MARSHALL
1920 MILLS
*1916 MITCHELL
1975 MITCHELL
1959 MONONA
1931 MONROE
*1917 MONTGOMERY
*1914 MUSCATINE
*1921 O'BRIEN
1940 OSCEOLA
*1921 PAGE
*1918 PALO ALTO
*1923 PLYMOUTH
1928 POCAHONTAS
*1918 POLK
1960 POLK
*1914 POTTAWATTAMIE
1929 POWESHIEK
*1916 RINGGOLD
1924 SAC

*1915 SCOTT
1961 SHELBY
*1915 SIOUX
*1903 STORY
1941 STORY
*1904 TAMA
1950 TAMA
1954 TAYLOR
*1927 UNION
*1915 VAN BUREN
1962 VAN BUREN
*1917 WAPELLO
*1925 WARREN
1930 WASHINGTON
*1918 WAYNE
1971 WAYNE
*1914 WEBSTER
1975 WEBSTER
*1918 WINNEBAGO
*1922 WINNESHIEK
1968 WINNESHIEK
*1920 WOODBURY
1972 WOODBURY
1922 WORTH
*1919 WRIGHT

KANSAS

*1904 ALLEN
*1938 ALLEN
1931 BOURBON
*1905 BROWN
1960 BROWN
1975 BUTLER
1974 CHASE
*1912 CHEROKEE
1926 CLAY
*1915 COWLEY
*1928 CRAWFORD
1973 CRAWFORD
*1927 DONIPHAN
1973 EDWARDS
1975 ELLIS
1965 FINNEY
1965 FORD
*1904 GARDEN CITY AREA
1960 GEARY
1969 GRANT
1968 GRAY
1961 GREELEY
*1912 GREENWOOD
1961 HAMILTON
1971 HARPER
1974 HARVEY
1968 HASKELL
1973 HODGEMAN
*1912 JEWELL
1928 JOHNSON
1963 KEARNY
1938 KINGMAN
*1926 LABETTE
1972 LANE
*1919 LEAVENWORTH
1964 LOGAN
1930 MARION
*1913 MONTGOMERY
1974 MORRIS
1963 MORTON
*1930 NEOSHO
*1903 PARSONS AREA
1968 PRATT
*1911 RENO
1966 RENO
1967 REPUBLIC
1974 RICE
*1906 RILEY
1975 RILEY & PART OF GEARY
*1903 RUSSELL

_____

* OUT OF PRINT ; NOT AVAILABLE FOR DISTRIBUTION

1959 SALINE
1965 SCOTT
1965 SEWARD
*1911 SHAWNEE
1970 SHAWNEE
1973 SHERMAN
1961 STANTON
1961 STEVENS
*1910 WESTERN KANSAS
       RECONNAISSANCE
1965 WICHITA
*1902 WICHITA AREA
*1927 WILSON
1931 WOODSON

KENTUCKY

1964 ADAIR
1969 BARREN
1963 BATH
1973 BOONE, CAMPBELL AND
       KENTON
1966 CALDWELL
1945 CALLOWAY
1973 CALLOWAY AND MARSHALL
*1912 CHRISTIAN
1964 CLARK
1974 DAVIESS & HANCOCK
1965 ELLIOTT
1974 ESTILL AND LEE
*1931 FAYETTE
1968 FAYETTE
1965 FOURTEEN CO. EASTERN KY.
       RECONNAISSANCE
1964 FULTON
*1921 GARRARD
1953 GRAVES
1972 GRAYSON
1968 HARRISON
1967 HENDERSON
1966 JEFFERSON
*1915 JESSAMINE
*1919 LOGAN
1975 LOGAN
*1905 MADISON
1973 MADISON
1950 MARSHALL
*1903 MASON
1970 MC CREARY-WHITLEY AREA
*1905 MCCRACKEN
1974 MENIFEE AND ROWAN AND
       NORTHWESTERN MORGAN
1930 MERCER
1967 METCALFE
1920 MUHLENBERG
1971 NELSON
1974 PULASKI
*1910 ROCKCASTLE
*1903 SCOTT
1916 SHELBY
*1902 UNION
*1904 WARREN

LOUISIANA

*1903 ACADIA
1962 ACADIA
*1928 BEAUREGARD
*1908 BIENVILLE
1962 BOSSIER
*1906 CADDO
*1910 CONCORDIA
*1904 DE SOTO
*1908 EAST AND WEST CARROLL
*1906 EAST BATON ROUGE
1968 EAST BATON ROUGE
*1912 EAST FELICIANA
1974 EVANGELINE

*1911 IBERIA
*1918 LA SALLE
*1915 LAFAYETTE
*1901 LAKE CHARLES AREA
*1909 LINCOLN
*1931 LIVINGSTON
*1921 NATCHITOCHES
*1903 NEW ORLEANS AREA
*1903 OUACHITA
1974 OUACHITA
*1916 RAPIDES
*1919 SABINE
1973 ST. JAMES AND ST. JOHN
       THE BAPTIST
*1917 ST. MARTIN
1959 ST. MARY
*1905 TANGIPAHOA
1968 TENSAS
1960 TERREBONNE
*1922 WASHINGTON
*1914 WEBSTER
*1907 WINN

MAINE

1970 ANDROSCOGGIN AND
       SAGADAHOC
*1917 AROOSTOOK
1964 AROOSTOOK NORTHEASTERN
       PART
1964 AROOSTOOK SOUTHERN PART
*1908 CARIBOU AREA
*1915 CUMBERLAND
1974 CUMBERLAND
*1909 ORONO AREA
1963 PENOBSCOT
1972 SOMERSET(SOUTHERN PART)
*1955 WALDO
*1952 YORK

MARYLAND

*1921 ALLEGANY
*1909 ANNE ARUNDEL
*1929 ANNE ARUNDEL
1973 ANNE ARUNDEL
*1917 BALTIMORE
*1900 CALVERT
*1928 CALVERT
1971 CALVERT
*1929 CAROLINE
1964 CAROLINE
*1919 CARROLL
1969 CARROLL
*1900 CECIL
*1927 CECIL
1973 CECIL
*1918 CHARLES
1974 CHARLES
*1922 DORCHESTER
*1963 DORCHESTER
*1907 EASTON AREA
*1919 FREDERICK
1960 FREDERICK
*1922 GARRETT
1974 GARRETT
*1901 HARFORD
*1927 HARFORD
1975 HARFORD AREA
*1916 HOWARD
1968 HOWARD
*1900 KENT
*1930 KENT
*1914 MONTGOMERY
1961 MONTGOMERY
*1901 PRINCE GEORGES
*1925 PRINCE GEORGES
1967 PRINCE GEORGES

*1931 QUEEN ANNES
1966 QUEEN ANNES
*1920 SOMERSET
1966 SOMERSET
*1900 ST. MARYS
*1923 ST. MARYS
*1929 TALBOT
1970 TALBOT
*1917 WASHINGTON
1962 WASHINGTON
*1921 WICOMICO
1970 WICOMICO
*1903 WORCESTER
*1924 WORCESTER
1973 WORCESTER

MASSACHUSETTS

*1923 BERKSHIRE
*1899 CONNECTICUT VALLEY AREA
*1903 CONNECTICUT VALLEY AREA
*1925 DUKES AND NANTUCKET
*1925 ESSEX
*1929 FRANKLIN
1967 FRANKLIN
*1928 HAMPDEN AND HAMPSHIRE
*1924 MIDDLESEX
*1920 NORFOLK, BRISTOL, AND
       BARNSTAL
*1911 PLYMOUTH
1969 PLYMOUTH
*1922 WORCESTER

MICHIGAN

1929 ALGER
*1901 ALLEGAN
*1904 ALMA AREA
1924 ALPENA
1923 ANTRIM
1967 ARENAC
*1924 BARRY
1931 BAY
*1902 BERRIEN
*1928 BRANCH
*1916 CALHOUN
*1906 CASS
1974 CHARLEVOIX
1939 CHEBOYGAN
1927 CHIPPEWA
1942 CLINTON
1927 CRAWFORD
*1930 EATON
1973 EMMET
*1912 GENESEE
1972 GENESEE
1972 GLADWIN
1966 GRAND TRAVERSE
1924 HILLSDALE
1941 INGHAM
1967 IONIA
1937 IRON
1925 ISABELLA
1926 JACKSON
*1922 KALAMAZOO
1927 KALKASKA
1926 KENT
1972 LAPEER
1973 LEELANAU
1961 LENAWEE
*1923 LIVINGSTON
1974 LIVINGSTON
1929 LUCE
*1923 MACOMB
1971 MACOMB
1922 MANISTEE
1939 MASON
*1927 MECOSTA

* OUT OF PRINT ; NOT AVAILABLE FOR DISTRIBUTION

1925 MENOMINEE
1950 MIDLAND
1960 MONTCALM
1930 MONTMORENCY
*1904 MUNISING AREA
*1924 MUSKEGON
1968 MUSKEGON
1951 NEWAYGO
*1938 OCEANA
1923 OGEMAW
1969 OSCEOLA
1931 OSCODA
*1922 OTTAWA
1972 OTTAWA
*1904 OWOSSO AREA
*1905 OXFORD AREA
*1903 PONTIAC AREA
*1940 PRESQUE ISLE
*1921 RECONNAISSANCE ONTONAGON
1924 ROSCOMMON
1938 SAGINAW
*1904 SAGINAW AREA
1961 SANILAC
1939 SCHOOLCRAFT
1974 SHIAWASSEE
*1929 ST. CLAIR
1974 ST. CLAIR
*1921 ST. JOSEPH
1926 TUSCOLA
*1922 VAN BUREN
1930 WASHTENAW
*1908 WEXFORD

MINNESOTA

*1916 ANOKA
*1906 BLUE EARTH
*1905 CARLTON AREA
1968 CARVER
*1906 CROOKSTON AREA
1965 CROW WING
1960 DAKOTA
1961 DODGE
1975 DOUGLAS
1957 FARIBAULT
1958 FILLMORE
*1913 GOODHUE
*1929 HENNEPIN
1974 HENNEPIN
*1929 HOUSTON
1930 HUBBARD
1958 ISANTI
*1923 JACKSON
1939 KANABEC
*1924 LAC QUE PARLE
1926 LAKE OF THE WOODS
     (RECONNAISSANCE)
1954 LE SUEUR
1970 LINCOLN
*1903 MARSHALL AREA
1955 MCLEOD
1927 MILLE LACS
1958 NICOLLET
1975 NOBLES
1974 NORMAN
*1923 OLMSTED
*1914 PENNINGTON
*1941 PINE
1972 POPE
*1914 RAMSEY
*1939 RED RIVER VALLEY AREA
*1909 RICE
1975 RICE
1949 ROCK
1942 ROSEAU
1959 SCOTT
1968 SHERBURNE
1973 STEELE

*1919 STEVENS
1971 STEVENS
1973 SWIFT
1965 WABASHA
*1926 WADENA
1965 WASECA
1968 WRIGHT

MISSISSIPPI

*1910 ADAMS
1970 ADAMS
*1921 ALCORN
1971 ALCORN
*1917 AMITE
*1904 BILOXI AREA
1958 BOLIVAR
1965 CALHOUN
*1915 CHICKASAW
1974 CHICKASAW
*1920 CHOCTAW
*1926 CLAIBORNE
1963 CLAIBORNE
*1914 CLARKE
1965 CLARKE
*1909 CLAY
*1915 COAHOMA
1959 COAHOMA
*1918 COVINGTON
1965 COVINGTON
*1905 CRYSTAL SPRINGS AREA
1959 DE SOTO
*1911 FORREST
*1922 GEORGE
1971 GEORGE
*1932 GREENE
*1915 GRENADA
1967 GRENADA
*1930 HANCOCK
*1924 HARRISON
1975 HARRISON
*1916 HINDS
*1908 HOLMES
1959 HUMPHREYS
1961 ISSAQUENA
*1927 JACKSON
1964 JACKSON
*1904 JACKSON AREA
*1907 JASPER
*1915 JEFFERSON DAVIS
*1913 JONES
*1912 LAFAYETTE
*1919 LAMAR
1975 LAMAR
*1910 LAUDERDALE
*1916 LEE
1973 LEE
1959 LEFLORE
*1912 LINCOLN
1963 LINCOLN
*1911 LOWNDES
*1917 MADISON
*1938 MARION
1972 MARSHALL
*1903 MCNEILL AREA
*1908 MONROE
1966 MONROE
*1906 MONTGOMERY
1975 MONTGOMERY
*1916 NEWTON
1960 NEWTON
*1910 NOXUBEE
*1907 OKTIBBEHA
1973 OKTIBBEHA
1963 PANOLA
*1918 PEARL RIVER
*1922 PERRY
*1918 PIKE

1968 PIKE
*1906 PONTOTOC
1973 PONTOTOC
*1907 PRENTISS
1957 PRENTISS
1958 QUITMAN
*1926 RANKIN
*1909 SCRANTON AREA
1962 SHARKEY
*1919 SIMPSON
*1902 SMEDES AREA
*1920 SMITH
1959 SUNFLOWER
1970 TALLAHATCHIE
1967 TATE
1966 TIPPAH
*1944 TISHOMINGO
1956 TUNICA
1968 WALTHALL
*1912 WARREN
1964 WARREN
1961 WASHINGTON
*1911 WAYNE
*1913 WILKINSON
*1912 WINSTON
1975 YAZOO
*1901 YAZOO AREA

MISSOURI

*1921 ANDREW
*1909 ATCHISON
*1916 BARRY
*1912 BARTON
1974 BARTON
*1908 BATES
1962 BOONE
*1915 BUCHANAN
*1921 CALDWELL
1974 CALDWELL
*1916 CALLAWAY
*1910 CAPE GIRARDEAU
*1912 CARROLL
*1912 CASS
*1909 CEDAR
*1918 CHARITON
*1920 COLE
*1909 COOPER
*1905 CRAWFORD
1964 DAVIESS
*1914 DE KALB
1971 DENT
*1914 DUNKLIN
*1911 FRANKLIN
*1913 GREENE
*1914 GRUNDY
*1914 HARRISON
*1953 HOLT
*1902 HOWELL
*1910 JACKSON
1954 JASPER
*1914 JOHNSON
*1917 KNOX
*1911 LACLEDE
*1920 LAFAYETTE
1975 LAFAYETTE
*1923 LAWRENCE
*1917 LINCOLN
*1945 LINN
1956 LIVINGSTON
*1911 MACON
*1910 MARION
1975 MARK TWAIN NATIONAL
     FOREST AREA
*1912 MILLER
*1921 MISSISSIPPI
1964 MONITEAU
*1915 NEWTON

_____

* OUT OF PRINT ; NOT AVAILABLE FOR DISTRIBUTION

*1913 NODAWAY
*1904 O'FALLON AREA
*1910 PEMISCOT
 1971 PEMISCOT
*1913 PERRY
*1914 PETTIS
*1912 PIKE
*1911 PLATTE
*1926 POLK
*1906 PUTNAM
*1913 RALLS
*1922 RAY
*1911 RECONNAISSANCE OZARK
       REGION
*1918 REYNOLDS
*1915 RIPLEY
*1919 SALINE
*1905 SCOTLAND
 1975 SCOTLAND
*1903 SHELBY
*1956 ST. CHARLES
*1918 ST. FRANCOIS
*1919 ST. LOUIS
*1912 STODDARD
*1917 TEXAS
*1904 WEBSTER
 1968 WORTH

MONTANA

 1944 BIG HORN VALLEY AREA
*1902 BILLINGS AREA
*1914 BITTERROOT VALLEY AREA
 1959 BITTERROOT VALLEY AREA
 1975 CARBON AREA
 1953 CENTRAL MONTANA
       (RECONNAISSANCE)
*1905 GALLATIN VALLEY AREA
*1931 GALLATIN VALLEY AREA
 1967 JUDITH BASIN AREA
*1929 LOWER FLATHEAD VALLEY
       AREA
 1939 LOWER YELLOWSTONE VALLEY
       AREA
 1940 MIDDLE YELLOWSTONE
       VALLEY AREA
*1928 MILK RIVER AREA
*1929 NORTHERN PLAINS OF
       MONTANA RECONNAISSANCE
 1971 POWDER RIVER AREA
 1967 TREASURE
 1960 UPPER FLATHEAD VALLEY
       AREA
 1943 UPPER MUSSELSHELL
       VALLEY AREA
 1958 WIBAUX
 1972 YELLOWSTONE

NEBRASKA

*1923 ADAMS
 1974 ADAMS
*1921 ANTELOPE
*1919 BANNER
*1954 BLAINE
*1921 BOONE
 1972 BOONE
*1916 BOX BUTTE
*1937 BOYD
*1938 BROWN
*1924 BUFFALO
 1974 BUFFALO
*1922 BURT
*1924 BUTLER
*1913 CASS
*1941 CASS
*1928 CEDAR
*1917 CHASE

 1956 CHERRY
*1918 CHEYENNE
*1927 CLAY
*1930 COLFAX
*1922 CUMING
 1975 CUMING
*1926 CUSTER
*1919 DAKOTA
*1915 DAWES
*1922 DAWSON
*1921 DEUEL
 1965 DEUEL
*1929 DIXON
*1916 DODGE
*1913 DOUGLAS
 1975 DOUGLAS & SARPY
*1931 DUNDY
 1963 DUNDY
*1916 FILLMORE
*1916 FORT LARAMIE AREA
*1926 FRANKLIN
*1939 FRONTIER
*1930 FURNAS
*1914 GAGE
 1964 GAGE
*1924 GARDEN
*1938 GARFIELD
*1938 GOSPER
*1903 GRAND ISLAND AREA
*1937 GREELEY
*1916 HALL
 1962 HALL
*1927 HAMILTON
*1930 HARLAN
 1974 HARLAN
*1938 HAYES
*1930 HITCHCOCK
 1970 HITCHCOCK
*1938 HOLT
 1964 HOOKER
*1920 HOWARD
 1974 HOWARD
*1921 JEFFERSON
 1975 JEFFERSON
*1920 JOHNSON
*1923 KEARNEY
*1904 KEARNEY AREA
*1926 KEITH
*1937 KEYA PAHA
*1916 KIMBALL
 1962 KIMBALL
*1930 KNOX
*1906 LANCASTER
 1948 LANCASTER
*1926 LINCOLN
 1975 LOGAN
*1937 LOUP
*1920 MADISON
 1969 MCPHERSON
*1922 MERRICK
*1917 MORRILL
*1922 NANCE
 1960 NANCE
*1914 NEMAHA
*1907 NORTH PLATTE AREA
*1925 NUCKOLLS
*1912 OTOE
 1950 OTOE
*1920 PAWNEE
*1921 PERKINS
*1917 PHELPS
 1973 PHELPS
*1928 PIERCE
*1923 PLATTE
*1915 POLK
 1974 POLK
*1919 RED WILLOW
 1967 RED WILLOW

*1915 RICHARDSON
 1974 RICHARDSON
*1937 ROCK
*1928 SALINE
*1905 SARPY
*1939 SARPY
*1913 SAUNDERS
 1965 SAUNDERS
*1913 SCOTTS BLUFF
 1968 SCOTTS BLUFF
*1914 SEWARD
 1974 SEWARD
*1918 SHERIDAN
*1931 SHERMAN
*1919 SIOUX
*1929 STANTON
*1903 STANTON AREA
*1927 THAYER
 1968 THAYER
 1965 THOMAS
*1914 THURSTON
 1972 THURSTON
*1932 VALLEY
*1915 WASHINGTON
 1964 WASHINGTON
*1917 WAYNE
 1975 WAYNE
*1923 WEBSTER
 1974 WEBSTER
*1911 WESTERN NEBRASKA
       RECONNAISSANCE
*1937 WHEELER
*1928 YORK

NEVADA

 1971 CARSON VALLEY AREA
*1909 FALLON AREA
 1975 FALLON-FERNLEY AREA
 1967 LAS VEGAS AND ELDORADO
       VALLEYS AREA
*1923 LAS VEGAS AREA
 1965 LOVELOCK AREA
*1923 MOAPA VALLEY AREA
 1968 PAHRANAGAT-PENOYER AREA
 1974 SURPRISE VALLEY-HOME
       CAMP
 1974 TAHOE BASIN

NEW HAMPSHIRE

 1968 BELKNAP
 1949 CHESHIRE AND SULLIVAN
 1943 COOS
 1939 GRAFTON
 1953 HILLSBORO
*1906 MERRIMACK
 1965 MERRIMACK
*1909 NASHUA AREA
 1959 ROCKINGHAM
 1949 STRAFFORD
 1973 STRAFFORD

NEW JERSEY

*1917 BELVIDERE AREA
 1925 BERGEN AREA
*1919 BERNARDSVILLE AREA
 1971 BURLINGTON
 1966 CAMDEN
*1915 CAMDEN AREA
 1926 CAMDEN AREA
*1919 CHATSWORTH AREA
*1913 FREEHOLD AREA
*1927 FREEHOLD AREA
 1962 GLOUCESTER
 1974 HUNTERDON
 1972 MERCER

---

* OUT OF PRINT : NOT AVAILABLE FOR DISTRIBUTION

```
*1917 MILLVILLE AREA
 1975 PASSAIC
 1969 SALEM
*1901 SALEM AREA
*1923 SALEM AREA
 1975 SUSSEX
*1911 SUSSEX AREA
*1902 TRENTON AREA
*1921 TRENTON AREA


            NEW MEXICO

 1958 BLUEWATER AREA
 1968 CABEZON AREA
 1958 CURRY
*1928 DEMING AREA
 1971 EDDY AREA
*1930 FORT SUMNER AREA
 1973 HARDING
 1973 HIDALGO
 1974 LEA
*1932 LOVINGTON AREA
*1912 MESILLA VALLEY AREA
*1912 MIDDLE RIO GRANDE
       VALLEY AREA
*1899 PECOS VALLEY
 1959 PORTALES AREA
*1930 RINCON AREA
 1967 ROOSEVELT
*1933 ROSWELL AREA
 1975 SANTA FE AREA
*1929 SOCORRO AND RIO PUERCO
       AREAS
 1960 SOUTHWEST QUAY AREA
*1950 THE DUNCAN AREA
 1970 TORRANCE AREA
 1974 TUCUMCARI AREA
 1975 VALENCIA
 1967 ZUNI MOUNTAIN AREA


            NEW YORK

 1942 ALBANY AND SCHENECTADY
 1956 ALLEGANY
*1904 AUBURN AREA
*1902 BIGFLATS AREA
*1905 BINGHAMPTON AREA
*1932 BROOME
 1971 BROOME
*1940 CATTARAUGUS
*1922 CAYUGA
 1971 CAYUGA
*1914 CHAUTAUQUA
*1932 CHEMUNG
 1973 CHEMUNG
*1918 CHENANGO
*1914 CLINTON
*1923 COLUMBIA
*1916 CORTLAND
 1961 CORTLAND
*1930 DELAWARE
*1907 DUTCHESS
 1955 DUTCHESS
*1929 ERIE
 1958 FRANKLIN
*1922 GENESEE
 1969 GENESEE
 1975 HERKIMER
*1923 HERKIMER AREA
*1911 JEFFERSON
 1960 LEWIS
*1908 LIVINGSTON
 1956 LIVINGSTON
*1903 LONG ISLAND AREA
*1902 LYONS AREA
*1906 MADISON
*1910 MONROE
*1938 MONROE
 1973 MONROE
*1908 MONTGOMERY
*1906 NIAGARA
*1947 NIAGARA
 1972 NIAGARA
```

```
*1913 ONEIDA
*1938 ONONDAGA
*1910 ONTARIO
 1958 ONTARIO AND YATES
*1912 ORANGE
 1939 ORLEANS
*1917 OSWEGO
 1940 OTSEGO
 1937 RENSSELAER
*1917 SARATOGA
*1915 SCHOHARIE
 1969 SCHOHARIE
*1942 SENECA
 1972 SENECA
 1925 ST. LAWRENCE
*1931 STEUBEN
 1975 SUFFOLK
*1928 SUFFOLK AND NASSAU
 1946 SULLIVAN
*1903 SYRACUSE AREA
 1953 TIOGA
*1905 TOMPKINS
*1920 TOMPKINS
 1965 TOMPKINS
*1940 ULSTER
*1909 WASHINGTON
 1975 WASHINGTON
*1919 WAYNE
*1901 WESTFIELD AREA
*1919 WHITE PLAINS AREA
*1938 WYOMING
 1974 WYOMING
*1916 YATES


         NORTH CAROLINA

*1901 ALAMANCE
 1960 ALAMANCE
*1915 ALLEGHANY
 1973 ALLEGHANY
*1915 ANSON
*1912 ASHE
*1903 ASHEVILLE AREA
 1955 AVERY
*1917 BEAUFORT
*1918 BERTIE
*1914 BLADEN
 1937 BRUNSWICK
*1920 BUNCOMBE
 1954 BUNCOMBE
*1926 BURKE
*1910 CABARRUS
*1917 CALDWELL
*1923 CAMDEN AND CURRITUCK
*1938 CARTERET
*1901 CARY AREA
*1908 CASWELL
 1975 CATAWBA
 1937 CHATHAM
*1921 CHEROKEE
 1951 CHEROKEE
*1906 CHOWAN
 1941 CLAY
*1916 CLEVELAND
*1915 COLUMBUS
*1929 CRAVEN
*1903 CRAVEN AREA
*1922 CUMBERLAND
*1915 DAVIDSON
*1927 DAVIE
*1905 DUPLIN
 1959 DUPLIN
*1920 DURHAM
*1907 EDGECOMBE
*1913 FORSYTH
 1931 FRANKLIN
*1909 GASTON
*1929 GATES
 1953 GRAHAM
*1910 GRANVILLE
*1924 GREENE
*1904 GREENVILLE AREA
*1920 GUILFORD
```

```
*1916 HALIFAX
*1916 HARNETT
*1922 HAYWOOD
*1954 HAYWOOD
*1907 HENDERSON
*1943 HENDERSON
*1916 HERTFORD
*1902 HICKORY AREA
*1918 HOKE
 1964 IREDELL
*1948 JACKSON
*1911 JOHNSTON
*1938 JONES
*1909 LAKE MATTAMUSKEET AREA
*1933 LEE
 1927 LENOIR
*1914 LINCOLN
 1929 MACON
 1956 MACON
*1942 MADISON
*1928 MARTIN
*1910 MECKLENBURG
*1952 MITCHELL
*1930 MONTGOMERY
*1919 MOORE
*1902 MT. MITCHELL AREA
*1926 NASH
*1906 NEW HANOVER
*1925 NORTHAMPTON
*1921 ONSLOW
*1918 ORANGE
*1937 PAMLICO
 1957 PASQUOTANK
*1912 PENDER
*1905 PERQUIMANS AND
       PASQUOTANK
*1928 PERSON
*1909 PITT
 1974 PITT
*1923 POLK
*1900 RALEIGH TO NEWBERN
*1913 RANDOLPH
*1911 RICHMOND
*1908 ROBESON
 1926 ROCKINGHAM
*1914 ROWAN
*1924 RUTHERFORD
*1923 SAMPSON
*1909 SCOTLAND
 1967 SCOTLAND
*1916 STANLY
*1901 STATESVILLE AREA
*1940 STOKES
*1937 SURRY
 1947 SWAIN
*1906 TRANSYLVANIA
*1948 TRANSYLVANIA
 1974 TRANSYLVANIA
*1920 TYRRELL
*1914 UNION
*1918 VANCE
*1914 WAKE
 1970 WAKE
 1942 WARREN
*1932 WASHINGTON
*1928 WATAUGA
 1958 WATAUGA
*1915 WAYNE
 1974 WAYNE
*1918 WILKES
*1925 WILSON
*1924 YADKIN
 1962 YADKIN
*1952 YANCEY


            NORTH DAKOTA

*1912 BARNES
 1944 BILLINGS
*1915 BOTTINEAU
 1975 BOWMAN
 1974 BURLEIGH
*1904 CANDO AREA
```

---

* OUT OF PRINT ; NOT AVAILABLE FOR DISTRIBUTION

*1905 CARRINGTON AREA
*1924 CASS
*1914 DICKEY
*1903 FARGO AREA
*1902 GRAND FORKS AREA
*1903 JAMESTOWN AREA
*1914 LA MOURE
 1971 LA MOURE AND PARTS OF
       JAMES RIVER VALLEY
*1921 MCHENRY
 1942 MCKENZIE
*1907 MCKENZIE AREA
 1951 MORTON
*1907 MORTON AREA
 1975 OLIVER
*1906 RANSOM
*1908 RECONNAISSANCE WESTERN
*1908 RICHLAND
 1975 RICHLAND CO. & SHEYENNE
       NAT. GRASSLAND AREA
*1917 SARGENT
 1964 SARGENT
 1968 STARK
 1918 TRAILL
 1966 TRI-COUNTY AREA
 1972 WALSH
 1974 WARD
 1970 WELLS
*1906 WILLISTON AREA

                OHIO

 1938 ADAMS
 1965 ALLEN
 1973 ASHTABULA
*1903 ASHTABULA AREA
*1938 ATHENS
*1909 AUGLAIZE
*1927 BELMONT
*1930 BROWN
 1927 BUTLER
 1971 CHAMPAIGN
 1958 CLARK
*1923 CLERMONT
 1975 CLERMONT
*1905 CLEVELAND AREA
 1962 CLINTON
 1968 COLUMBIANA
*1902 COLUMBUS AREA
*1904 COSHOCTON
 1969 DELAWARE
 1971 ERIE
 1960 FAIRFIELD
 1973 FAYETTE
*1922 FULTON
*1915 GEAUGA
*1915 HAMILTON
 1973 HANCOCK
 1974 HENRY
 1955 HURON
*1925 LAKE
 1938 LICKING
 1939 LOGAN
 1934 LUCAS
*1917 MAHONING
 1971 MAHONING
*1916 MARION
*1906 MEIGS
*1916 MIAMI
 1974 MONROE
*1900 MONTGOMERY
*1925 MUSKINGUM
*1928 OTTAWA
*1914 PAULDING
 1960 PAULDING
*1914 PORTAGE
 1969 PREBLE
*1930 PUTNAM
 1974 PUTNAM
*1912 RECONNAISSANCE OF STATE
       OF OHIO
 1975 RICHLAND
 1967 ROSS

*1917 SANDUSKY
 1940 SCIOTO
*1913 STARK
 1971 STARK
 1974 SUMMIT
*1902 TOLEDO AREA
*1914 TRUMBULL
 1954 TUSCARAWAS
 1975 UNION
 1972 VAN WERT
 1938 VINTON
 1973 WARREN
*1926 WASHINGTON
*1905 WESTERVILLE AREA
 1966 WOOD
*1904 WOOSTER AREA

              OKLAHOMA

 1965 ADAIR
*1939 ALFALFA
 1975 ALFALFA
 1962 BEAVER
 1968 BLAINE
*1914 BRYAN
 1973 CADDO
*1917 CANADIAN
*1938 CARTER
 1970 CHEROKEE AND DELAWARE
*1943 CHOCTAW
 1960 CIMARRON
 1954 CLEVELAND
 1974 COAL
 1967 COMANCHE
 1963 COTTON
*1931 CRAIG
 1973 CRAIG
 1959 CREEK
 1963 DEWEY
 1966 ELLIS
*1939 GARFIELD
 1967 GARFIELD
*1931 GRANT
*1937 GREER
 1967 GREER
 1960 HARPER
 1975 HASKELL
 1968 HUGHES
 1961 JACKSON
 1973 JEFFERSON
*1915 KAY
 1967 KAY
 1962 KINGFISHER
*1931 KIOWA
 1931 LE FLORE
 1970 LINCOLN
 1960 LOGAN
 1966 LOVE
*1940 MAJOR
 1969 MAJOR
*1937 MAYES
 1975 MAYES
 1974 MCCURTAIN
*1938 MCINTOSH
*1939 MURRAY
*1913 MUSKOGEE
 1956 NOBLE
 1952 OKFUSKEE
*1906 OKLAHOMA
 1969 OKLAHOMA
 1968 OKMULGEE
 1964 OTTAWA
 1959 PAWNEE
*1916 PAYNE
*1937 PITTSBURG
 1971 PITTSBURG
*1941 PONTOTOC
 1973 PONTOTOC
*1914 ROGER MILLS
 1963 ROGER MILLS
 1966 ROGERS
 1970 SEQUOYAH

 1964 STEPHENS
*1930 TEXAS
 1961 TEXAS
*1930 TILLMAN
 1974 TILLMAN
*1906 TISHOMINGO AREA
*1942 TULSA
 1968 WASHINGTON
*1941 WASHITA
 1939 WOODS
*1938 WOODWARD
 1963 WOODWARD

                OREGON

 1973 ALSEA AREA
 1949 ASTORIA AREA
 1954 BAKER AREA
*1903 BAKER CITY AREA
 1920 BENTON
 1975 BENTON
*1921 CLACKAMAS
 1929 COLUMBIA
 1970 CURRY AREA
 1958 DESCHUTES AREA
 1925 EUGENE AREA
 1926 GRANDE RONDE VALLEY AREA
*1912 HOOD RIVER-WHITE SALMON
       RIVER AREA
 1919 JOSEPHINE
*1908 KLAMATH RECLAMATION
       PROJECT
 1924 LINN
*1927 MARION
 1972 MARION
*1909 MARSHFIELD AREA
*1911 MEDFORD AREA
*1919 MULTNOMAH
 1922 POLK
 1966 PRINEVILLE AREA
*1903 SALEM AREA
 1964 SHERMAN
 1973 SOUTH UMPQUA AREA
 1964 TILLAMOOK AREA
 1975 TROUT CREEK-SHANIKO AREA
 1948 UMATILLA AREA
*1919 WASHINGTON
*1917 YAMHILL AREA
 1974 YAMHILL AREA

             PENNSYLVANIA

*1904 ADAMS
 1967 ADAMS
*1939 ARMSTRONG
*1911 BEDFORD
*1909 BERKS
 1970 BERKS
*1915 BLAIR
*1911 BRADFORD
*1946 BUCKS
 1975 BUCKS AND PHILADELPHIA
*1915 CAMBRIA
 1962 CARBON
*1907 CENTRE
*1905 CHESTER
 1963 CHESTER AND DELAWARE
 1958 CLARION
*1916 CLEARFIELD
 1966 CLINTON
 1967 COLUMBIA
 1954 CRAWFORD
 1972 DAUPHIN
*1910 ERIE
 1960 ERIE
 1973 FAYETTE
*1938 FRANKLIN
 1975 FRANKLIN
 1969 FULTON
*1921 GREENE
*1944 HUNTINGDON
*1931 INDIANA

_____
* OUT OF PRINT ; NOT AVAILABLE FOR DISTRIBUTION

1968 INDIANA
1964 JEFFERSON
*1907 JOHNSTOWN AREA
*1914 LANCASTER
1959 LANCASTER
*1900 LANCASTER AREA
*1901 LEBANON AREA
*1912 LEHIGH
1963 LEHIGH
*1903 LOCKHAVEN AREA
*1923 LYCOMING
*1917 MERCER
1971 MERCER
*1905 MONTGOMERY
1967 MONTGOMERY
1955 MONTOUR AND
     NORTHUMBERLAND
1974 NORTHAMPTON
1969 PIKE
1958 POTTER
*1908 RECONNAISSANCE
     NORTHWESTERN
*1909 RECONNAISSANCE
     SOUTHWESTERN
*1910 RECONNAISSANCE
     SOUTH CENTRAL
*1911 RECONNAISSANCE
     NORTHEASTERN
*1912 RECONNAISSANCE
     SOUTHEASTERN
1973 SUSQUEHANNA
*1929 TIOGA
*1946 UNION
1975 VENANGO
*1910 WASHINGTON
*1938 WAYNE
1968 WESTMORELAND
*1929 WYOMING
*1912 YORK
1963 YORK

PUERTO RICO

*1902 ARECIBO TO PONCE
1965 LAJAS VALLEY AREA
1975 MAYAGUEZE AREA OF
     WESTERN PUERTO RICO
1942 PUERTO RICO

RHODE ISLAND

*1939 KENT AND WASHINGTON
*1942 NEWPORT AND BRISTOL
*1943 PROVIDENCE
*1904 RECONNAISSANCE OF RHODE
     ISLAND

SOUTH CAROLINA

1937 ABBEVILLE
*1902 ABBEVILLE AREA
*1909 ANDERSON
*1913 BAMBERG
1966 BAMBERG
*1912 BARNWELL
*1916 BERKELEY
1963 CALHOUN
*1903 CAMPOBELLO AREA
1971 CHARLESTON
*1904 CHARLESTON AREA
*1905 CHEROKEE
1962 CHEROKEE
*1912 CHESTER
*1914 CHESTERFIELD
*1910 CLARENDON
*1909 CONWAY AREA
1960 DARLINGTON
*1902 DARLINGTON AREA
1931 DILLON
*1915 DORCHESTER
1938 EDGEFIELD
*1911 FAIRFIELD

*1914 FLORENCE
1974 FLORENCE AND SUMTER
*1911 GEORGETOWN
*1921 GREENVILLE
1975 GREENVILLE
1929 GREENWOOD
*1915 HAMPTON
*1918 HORRY
1919 KERSHAW
*1904 LANCASTER
1973 LANCASTER
1975 LAURENS AND UNION
*1907 LEE
1963 LEE
*1922 LEXINGTON
*1917 MARLBORO
1965 MARLBORO
*1918 NEWBERRY
1960 NEWBERRY
*1907 OCONEE
1963 OCONEE
*1913 ORANGEBURG
*1904 ORANGEBURG AREA
1943 PICKENS
1972 PICKENS
*1916 RICHLAND
*1909 SALUDA
1962 SALUDA
*1921 SPARTANBURG
1968 SPARTANBURG
*1907 SUMTER
1943 SUMTER
*1913 UNION
1928 WILLIAMSBURG
*1905 YORK
1965 YORK

SOUTH DAKOTA

*1920 BEADLE
*1907 BELLEFOURCHE AREA
1971 BENNETT
1959 BROOKINGS
*1903 BROOKINGS AREA
*1925 BROWN
1966 CODINGTON
1974 DAVISON
*1923 DOUGLAS
1922 GRANT
1963 HAND
1975 HUGHES
*1925 HYDE
1973 LAKE
1975 MARSHALL
*1921 MCCOOK
1975 MELLETTE
1964 MINNEHAHA
*1926 MOODY
*1909 RECONNAISSANCE WESTERN
     SOUTH DAKOTA
1971 SHANNON
1975 SULLY
1974 TODD
1921 UNION
*1923 WALWORTH
1969 WASHABAUGH

TENNESSEE

1947 BEDFORD
1953 BENTON
1959 BLOUNT
1958 BRADLEY
1953 CARTER
1948 CLAIBORNE
1955 COCKE
*1908 COFFEE
1959 COFFEE
1950 CUMBERLAND
*1903 DAVIDSON
1955 DECATUR
1972 DEKALB

*1923 DICKSON
1965 DYER
1964 FAYETTE
1958 FRANKLIN
*1907 GILES
1968 GILES
*1906 GRAINGER
1948 GRAINGER
1958 GREENE
*1904 GREENEVILLE AREA
1946 HAMBLEN
1947 HAMILTON
*1926 HARDIN
1963 HARDIN
*1905 HENDERSON
1960 HENDERSON
*1922 HENRY
1958 HENRY
1958 HOUSTON
1946 HUMPHREYS
*1913 JACKSON
1941 JEFFERSON
1956 JOHNSON
1955 KNOX
1969 LAKE
*1904 LAWRENCE
1959 LAWRENCE
1946 LINCOLN
1961 LOUDON
*1906 MADISON
1958 MARION
*1923 MAURY
1959 MAURY
1957 MCMINN
*1919 MEIGS
1974 MEIGS
*1901 MONTGOMERY
1975 MONTGOMERY
1953 NORRIS AREA
1973 OBION
*1908 OVERTON
*1953 PERRY
*1903 PIKEVILLE AREA
*1912 PUTNAM
1963 PUTNAM
1948 RHEA
1942 ROANE
*1912 ROBERTSON
1968 ROBERTSON
1956 SEVIER
*1916 SHELBY
1970 SHELBY
1953 STEWART
1953 SULLIVAN
*1909 SUMNER
1967 WARREN
1958 WASHINGTON
1964 WILLIAMSON

TEXAS

*1904 ANDERSON
1975 ANDERSON
1974 ANDREWS
*1912 ARCHER
1965 ARMSTRONG
*1904 AUSTIN AREA
1963 BAILEY
*1907 BASTROP
*1938 BEE
*1916 BELL
1966 BEXAR
1975 BORDEN
*1918 BOWIE
*1902 BRAZORIA AREA
*1914 BRAZOS
*1958 BRAZOS
*1948 BROWN
*1907 BROWNSVILLE AREA
*1941 CAMERON
*1908 CAMP
1962 CARSON

---

* OUT OF PRINT ; NOT AVAILABLE FOR DISTRIBUTION

*1937 CASS
1974 CASTRO
*1959 CHEROKEE
1963 CHILDRESS
1964 COCHRAN
1974 COKE
*1922 COLEMAN
1974 COLEMAN
*1930 COLLIN
1969 COLLIN
1973 COLLINGSWORTH
*1907 COOPER AREA
*1908 CORPUS CHRISTI AREA
1974 COTTEL
1966 CROSBY
1975 DALLAM
*1920 DALLAS
1960 DAWSON
1968 DEAF SMITH
*1918 DENTON
*1922 DICKENS
1970 DICKENS
*1943 DIMMIT
*1916 EASTLAND
1971 EL PASO
*1910 ELLIS
1964 ELLIS
*1920 ERATH
1973 ERATH
*1932 FALLS
*1946 FANNIN
1966 FISHER
1964 FOARD
1960 FORT BEND
*1908 FRANKLIN
*1918 FREESTONE
*1929 FRIO
1965 GAINES
*1930 GALVESTON
1975 GARZA
1975 GILLESPIE
1966 GRAY
*1909 GRAYSON
1974 HALE
1967 HALL
1960 HANSFORD
*1932 HARDEMAN
1972 HARDEMAN
*1922 HARRIS
*1912 HARRISON
1961 HASKELL
1974 HEMPHILL
*1906 HENDERSON
*1923 HENDERSON
*1925 HIDALGO
1965 HOCKLEY
*1905 HOUSTON
1969 HOWARD
*1939 HUNT
*1903 JACKSONVILLE AREA
*1913 JEFFERSON
1965 JEFFERSON
1974 JIM HOGG
1972 JONES
*1940 KAUFMAN
1973 KENT
1967 KINNEY
1962 LAMB
*1906 LAREDO AREA
*1905 LAVACA
*1905 LEE
1975 LIPSCOMB
*1917 LUBBOCK
*1903 LUFKIN AREA
1959 LYNN
1975 MARTIN
*1942 MAVERICK
1974 MCCULLOCH
1958 MCLENNAN
1967 MENARD
*1928 MIDLAND
1973 MIDLAND

*1925 MILAM
1969 MITCHELL
1972 MONTGOMERY
1975 MOORE
*1909 MORRIS
1925 NACOGDOCHES
*1903 NACOGDOCHES AREA
*1926 NAVARRO
1975 NAVARRO
1965 NUECES
1973 OCHILTREE
1975 PANOLA
*1903 PARIS AREA
*1930 POLK
*1929 POTTER
*1930 RANDALL
1970 RANDALL
*1910 RECONNAISSANCE CENTRAL
        GULF COAST
*1919 RECONNAISSANCE NORTHWEST
*1910 RECONNAISSANCE PANHANDLE
*1909 RECONNAISSANCE SOUTH
*1913 RECONNAISSANCE SOUTH
        CENTRAL
*1911 RECONNAISSANCE SOUTHWEST
*1928 RECONNAISSANCE TRANS-
        PECOS AREA
*1922 RECONNAISSANCE WEST
        CENTRAL
*1919 RED RIVER
*1922 REEVES
*1907 ROBERTSON
*1923 ROCKWALL
1970 RUNNELS
*1904 SAN ANTONIO AREA
*1906 SAN MARCOS AREA
*1916 SAN SABA
*1931 SCURRY
1973 SCURRY
1975 SHERMAN
*1915 SMITH
1972 STARR
1975 STONEWALL
1968 SUTTON
1974 SWISHER
*1920 TARRANT
*1915 TAYLOR
1974 TERRELL
1962 TERRY
*1931 THE SOILS OF TEXAS
*1909 TITUS
1974 TRAVIS
*1928 VAN ZANDT
*1902 VERNON AREA
*1927 VICTORIA
*1905 WACO AREA
1975 WARD
*1913 WASHINGTON
1974 WHARTON
*1932 WHEELER
1975 WHEELER
1962 WIBARGER
*1924 WICHITA
*1926 WILLACY
*1938 WILLIAMSON
*1901 WILLIS AREA
*1907 WILSON
*1903 WOODVILLE AREA
*1964 YOAKUM
*1940 ZAVALA

UTAH

*1920 ASHLEY VALLEY AREA
*1904 BEAR RIVER AREA
1960 BERYL-ENTERPRISE AREA
1975 BOX ELDER
*1913 CACHE VALLEY AREA
1974 CACHE VALLEY AREA
1970 CARBON-EMERY AREA
1968 DAVIS-WEBER
*1919 DELTA AREA

*1959 EAST MILLARD AREA
*1939 PRICE AREA
*1903 PROVO AREA
*1899 RECONNAISSANCE SANPETE,
        CACHE, AND UTAH
1958 RICHFIELD AREA
*1959 ROOSEVELT-DUCHESNE AREA
1946 SALT LAKE AREA
1974 SALT LAKE AREA
*1899 SALT LAKE VALLEY AREA
1962 SAN JUAN AREA
*1900 SEVIER VALLEY AREA
*1921 UINTA RIVER VALLEY AREA
1972 UTAH(CENTRAL PART)
*1942 VIRGIN RIVER VALLEY AREA
*1900 WEBER AREA

VERMONT

1971 ADDISON
1974 CHITTENDEN
1959 GRAND ISLE
*1937 RECONNAISSANCE OF ENTIRE
        STATE
*1904 VERGENNES AREA
*1916 WINDSOR

VIRGINIA

*1917 ACCOMACK AND NORTHAMPTON
*1940 ALBERMARLE
*1902 ALBERMARLE AREA
*1904 APPOMATTOX
*1937 AUGUSTA
*1901 BEDFORD AREA
1954 BLAND
*1909 CAMPBELL
1967 CARROLL
1974 CHARLOTTE
*1906 CHESTERFIELD
*1952 CULPEPER
1963 FAIRFAX
*1915 FAIRFAX AND ALEXANDRIA
1956 FAUQUIER
1958 FLUVANNA
*1914 FREDERICK
*1930 GRAYSON
1938 HALIFAX
*1905 HANOVER
*1914 HENRICO
1975 HENRICO
1941 ISLE OF WIGHT
1953 LEE
*1903 LEESBURG AREA
1960 LOUDOUN
*1905 LOUISA
1975 MADISON
1962 MATHEWS
1956 MECKLENBURG
*1907 MONTGOMERY
*1932 NANSEMOND
*1903 NORFOLK AREA
1959 NORFOLK AREA
1963 NORTHUMBERLAND AND
        LANCASTER
1960 NOTTOWAY
*1927 ORANGE
1971 ORANGE
*1918 PITTSYLVANIA
1958 PRINCE EDWARD
*1901 PRINCE EDWARD AREA
1945 PRINCESS ANNE AREA
1961 RAPPAHANNOCK
*1931 ROCKBRIDGE
1945 RUSSELL
1951 SCOTT
*1948 SMYTH
*1937 SOUTHAMPTON
1974 STAFFORD AND KING GEORGE
1948 TAZEWELL
1945 WASHINGTON

_____

* OUT OF PRINT ; NOT AVAILABLE FOR DISTRIBUTION

1954 WISE
*1905 YORKTOWN AREA

VIRGIN ISLANDS

1932 RECONNAISSANCE OF ST.
     CROIX ISLAND
1970 VIRGIN ISLANDS OF
     THE U.S.

WASHINGTON

1967 ADAMS
*1907 BELLINGHAM
*1916 BENTON
1971 BENTON
1975 CHELAN AREA
1951 CLALLAM
1972 CLARK
1973 COLUMBIA AREA
1974 COWLITZ AREA
*1905 EVERETT AREA
*1914 FRANKLIN
1974 GARFIELD AREA
*1912 HOOD-RIVER WHITE SALMON
     AREA
*1905 ISLAND
1958 ISLAND
1975 JEFFERSON AREA
1952 KING
1973 KING AREA
*1939 KITSAP
1945 KITTITAS
1954 LEWIS
1960 MASON
1955 PIERCE
*1911 QUINCY AREA
*1911 RECONNAISSANCE
     SOUTHWESTERN
1929 RECONNAISSANCE COLUMBIA
     BASIN AREA
*1909 RECONNAISSANCE EASTERN
     PART PUGET SOUND BASIN
*1910 RECONNAISSANCE WEST PART
     OF PUGET SOUND BASIN
1962 SAN JUAN
1960 SKAGIT
1956 SKAMANIA
1947 SNOHOMISH
1917 SPOKANE
1968 SPOKANE
*1913 STEVENS
1958 THURSTON
1964 WALLA WALLA
*1902 WALLA WALLA AREA
*1918 WENATCHEE AREA
1953 WHATCOM
1958 YAKIMA
*1901 YAKIMA AREA

WEST VIRGINIA

1968 BARBOUR
*1917 BARBOUR AND UPSHUR
1966 BERKELEY
*1913 BOONE

*1918 BRAXTON AND CLAY
1974 BROOKE, HANCOCK AND OHIO
*1910 CLARKSBURG AREA
*1919 FAYETTE
1975 FAYETTE AND RALEIGH
*1922 GRANT AND MINERAL
1941 GREENBRIER
1972 GREENBRIER
*1927 HAMPSHIRE
*1930 HARDY AND PENDLETON
*1911 HUNTINGTON AREA
1961 JACKSON AND MASON
1973 JEFFERSON
*1916 JEFFERSON, BERKELEY, AND
     MORGAN
*1912 KANAWHA
*1915 LEWIS AND GILMER
*1913 LOGAN AND MINGO
1960 MARSHALL
*1914 MCDOWELL AND WYOMING
*1923 MERCER
*1907 MIDDLEBOURNE AREA
*1925 MONROE
1965 MONROE
*1911 MORGANTOWN AREA
*1920 NICHOLAS
*1908 PARKERSBURG AREA
*1938 POCAHONTAS
*1910 POINT PLEASANT AREA
*1912 PRESTON
1959 PRESTON
*1914 RALEIGH
*1931 RANDOLPH
*1909 SPENCER AREA
*1924 SUMMERS
*1921 TUCKER
1967 TUCKER-RANDOLPH
*1905 UPSHUR
*1918 WEBSTER
*1906 WHEELING AREA
1970 WOOD AND WIRT

WISCONSIN

*1920 ADAMS
1958 BARRON
*1910 BAYFIELD
1961 BAYFIELD
*1929 BROWN
1974 BROWN
*1913 BUFFALO
1962 BUFFALO
*1925 CALUMET
*1911 COLUMBIA
*1930 CRAWFORD
1961 CRAWFORD
*1913 DANE
*1916 DOOR
1975 DUNN
*1911 FOND DU LAC
1973 FOND DU LAC
1961 GRANT
*1922 GREEN
1974 GREEN
1922 GREEN LAKE
*1910 IOWA
1962 IOWA

*1918 JACKSON
*1902 JANESVILLE AREA
*1912 JEFFERSON
*1911 JUNEAU
*1919 KENOSHA AND RACINE
1970 KENOSHA AND RACINE
*1911 KEWAUNEE
*1911 LA CROSSE
1960 LA CROSSE
1966 LAFAYETTE
*1926 MANITOWOC
1975 MARQUETTE
*1916 MILWAUKEE
1971 MILWAUKEE AND WAUKESHA
*1923 MONROE
*1918 OUTAGAMIE
1970 OZAUKEE
1964 PEPIN
*1923 PIERCE
1968 PIERCE
*1905 PORTAGE
*1915 PORTAGE
*1906 RACINE
*1913 RECONNAISSANCE
     NORTHEASTERN
*1909 RECONNAISSANCE MARINETTE
*1914 RECONNAISSANCE NORTH
     PART OF NORTHWESTERN
*1914 RECONNAISSANCE NORTH
     PART OF NORTH CENTRAL
*1915 RECONNAISSANCE SOUTH
     PART OF NORTH CENTRAL
1959 RICHLAND
*1917 ROCK
1974 ROCK
*1925 SAUK
*1924 SHEBOYGAN
*1904 SUPERIOR AREA
*1927 TREMPEALEAU
*1928 VERNON
1969 VERNON
*1903 VIROQUA AREA
*1920 WALWORTH
1971 WALWORTH
1971 WASHINGTON
*1921 WASHINGTON AND OZAUKEE
*1910 WAUKESHA
*1917 WAUPACA
*1909 WAUSHARA
*1927 WINNEBAGO
*1915 WOOD

WYOMING

*1928 BASIN AREA
1955 CAMPBELL
*1917 FORT LARAMIE AREA
1971 GOSHEN(SOUTHERN PART)
1939 JOHNSON
1975 JOHNSON
*1903 LARAMIE AREA
1974 RIVERTON AREA
1939 SHERIDAN
*1927 SHOSHONE AREA
1969 TETON AREA IDAHO-WYOMING
1940 UINTA
*1926 WHEATLAND AREA

---

* OUT OF PRINT ; NOT AVAILABLE FOR DISTRIBUTION

Module I-7

COSTING LAND APPLICATION SYSTEMS

SUMMARY

This module expands on the concepts of cost estimation and comparison of costs among various treatment alternatives which were presented in Module I-4, "Treatment Systems, Effluent Qualities, and Costs." The need for useful published cost data is stressed in this module. Criteria for selecting cost references are presented, and examples of charts and graphs from several of these are used in comparing land application and conventional treatment schemes.

Several critical cost factors, referred to here as "breakpoint issues" are identified, each of which can exert a large influence on land application feasibility. A summary of generalized cost comparisons is made. Several pertinent cost references are listed, and the importance of keeping up to date with new reference material is pointed out to land treatment site designers.

CONTENTS

OBJECTIVES

Upon completion of this module, the reader should be able to:

1. Define and discuss at least three "break point" issues of importance in evaluating cost effectiveness of land application systems.
2. Give the range of sludge handling costs as a percentage of conventional treatment costs for the treatment systems discussed.
3. Use several of the available cost references to make comparisons between conventional and land application systems.

INTRODUCTION

In Module I-4, "Treatment Systems, Effluent Qualities, and Costs," an effort is made to emphasize how site specific needs in waste treatment are met through the selection of system components. It is pointed out that various permutations of system components are possible and that it is the option of the designer to select appropriate components and integrate them into a functional system.

However, that very flexibility of design options creates severe difficulties in formulating costing estimates. The number of options available to handle site specific problems is great. Specific cost listings for each option become impractical. Thus, the objective of this module is to give the reader some general insights into relative costs and introduce some costing literature and representative problems.

Limitations of this Module

There are two significant limitations imposed on this module.

1. Discussions are to be confined only to selected, exemplary systems.
2. Published costing information is scarce, usually dated, and sometimes contains uncom-

mon units or information that is difficult to interpret and compare with other publications.

Clearly, these two factors make a general discussion of the subject difficult.

Criteria for Selecting Literature

The literature selected for this module was accepted with the following reservations:

1. While the data, tables, graphs, and accompanying values are realistic representations of costing information, all values are considered to be outdated. No attempt is made here to update them. The method usually used by designers to update cost data is the "cost index," which may be used on any cost figures for which the date of development is known. A cost index is computed using known inflation rates for labor, materials, and other components of construction project costs, and related to a standard value at some past date. Two indexes are recommended:
   a. The ENR cost index is a measure of general heavy construction costs. It is printed periodically in *Engineering News Record* and is figured for selected cities around the U.S.
   b. The EPA construction cost index covers construction costs related to wastewater treatment, storage, and conveyance systems. It is also periodically updated and varies from city to city. This index is divided into the Sewage Treatment Plant C.C.I. and the Sewer C.C.I.

   *In order to determine the most up-to-date rates for labor, materials, and other construction needs, two indexes should be consulted: Engineering News-Record *magazine and the Sewage Treatment Plant C.C.I.-Sewer C.C.I. of the EPA.*

2. The most useful information (for the purposes of this module) is *comparative costs* between systems rather than the dollar-and-cents costs of a specific system. It is assumed that relative costs will remain more stable despite changes in absolute costs.
3. References used in this module were selected because:
   a. They represent typical presentations of costing information and are assumed to reflect close approximations to the "real world."
   b. They are readily available to designers across the country.
   c. They have much explanatory, relevant information a reader may wish to explore on his own time.
   d. Readers will often have professional access to other costing information preferred by their respective firms or governmental agencies and not necessarily available to the public or for reproduction here.
4. Only a very few of all available options of system design are considered. Those designs which have been selected are simply examples. No "favored" or "preferred" status is to be implied.

---

*This and other italicized summaries are intended to highlight key ideas, provide a basis for later review or to aid in skimming sections that are relatively familiar. They can be ignored in a complete reading of the text.

GENERAL OVERVIEW OF RELATIVE COSTS

In Module I-4, "Treatment Systems, Effluent Qualities, and Costs," a distinction is made between

- pretreatment (systems that partially renovate wastes before land application), and
- land application systems.

This module will emphasize that distinction. The major organization of the module is a division of costing information between pretreatment and land application. In this way, the cost of a total system can be estimated more easily as the sum of the costs of pretreatment and land application components.

Comparing Components that Affect Costs

Before specific costs are considered, it may be useful to review something of the complexities of pretreatment and land application components.

An initial glance at Figures 1 and 2 shows that both pretreatment (Figure 1) and land application (Figure 2) are divided into a number of major component parts. Each, in turn, is divided into two or more units which may or may not be mutually exclusive.

The design of a given system will include a blending and matching of the appropriate component units given in Figures 1 and 2. The cost of the system, however, will be related to the complexity of the final system. Where at least secondary pretreatment precedes land application, the complexity of the system may become sufficient to defeat cost competitiveness with, say, tertiary treatment. This concept was emphasized in Module I-4.

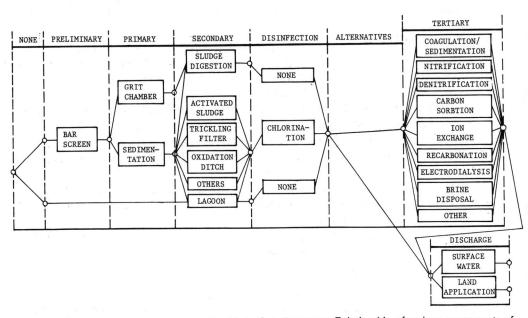

Figure 1. Pretreatment system components with tertiary treatment. Relationship of various components of sewage treatment systems not utilizing land application.

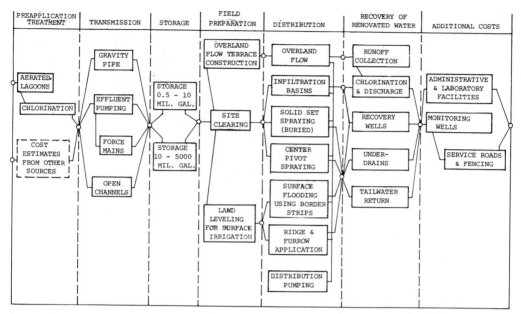

Figure 2. System components used in land application. Relationship of various components of sewage treatment by land application (from Pound, C. E., *et al.*, 1975).

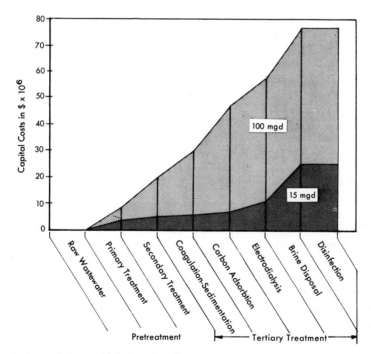

Figure 3. Cumulative capital costs. Relative values for wastewater pretreatment of increasing complexity and tertiary treatment at two flow rates. From Stephan, D. G. and L. W. Weinberger. Wastewater reuse—has it arrived? *J. Water Pollut. Contr. Fed.*, **40**(4): 529–539.

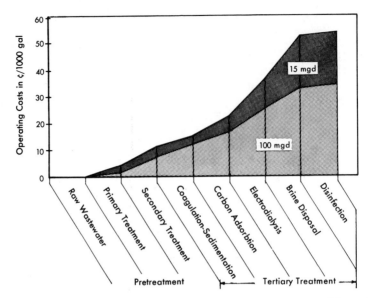

Figure 4. Cumulative operating costs. Relative values for wastewater pretreatment of increasing complexity and tertiary treatment at two flow rates. From Stephan, D. G. and L. W. Weinberger. Wastewater reuse—has it arrived? *J. Water Pollut. Contr. Fed.*, **40**(4): 529–539.

Relative Cost of Pretreatment Varies with Complexity, Size of System

Pretreatment Costs for Wastewaters.   The relative costs of wastewater pretreatment are given in Figures 3 and 4. Comparative capital costs appear in Figure 3 and comparative operating costs appear in Figure 4. As expected, costs increase across the board as wastewater pretreatment complexities increase. But while capital costs (Figure 3) increase dramatically, especially for higher volume flows, relative operating costs are highest for smaller volume plants at any given level of pretreatment complexity. That trend is quite independent of the specific wastewater treatment employed.

> *Costs increase across the board as wastewater pretreatment becomes more complex; operating costs are highest for smaller volume plants.*

Pretreatment Costs for Sludges.   In general, costing for sludge treatment follows patterns remarkably different from those seen in wastewaters. First, there is no apparent across-the-board trend.

Secondly, sludge handling costs vary considerably depending on the design for wastewater treatment. The general complexity of estimating costs for sludge handling is illustrated in Figures 5 and 6.

Clearly, sludge handling represents a sizable fraction of pretreatment capital costs, ranging roughly from 10% (option 5, trickling filter) to 46% (option 7, activated sludge) for the 1 mgd facilities included in Figure 5. Operating costs represent about the same range (11% for option 5, primary treatment, to 36% for option 1, activated sludge).

Cost Comparison Between Pretreatment and Land Application

In general, capital costs for land application regimes are roughly equal to primary pretreatment. Operating costs range from the level of primary treatment to a value approaching that of trickl-

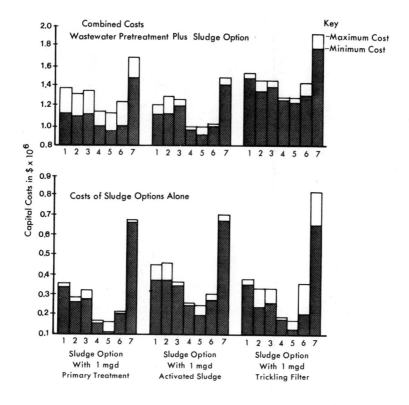

Sludge Options

   1. Gravity, Chemical, Vacuum Filtration, Incineration, Landfill
   2. Chemical, Centrifuge, Incineration, Landfill
   3. Gravity, Porteous, Vacuum Filtration, Incineration, Landfill
   4. Gravity, Digestion, Sand Drying, Landfill
   5. Gravity, Digestion, Land Spreading
   6. Gravity, Digestion, Vacuum Filtration, Landfill
   7. Gravity, Digestion, Vacuum Filtration, Ocean Dumping

Figure 5. Comparative capital costs for selected sludge options occurring in conjunction with three wastewater pretreatment regimes (adapted from the Battelle Report, 1974).

ing filter operation, as illustrated in Figure 7 for 1 mgd flow rate. The land application costs in Figure 7 are independent of the pretreatment cost. As a rough rule-of-thumb, this pattern is consistent across most flow rates.

Capital and Operating Costs vs. Flow Rates. In Module I-4, "Treatment Systems, Effluent Qualities, and Costs," land treatment is compared to tertiary treatment in terms of efficiency and cost. A more precise feeling for the relative numbers involved in tertiary treatment and land application cost comparison is obtained from Figures 8 and 9. Those values summarize information about a variety of tertiary treatment and land application options. While the options given in Figure 8 may be familiar, examine the options of Figure 9 more closely. Note that the costs for rapid infiltration are consistently lowest at all flows and that the application rate is 12 in./wk (30 cm/wk) compared to 2 in./wk (5 cm/wk) for other options. Costs related to the remaining land application options are competitive with each other although spray irrigation tends to be higher priced overall.

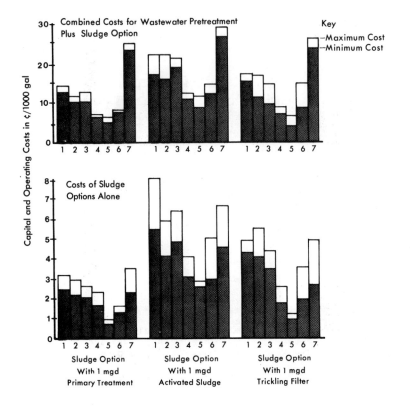

Figure 6. Comparative operating costs for selected sludge options occurring in conjunction with three pretreatment regimes (adapted from the Battelle Report, 1974).

Break-Point Issues.   The important point here, however, is the comparison between costs of pretreatment plus land application with costs of physical-chemical tertiary treatment. From what has been said earlier (especially with regard to Figure 7), primary pretreatment plus land application normally is cheaper than tertiary treatment. However, when secondary pretreatment costs are combined with land application, total costs begin to approach and sometimes exceed those of physical-chemical tertiary treatment. Costing factors which favor pretreatment-land application to tertiary treatment (or vice versa) can arise from very site specific situations, some of which are discussed below.

> *Most important is to compare costs of pretreatment plus land application with costs of physical-chemical tertiary treatment.*

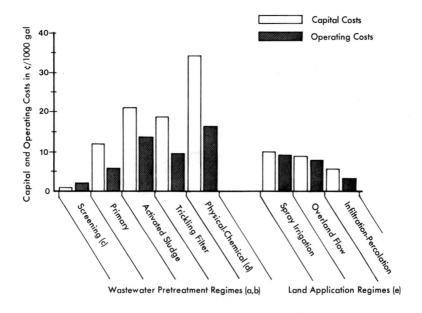

(a) Capital Cost at Sewage Treatment Plant Construction Cost (STPCC) Index 192.8, Amortized Over 25 Years at 7% Interest.
(b) Operating Costs Updated 192.8/119.1 = 1.62 Times Reported Costs
(c) Arbitrary 40 Mesh Screen (Water Resources Engineers, 1968)
(d) Coagulation-Sedimentation (Lime and Ferrous Sulfate) Plus Granular Carbon Adsorption Costs
(e) Estimated 1973 Dollars, Engineering News-Record Construction Costs (ENRCC) and STPCC Index 192.

Note: STPCC = Sewage Treatment Plant Construction Cost
       ENRCC = Engineering News-Record Construction Cost

Figure 7. Relative costs in pretreatment and land application regimes for capital and operating expenses at 1 mgd flow (adapted from Pound and Crites, 1975).

If *land values* are higher than the $500/acre assumed in the data of Figure 7, or if prevailing laws force the purchase of extra large buffer zones around a given site, land application would become less cost effective compared to conventional secondary treatment. Along with land values, *transportation* of material from its source to the land application site must be considered. In general, land values decrease with distance from municipal areas while transportation costs increase. In Module I-4, "Treatment Systems, Effluent Qualities and Costs," this factor is addressed with the aid of Figure 10. Even though the presentation is merely an idealized version, it conveys the relative narrowness of optimum conditions for minimum transportation/land cost ratios.

The *pumping head* factor may be determined by the topography of a site. Also, the design requirements of spray rigs may require high pressure pumping. The costs for distribution pumping at 50, 150, and 300 feet total heads are given in Figure 11.

Certain *construction factors* may appear which interfere with cost effectiveness of land application systems. For example, Figure 12 presents pipe costs, arrangements, and spacings for spray irrigation systems. In each case, the costs involved for even the most extreme situ-

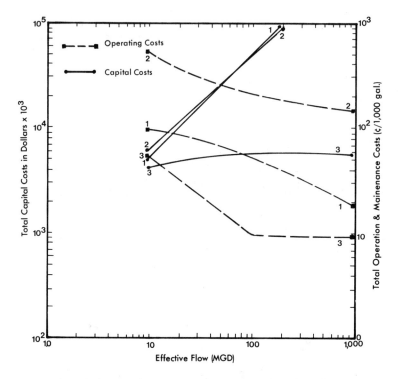

1. Nitrification/Dentrification with Sludge Digestion & Land Spreading.
2. Clarification/Carbon Absorption with Sludge Recalcination, Digestion & Land Spreading.
3. Filtration/Carbon Absorption with Incineration of Chemical Sludge.

Figure 8. Comparative capital costs and operation-maintenance costs for various tertiary treatment regimes (adapted from Battelle Report, 1974).

ations amount to only a few thousand dollars. That is only a small fraction of the system cost, but again the margin for cost effectiveness is narrow and may be closed by such site specific requirements.

Recovery wells may be needed, especially in rapid infiltration systems. In general, flooding is much cheaper than spraying, but in some cases there may be the cost of preparing recovery wells. Some comparative costs for recovery wells are given in Figure 13.

Flooding of wastewater is generally cheaper than spraying of wastewater.

Underdraining may be needed for systems which cannot accept the hydraulic loading imposed on them without some method of preventing soil waterlogging. Some representative costs for underdraining are given in Figure 14.

Monitoring systems are dictated by both prudence and legal requirements. Common monitoring devices include suction lysimeters, surface grab samples, or monitoring wells. Total costs depend on both the type of installation(s) used and their numbers. A quick overview of one such cost, monitoring wells, is given in Figure 15.

Total costs of monitoring systems depend on both the type of installation used and the number of devices used in the system.

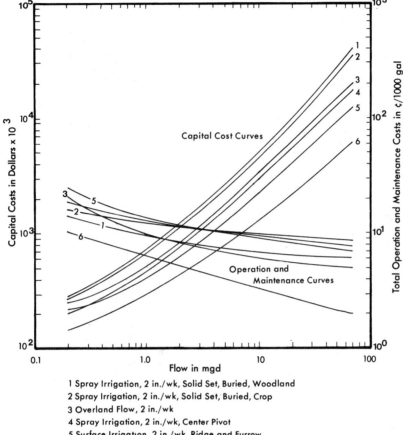

1 Spray Irrigation, 2 in./wk, Solid Set, Buried, Woodland
2 Spray Irrigation, 2 in./wk, Solid Set, Buried, Crop
3 Overland Flow, 2 in./wk
4 Spray Irrigation, 2 in./wk, Center Pivot
5 Surface Irrigation, 2 in./wk, Ridge and Furrow
6 Infiltration/Percolation, 12 in./wk, 50 ft Recovery Wells

Figure 9. Comparative capital costs and operation-maintenance costs for various land application regimes (adapted from Pound, *et al.*, 1975, pp. 38–49).

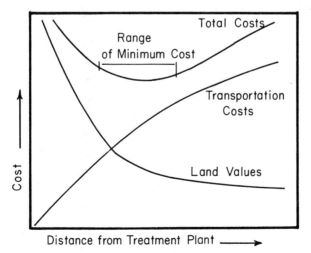

Figure 10. Minimum costs represent a tradeoff between land values and transportation costs (Battelle Report, 1974, p. 157).

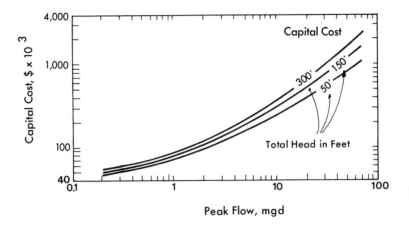

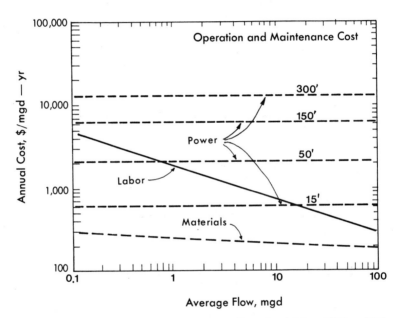

Figure 11. Pumping costs increase with head (Pound and Crites, 1975, p. 103).

Agricultural profit is often proposed as a source of income sufficient to offset a significant proportion of operation costs. Certainly there is no doubt that the value of agricultural products will increase in the future, but that does not mean in all cases that crops will offset operational costs in land application. Lands irrigated by wastewaters require careful husbandry to produce high cash crops. That requires talent and capital into which many municipalities are unable or unwilling to invest. Even forage crops require harvesting and other care which reduce the magnitude of profit. Nevertheless, some profit from crops may be realized with careful planning. Also, water and sludges may be sold where there is a demand. However, the usual experience is that any income represents only a partial recovery of costs.

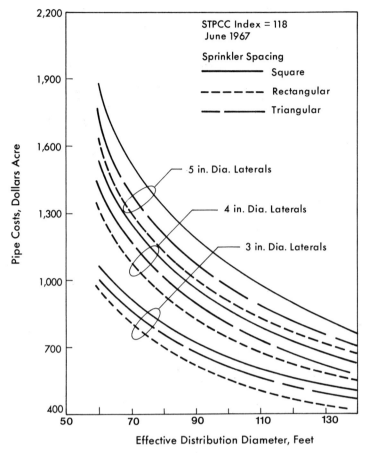

Figure 12. Pipe costs for spray irrigation decrease with smaller diameter pipes and larger area served by a given pipe (Pound and Crites, 1975, p. 146).

Although some profit from crops may be realized with careful planning of the land application system, any income represents only a partial recovery of costs in almost all cases.

The careful *selection of system components* is one of the more effective activities entering into break-point decisions. This was emphasized at the beginning of this module but deserves further consideration. A designer who is obliged to include secondary pretreatment before land application may favor lagooning or aerated lagoons rather than, say, an activated sludge pretreatment, provided that the discharge from the lagoons satisfies regulatory agency requirements for secondary treatment prior to land application.

The careful selection of system components is one of the more effective activities entering into break-point decisions.

The *cost effectiveness* of waste treatment systems must be reported at some point in the earlier planning stages. Such cost effectiveness is defined in the *Federal Register* (Quarles, 1973).

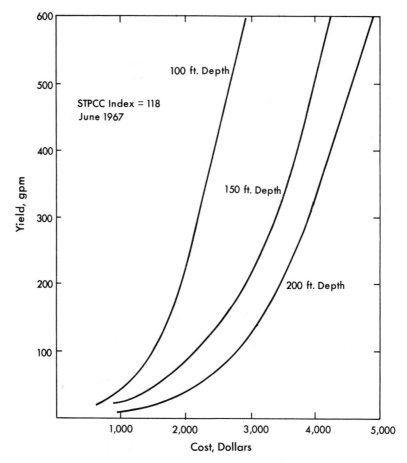

Figure 13. Costs for recovery wells increase with depth and expected yield (Pound and Crites, 1975, p. 154).

Summary of Generalizations

To achieve high quality effluent a waste treatment system must be designed to site specific limitations. Few effective rule-of-thumb generalizations can be formulated. However, some such generalizations are useful in the initial planning stages.

Source to Site Distance Limits.   One obvious place to look for some generalization would be in the distance from waste source to land application. In cases where transmission costs are very high, land application has a substantially reduced cost effectiveness versus tertiary treatment. Would it therefore be possible to state that, say, a 10 mile transmission is prohibitive-or 15 miles or 20 miles?

By returning to Figure 10, the implausibility of a general rule in this area becomes apparent. The cost of a system depends on two functions: land value and transportation. Each of these are under the economic constraints of the community. In larger communities land values may remain high for many miles in all directions, diminishing or even obscuring any optimum cost range. Yet, while a community may find tertiary treatment for wastewaters to be cost effec-

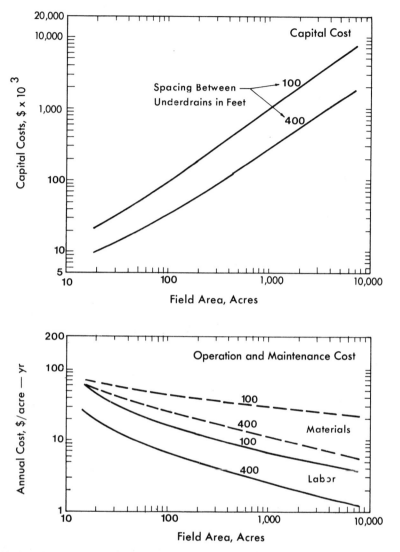

Figure 14. Underdrain capital costs increase with the area served while operation and maintenance costs decline (Pound and Crites, 1975, p. 105).

tive, long-range transport of sludges may be economically acceptable. Thus, Chicago can send its sludges many miles downstream for a land reclamation project, or Philadelphia can ship sludge some 150 miles to an ocean dumping site. Small communities may not be able to transport waste matter more than a half dozen miles or so without losing cost effectiveness. The cost effectiveness of the transmission distance for sludges and wastewaters depends considerably on local conditions. However, for any given situation, estimates should be available for both land and transportation or piping costs.

The optimum cost for a system depends on land value and transportation; each of these factors are determined by the economic constraints of the community.

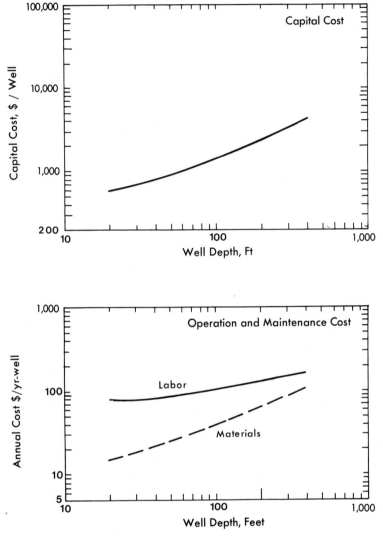

Figure 15. Costs of monitoring wells depend on depth (Pound and Crites, 1975, p. 117).

Head Limitations.   To approach the problem of pumping costs for land application systems, assume that the values presented in Figure 7 are representative of a given system. A system employing primary treatment plus spray irrigation would involve a capital outlay of 23.4¢/ 1000 gal. Therefore, given the above pretreatment and application combinations, costs to over- come a head disadvantage may amount to 10¢/1,000 gal. (or some 43% of the total land treat- ment capital costs) before losing its cost advantage to tertiary treatment. However, a trickling filter-spray irrigation combination costing 29¢/1,000 gal. could tolerate a head disadvantage of only some 16.5% of the total capital cost before losing cost effectiveness to tertiary treatment. This cost differential is equivalent to a pumping head of about 300 feet of water.

Operating expenses are more critical in this matter than capital expenses. A combination of the operating expenses of preliminary treatment and spray irrigation would be about 12¢/1,000 gal. less than operating costs for tertiary treatment. The operating costs of the trickling filter and spray irrigation combination would be 3.1¢/1,000 gal. in excess of tertiary treatment.

Land Application Costs. A third question which may be asked concerns the relative costs of the various land application regimes.

Evidence from Figures 7 and 9 suggests that rapid infiltration would be the least costly system to construct and operate. But rapid infiltration systems require very specific soils (high infiltration-percolation) and deep water tables. It may be possible to modify marginally acceptable sites by underdraining or even by using a series of recovery wells. But both systems are costly (Figures 13 and 14). Again, the cost margin is narrow and a final decision may depend on yet other site specific issues.

> *Evidence suggests that rapid infiltration is the cheapest application regime but requires highly specific soil conditions.*

Volume of Flow. A fourth area of interest is the effect of volume on the feasibility of land application. If there is some costing limitation to land application at some volume of flow, a point should appear in land application cost (Figure 9) where costs climb prohibitively with respect to tertiary treatment (Figure 8).

Notice, however, that no such limiting point is apparent. For 0.1 to 1 mgd flows, capital costs of land application run from about 1.5×10^5 to 7×10^5. At these low flows, land application is distinctly advantageous and many land application systems of that approximate range of flow are built. Flow rates for 1-10 mgd have capital costs ranging from about 3×10^5 to 5×10^6 for land application and 4×10^6 to 6.5×10^6 for tertiary treatment (@ 10 mgd). In general, land application tends to maintain its cost advantage through the range of wastewater flows.

Examination of operating costs reveals that with increasing effective flow, operating costs for land application remain under those for tertiary treatment, at least up to 100 mgd. That makes it even less likely that cost-effective limitations for land application systems are related to an increase in volume of wastewater handled.

> *Even when effective volume of flow is increased, operating costs for land application remain less than those for tertiary treatment, at least up to 100 mgd.*

Specific Cost Estimates Depend on Valid, Current Data

Available Literature. Engineering proposals will most often be evaluated on the basis of an economic comparison with alternatives which are also technically capable of achieving the project goals. The problem faced by land treatment designers is the same as that for designers of other engineered systems—obtaining valid, up-to-date cost data. The references listed on the next page should be adequate to provide land treatment cost data and comparison with "conventional" alternatives. This list is not meant to be complete. Other references are available and more will be forthcoming. The designer should keep abreast of the materials on costing being produced by EPA, Corps of Engineers, and other sources in order to maintain an up-to-date cost reference file, to be used in conjunction with data from past experience of his firm or agency. The references given here meet the "criteria for selecting literature" given in the first section of this module. The graphs and charts excerpted from some of these references in the section "General Overview of Relative Costs" will suggest possible uses of the references cited.

> *Land treatment designers should keep abreast of all costing materials published by EPA and other sources.*

A list of some useful cost references for land treatment and conventional systems is as follows (complete titles, etc. will be found in the Bibliography):

- Battelle Institute, 1974. "Municipal Sewage Treatment"—Performance as well as cost comparisons of eleven wastewater treatment strategies, some including land application, and twelve sludge handling options. Also, transportation costs and other data.
- Pound, Crites, and Griffes, 1975. "Costs of Wastewater Treatment by Land Application"—Costs for all phases of land application systems for preliminary and detailed cost estimates. Keyed to EPA Construction Cost Index.
- Pound, Crites, and Smith 1975. "Cost Effective Comparison of Land Application and AWT"—Variables included are site conditions, distance to site, flows, and land prices.
- DiGregorio, 1968. "Cost of Wastewater Treatment Processes"—Conventional preliminary, primary, secondary, sludge dewatering, three forms of tertiary and package plants.
- Smith and McMichael, 1969. "Cost and Performance of Tertiary Processes"—Most standard tertiary processes.
- VanNote, *et al.*, 1975. "Guide to Selection of Cost-Effective Systems"—Costs of unit processes and systems based on them and methods of determining cost effectiveness.

BIBLIOGRAPHY

Battelle Memorial Institute, Final Report. 1974. Evaluation of municipal sewage treatment alternatives. Prepared for Council on Environmental Quality in association with the EPA. Contract EQC 316.

DiGregorio, D. 1968. Cost of wastewater treatment processes. Prepared for the Federal Water Pollution Control Administration. Contract 14-20-60, Report No. TWRC-6.

Downing, P. 1969. The economics of urban sewage disposal. Praeger, New York, N.Y.

Guarino, C. F., M. D. Nelson, S. A. Townsend, T. E. Wilson, and E. F. Ballotti. 1975. Land and sea solids management alternatives in Philadelphia. *J. Water Pollut. Contr. Fed.*, 47(11):2551–2564.

Michel, R. 1969. Costs and manpower for municipal wastewater treatment plants operation and maintenance, 1965–1968. *J. Water Pollut. Contr. Fed.*, 41(3):335–354.

Pound, C. E., R. W. Crites, and D. A. Griffes. 1975. Costs of wastewater treatment by land application. Prepared for the Office of Water Program Operations. EPA-430/9-75-003.

Pound, C. E., R. W. Crites, and R. G. Smith. 1975. Cost-effective comparison of land application and advanced wastewater treatment. Office of Water Program Operations. EPA-430/9-75-016.

Quarles, J. 1973. Cost effectiveness analysis guidelines. *Fed. Reg.*, 38(174):24639–24640.

Smith, R. and W. F. McMichael. 1969. Costs and performance estimates for tertiary wastewater treatment processes. Prepared for the Federal Water Pollution Control Administration. Report No. TWRC-9.

Smith R. and R. Eilers. 1970. Cost to the consumer for collection and treatment of wastewater. U.S. EPA. Cincinnati, Ohio.

Stephan, D. G. and L. W. Weinberger. 1968. Wastewater reuse—has it "arrived?" *J. Water Pollut. Contr. Fed.*, 40(4):529–539.

VanNote, R. H., P. Herbert, R. Patel, C. Chupek, L. Feldman. 1975. A guide to the selection of cost-effective wastewater treatment systems. Office of Water Program Operations. EPA-430/9-75-002.

Water Resources Engineers, Inc. 1968. Cannery wastes treatment, utilization, and disposal. California State Water Resources Control Board, Publication No. 39.

Young, C. E. and G. A. Carlson. 1975. Land treatment versus conventional advanced treatment of municipal wastewater. *J. Water Pollut. Contr. Fed.*, 41(3):335–354.

APPENDIX

This Appendix contains two optional exercises in the use of some of the reference materials mentioned in the text of the module.

The first exercise (Appendix A) is a sample costing problem, which includes a worksheet and an answer sheet. The sample problem requires the use of two references:

- Battelle Report ("Municipal Sewage Treatment—A Comparison of Alternatives," 1974).
- Pound Report ("Costs of Wastewater Treatment by Land Application," 1975).

The second exercise (Appendix B) is a "self evaluation" of the reader's familiarity with the two references listed above, by answering a variety of questions pertaining to data found in them.

APPENDIX A

SAMPLE PROBLEM

This is a problem for estimating the cost of a land application system. This part of Module I-7 is optional.

Determine pre-application costs using the data and procedures outlined in the Battelle Report and Stage I costs using the Pound Report.

Answers (with some comments) are given. The Battelle Report and Pound Report data sheets are included for the convenience of the reader.

A small municipality in a northern latitude has been urged to treat its estimated 1.2 mgd sewage flow by activated sludge with discharge to land through center pivot spray irrigation applied at 1.8 in./day. Sludge is to be thickened by flotation, digested, and spread onto the land. The prevailing construction index (EPA) is 180, the local multiplier is 1.6. Land values at the proposed site are $600/acre, power costs are 0.035¢/kwh, chlorine costs $0.08/lb. The land site is 2.4 miles from the treatment plant and 20-foot elevation. Sludge is to be transported to local farms for a round trip of 6 miles at $0.12/ton-mile round trip. Amortization will be over 20 years at 10%. The amortization factor will be 0.117. Land application will be for 40 weeks. Storage in a lined reservoir will be needed. Local labor costs are $7.50 per hour. Spraying will be done on grasses and a 200-foot buffer zone is required.

SAMPLE WORKSHEET

Assumptions

      Plant Type -

      Flow Rate   -

      Prevailing Construction Index - EPA -

                                       ENR -

      Local Multiplier -

      Local Land Value - $ /acre

      Local Cost of Labor - $ /hr (weighted average for operating labor
                                       and supervision)

      Local Cost of Power - $ /kW-hr

Prevailing Cost of Chemicals

_____ @ $_____/lb

_____ @ $_____/lb

_____ @ $_____/lb

_____ @ $_____/lb

Transport Distance for Sludge   miles round trip

Transport Cost for Sludge $/ton-mile

Transport Distance for Effluent   miles

Transport Cost for Effluent $/1000 gal.

Amortization Basis _____%

_____years

    Factor   _____

Capital Costs   Estimated Cost

1. Running Total Base Cost on Profile Sheet $_____ for _____ flow

2. Flow Change Multiplier = _____ : Flow Adjusted Cost = $_____

3. National Cost Factor = (/175) = _____

    Price Index Adjusted Cost = $_____

4. Local Multiplier = $_____

5. Total Adjusted Cost = $_____

6. Base Land Requirement from Profile Sheet _____ acres

7. Land Requirement Multiplier = (____/_____)$^{.6}$ = _____

8. Adjusted Land Requirement = _____ x _____ = _____ acres

9. Adjusted Land Costs = _____ x _____ = $_____

10. Total Capital Expenditures = $_____

Operating Costs

Labor

1. Base Labor Requirement on Profile Sheet   _____ man years

2. Labor Multiplier (_____/_____)$^{.58}$ = _____ man years

3. Adjusted Labor Requirement =   _____ man years

Electric

4. Base Electrical Requirement on Profile Sheet _____ kW-hr/day

5. Electrical Multiplier = (_____/_____)$^{.55}$ = _____

6. Adjusted Electrical Requirement = _____ x _____ = _____ kW-hr/day

Chemical

7. Base Chemical Requirements on Profile Sheet _____ lb/day

8. Chemical Multiplier = (_____/_____)$^{1.0}$ = _____

9. Adjusted Chemical Requirement = _____ x _____ = _____ lb/day

Fuel

10. Base Fuel Requirement on Profile Sheet _____ Btu/day

11. Fuel Multiplier = (_____/_____)$^{1.0}$ = _____

12. Fuel Requirement = _____ x _____ = _____ Btu/day

Sludge

13. Base Quantity of Sludge Requiring Transportation _____Tons/day

14. Sludge Multiplier (_____/_____) = _____

15. Adjusted Quantity of Sludge Requiring Transportation _____Tons/day

16. Volume of Effluent Requiring Transportation_____1000 gal/day

Summation

17. Daily Labor Cost _____ x _____ x 8 = $_____/day

18. Daily Electrical Cost _____ x _____ = $_____/day

19. Daily Chemical Cost_____ x _____ = $_____/day

20. Daily Fuel Cost _____ x _____ = $_____/day

21. Daily Solids Transportation Cost _____tons/day x _____tons/mi x ____mi =

                                                    $_____/day

22. Total Daily Cost _____ + _____ + _____ + _____ +

                                                  = $_____/day

23. Total Cost/1000 gal. _____ ÷ _____ = $_____/1000 gal.

24. Cost for Effluent Transportation _____ x _____ x _____ = $____/1000 gal.

25. Adjusted Operating Cost _____ + _____ = $_____/1000 gal.

26. Adjusted Amortization Cost @ 10% for 20 Years (_____x_____) ÷ (365 x ___)

                                                  = $_____/1000 gal.

27. Total Adjusted Operating Cost _____ + _____ = $_____/1000 gal.

Table 3

Sample Stage I Cost Calculation Sheet

Alternative No. _____   Average Flow _____mgd

Type of System _____   Analysis Date _____

Cost Component	Total Capital Cost $	Amortized Capital Cost, ¢/1,000 gal.	O&M Cost, ¢/1,000 gal.	Total Cost, ¢/1,000 gal.
Preapplication treatment				
_____	_____	_____	_____	_____
_____	_____	_____	_____	_____
_____	_____	_____	_____	_____
Transmission-conveyance				
_____, _____ mi	_____	_____	_____	_____
Transmission - pumping	_____	_____	_____	_____
Storage period				
_____ wks	_____	_____	_____	_____
Application systems				
_____				
@ _____ in./wk	_____	_____	_____	_____

Table 3 (continued)

Underdrains

SUBTOTAL, BASE DATE[a] _____ _____ _____ _____

  Trend factor[b] _____ _____ _____ _____

SUBTOTAL, ANALYSIS DATE _____ _____ _____ _____

Crop revenues   (_____) (_____)

Land cost _____ acres _____ _____ _____ _____

  @ _____ per acre

        TOTAL COST _____ _____ _____ _____

---

a. February 1973.

b. Trend factor = EPA Sewer Construction Cost Index for analysis date at appropriate location ÷ 194.2.

Sample Worksheet (From the Battelle Report, pp. 151-154)

Assumptions

      Plant Type - Strategy #6, Sludge Option 5 (Battelle Rpt. p.92,94)

      Flow Rate - 1.2 mgd

      Prevailing Construction Index - EPA - 180
                                            ENR -

      Local Multiplier - 1.6

      Local Land Value - $600/acre

      Local Cost of Labor - $7.50/hr (weighted average for operating labor and supervision)

      Local Cost of Power - $0.035/kW-hr

      Prevailing Cost of Chemicals

Chlorine	@ $ 0.08		/lb
_____	@ $ _____		/lb
_____	@ $ _____		/lb

      Transport Distance for Sludge   10   miles round trip

      Transport Cost for Sludge $ 0.12 $/ton-mile

      Transport Distance for Effluent   2.4   miles

      Transport Cost for Effluent   N.A. $/1000 gal.

      Amortization Basis   10   %

                       20   years

         Factor   0.117

Capital Costs   Estimated Cost

      1. Running Total Base Cost on Profile Sheet $ 4,210,000 for   1 mgd   flow

      2. Flow Change Multiplier = $(1.2/1)^{0.6}$=1.116 : Flow Adjusted Cost =
                                              $ 4,698,360

3. National Cost Factor = (180/175) = __1.029__
   Price Index Adjusted Cost = $1.029 x 4,698,360 = $4,832,599

4. Local Multiplier = __1.6__

5. Total Adjusted Cost = $1.6 x 4,832,599 = 7,732,158

6. Base Land Requirement from Profile Sheet 19 + 15.4 = 34.4 acres

7. Land Requirement Multiplier = (__1.2__ / __1__)$^{.6}$ = __1.116__

8. Adjusted Land Requirement = __1.116__ x __34.4__ = __38.4__ acres

9. Adjusted Land Costs = __38.4__ x __$600__ = $ 23,034

10. Total Capital Expenditures = $ 7,755,192

Operating Costs

Labor

1. Base Labor Requirement on Profile Sheet __3.2 + 7.9 + 7.9 = 19__ man years

2. Labor Multiplier (__1.2__ / __1__)$^{.58}$ = __1.112__ man years

3. Adjusted Labor Requirement = __1.112 x 19 = 21.12__ man years

Electric

4. Base Electrical Requirement on Profile Sheet __1270 + 373 + 1210 =__ __6214__ kW-hr/day

5. Electrical Multiplier = (__1.2__ / __1__)$^{.55}$ = __1.105__

6. Adjusted Electrical Requirement = __1.105__ x __6214__ = __6869__ kW-hr/day

Chemical

7. Base Chemical Requirements on Profile Sheet 670 + 58 = 728 lb/day

8. Chemical Multiplier = (__1.2__ / __1__)$^{1.0}$ = __1.2__

9. Adjusted Chemical Requirement = __1.2__ x __728__ = __874__ lb/day

Fuel

10. Base Fuel Requirement on Profile Sheet __N.A.__ Btu/day

11. Fuel Multiplier = (__N.A.__ / ____)$^{1.0}$ =

12. Fuel Requirement = __N.A.__ x ____ = Btu/day

Sludge

13. Base Quantity of Sludge Requiring Transportation __$\frac{10,800 + 12,500 + 14,000}{2,000} = 18.6$__ Tons/day

14. Sludge Multiplier (__1.2__ / __1__) = __1.2__

15. Adjusted Quantity of Sludge Requiring Transportation 18.6 x 1.2 = __22.4__ Tons/day

16. Volume of Effluent Requiring Transportation __N.A.__ 1000 gal/day

Summation

17. Daily Labor Cost __21.12__ x __7.50__ x 8 = $ __1267.20__ /day

18. Daily Electrical Cost __6869__ x __0.035__ = $ __240.42__ /day

19. Daily Chemical Cost __874__ x __0.08__ = $ __69.92__ /day

20. Daily Fuel Cost __N.A.__ x ____ = $ __-__ /day

21. Daily Solids Transportation Cost __22.4__ tons/day x$__0.12__ tons/mi x __6__ mi =
    $ __16.13__ /day

22. Total Daily Cost $1267.20+ $240.42 + $69.92 + N.A. + $16.13
$$= \$ \ \$1593.67 \qquad /day$$

23. Total Cost/1000 gal. $1593.67 \div 1200 = \$ 1.33$ /1000 gal.

24. Cost for Effluent Transportation N.A. x _____ x _____ = $ _____ /1000 gal.

25. Adjusted Operating Cost 0.00 +1.33/100= $ 1.33 /1000 gal.

26. Adjusted Amortization Cost @ 10% for 20 Years $(7,755,192 \times 0.117) \div (365 \times 1200)$
$$= \$ \qquad \$2.07 \qquad /1000 \ gal.$$

27. Total Adjusted Operating Cost $1.33 + $2.07 = $ 3.47 /1000 gal.

Table 3

Sample Stage I Cost Calculation Sheet

Alternative No. ___1___   Average Flow ___1.2___ mgd

Type of System SPRAY IRRIGATION, PIVOT   Analysis Date ___-___

Cost Component	Total Capital Cost $	Amortized Capital Cost, c/1,000 gal.	O&M Cost, c/1,000 gal.	Total Cost, c/1,000 gal.
Preapplication treatment	7 755 192	149.9	133	347.00
Transmission-conveyance FORCE MAIN 2.4 mi	(86000 x 2.4 =) 206 400	(1.8 x 2.4 =) 4.32	(0.028 x 2.4 =) 0.067	4.39
Transmission - pumping (1)	210 000	4.50	2.3	6.80
Storage period 12 wks	(160000 x 2.2 =)(2) 352 000	(3.00 x 2.2=) 6.60	(0.43 x 2.2=) 0.946	7.55
Application systems (3) SPRAY, PIVOT @ 1.8 in./wk	500 000	9.0	10.2	19.20
Underdrains SUBTOTAL, BASE DATE[a]	9 023 592	174.3	146.5	384.94
Trend factor[b] (180)	0.93	0.93	0.93	0.93
SUBTOTAL, ANALYSIS DATE	8 391 941	162.1	136.2	357.99
Crop revenues			(none)	(none)
Land cost 380 acres @ $600 per acre	22 800	2.93(4)	-	2.93
TOTAL COST	8 691 941	165.03	136.2	360.92

a. February 1973

b. Trend factor = EPA Sewer Construction Cost Index for analysis date at
    appropriate location ÷ 194.2.

1. The site is only 20 ft elevation, but the pumping head must be much greater
    to obtain the desired spray. Using these data derived for an effective
    head of 150 will give a spray head of 150-20=130 ft or somewhat less than
    design specs.

2. See comment, p. 30: for full lining of storage, multiply by 2.2.

3. Note that these curves require EFFECTIVE FLOW. The effective flow
    of this system is: (52/40) x 1.2 = 1.56 MGD. This is caused by
    less than full year application.

4. Amortized cost = 0.0154 x (tot. capital cost of land/average
    design flow).

Appendix B

A SELF EVALUATION

(Optional)

The object of these questions is to obtain some indication of how
familiar the reader is with the literature in terms of both locating pertinent
information and using tables, nomograms, graphs, and other aids.

Answers are provided.

1. What is meant by the term "strategy" as used in both Battelle and Pound?

    _____

    _____

2. What is meant in Pound, et al. by "Stage I" and "Stage II"? _____

    _____

    _____

3. Are schematics provided for specifying sludge options in the Battelle
    report? If so, how many options are specified? _____

4. Specify energy requirements (kWh), total capital costs, and total opera-
    ting costs for a trickling filter with discharge to surface water,
    sludge handling by gravity, digestion, and land spreading, for 1 mgd,
    10 mgd, and 100 mgd using the Battelle Report.

	Energy (kWh)	Total Cap Cost	Total Op Cost
1 mgd	_____	_____	_____
10 mgd	_____	_____	_____
100 mgd	_____	_____	_____

5. How much land is required for a 1 mgd flow at an application of 2.0 in./
    week for 32 weeks of the year? Answer for conditions of no buffer zone
    and 200 ft buffer zone. _____

A SELF EVALUATION (continued)

6. What is the capital cost in $/LF of a 10 inch gravity pipe buried to a depth of 9 ft under wet conditions? _____

7. Assuming a land value of $500 per acre, what would land costs be for a 5 mgd system operating 40 weeks at 1.5 in./week? _____

_____

8. Using the quick comparisons given in the Batelle Report, determine the following:

   a) Are the labor requirements for a 10 mgd operation, employing strategy #10, greater or less than for a similar 1000 mgd plant? _____

   _____

   b) Which three strategies produce the greatest volume of sludge (identify by number)? _____

   _____

   c) Which strategy removes the most phosphorus? _____

   _____

9. Give two methods of updating cost estimates. _____

_____

_____

SUGGESTIONS

1. A "strategy" is a system of facilities which will provide some stated degree of treatment of wastewaters and sludges (Battelle, pp. 4–12).
2. "Stages" refer to degrees of complexities of listing the general components of Land Application Systems. Stage I has five components: Preapplication treatment, transmission, storage, application systems, and recovery of renovated water. Stage II has seven components: preapplication treatment, transmission, storage, field preparation, distribution, recovery of renovated water, and additional costs. (Pound, et al., pp. 24–61).
3. Twelve sludge options, with schematics, are specified in Battelle, pp. 13–24.
4. From Battelle, pp. 78–81 (Strategy #3).

	Energy (kWh)	Total Capital Cost	Total Operating Cost
1 mgd	450	$ 1.24–1.29 × 10^6	4.8–7.0¢/1000 gal.
10 mgd	1774	$ 4.14–4.32 × 10^6	1.8–2.8¢/1000 gal.
100 mgd	4790	$ 27.8–28.2 × 10^6	2.2–2.5¢/1000 gal.

5. No buffer zone: 250 acres.
   200 ft buffer zone: 325 acres (Pound, et al., p. 26. Why is the nomogram on p. 63 inappropriate for answering this problem?).
6. See Pound, et al., pp. 72–73. Cost under normal conditions would be about $12/LF, but the wet conditions require an adjustment factor (given on p. 72) of 1.20, therefore capital cost = 1.20 × $12/LF + $14.40/LF. (Why was the information on pages 32–33 not used to answer this question?).

7. Using Pound, *et al.*, pp. 62–63, total acres needed would be about 1,100 acres @ $500/acre = $550,000.
8. Battelle Report:
   a. Page 28, Figure 22-A: higher.
   b. Page 30, Figure 24-E: strategies 8, 9, and 10.
   c. Page 31, Figure 25-B: none of the strategies remove phosphorus. They all send the same relative amount for disposal.
9. *Engineering News Record* and EPA's Sewage Treatment Plant Construction Cost Index (Battelle Report, p. 143, second to last paragraph).

Module I-8

SOCIETAL CONSTRAINTS

SUMMARY

This module is intended as an introduction to the legal and societal considerations which must be appraised when land application systems are designed. Module I-8, "Societal and Legal Constraints," serves as an introduction to the federal legislation and state guidelines pertaining to land treatment which will be discussed in greater detail in Module 1-9, "Legal Aspects."

The main thrust of this module is to point out some of the concerns that a community is likely to express regarding land treatment proposals, and to illustrate the importance of dealing openly with the community to foster public participation in the decision-making process, thereby easing the way for more complete public acceptance of a project. The need for public acceptance of land application systems should be obvious to the design engineer. While each system must meet the provisions of federal and state guidelines to be approved for construction, local authorities can still block projects by various ordinances, legal action, and general unwillingness to consider specific options.

Zoning ordinances, the various planning and zoning boards, public acceptance, community concern, economic and aesthetic factors are some of the concepts discussed in relation to land application. To illustrate each of these concepts, and the interrelationships among the various local bodies in a well thought out public acceptance campaign, a case history is presented.

The example given in the Appendix (p. 188) is the sequence of events of an actual land application proposal by a food processing industry, illustrating the problems encountered with local government bodies and private citizens. The Appendix example depicts events which have actually occurred, but all the names given are fictitious.

CONTENTS

OBJECTIVES

After reviewing this module, the reader should be able to do the following:

1. Name the federal law which revived interest in land application as a waste management alternative.
2. Explain the levels of government regulation which a design group must consider when planning for a land application system. Discuss possible influences of the municipality, township, county, regional planning authority, state, sanitary district, nation.
3. Discuss briefly the importance of good relations in the community in which the system is to be sited.
4. Describe the methods that are most successful for gaining public acceptance of land application. Discuss them in relation to the examples given in this module.
5. Discuss the major objections a community might have against the installation of a land treatment system. Give arguments against these objections.

INTRODUCTION

Most of the available information on land application of wastes focuses on the technical aspects of this waste management alternative. Equally important to the success of land application systems is its acceptance by the public. The social and economic aspects are the most difficult for the project engineer to define and evaluate.

Public acceptance is often cited as a key determinant for the success of a land application project. Even if a site has all the appropriate characteristics for waste application, it may be inappropriate from the standpoint of the community in which it is located. It is costly to go through engineering studies and identify a site for waste application, and subsequent rejection by the community would make the process even more costly. To minimize the chance of the site being rejected on social grounds, the engineer must work with the community to ensure acceptance both of the general system design and the chosen site.

Public acceptance is a determining factor in the success of land treatment of wastes.

*This and other italicized summaries are intended to highlight key ideas, provide a basis for later review or to aid in skimming sections that are relatively familiar. They can be ignored in a complete reading of the text.

Public concern focuses on several specific issues. Is such a system legal? What federal and state regulations must be met? Will the proposed project meet these regulations? Legal requirements are discussed in greater detail in Module I-9, "Legal Aspects."

Fear of disease being spread from a land application system is another factor that may prevent the public from accepting a land application system in their community. Such fear would be reduced if the public had a better understanding of the treatment processes utilized prior to land application and of the mechanisms that reduce the disease potential after the wastes are applied to the land. Module II-5 "Pathogens," discusses the effects of pretreatment and land application processes on pathogens.

The public's fear of disease from land treatment can be allayed by informing them about appropriate processes that are used to protect public health.

Of public health concern is the effect of toxic elements released to the environment at a land application site. No instance of toxic element poisoning of humans has been associated with land application systems. The fate of toxic elements in land application systems is discussed in Module II-4, "Potentially Toxic Elements."

Fear of toxic elements is another public reaction to land treatment. No cases of toxic element poisoning of humans have been associated with land treatment.

Legal and health concerns are generally associated with proposed land application systems. Other concerns will be more specific to individual communities. These may include economic, aesthetic, political, and attitudinal concerns.

Public acceptance of land application as a waste management alternative is necessary. It is not sufficient, however, merely to address these concerns to the community. The engineer should work with the community in getting a land application project accepted. It is necessary to work with the community to discover just what specific concerns exist. Not only will a close working relationship between the project engineer and the community help to identify existing and potential problems, but it will increase the chances for final public acceptance of the project. Local government officials, community leaders, and members of special interest groups are most likely to have the greatest interaction with the project engineer.

The project engineer should work closely with the community from the very beginning to discover its concerns and to discuss them.

It is necessary to include the general public in the planning stages of a land application system. The public should be invited to participate in the planning process, and the engineer must be willing to incorporate community-generated suggestions. An effective public information program is necessary to keep the community well informed as to the progress of the land application project.

The engineer should invite the public to participate in the planning, and should be willing to incorporate public suggestions into the final decision.

LEGAL RESTRICTIONS ON LAND APPLICATION SYSTEMS

Land Application is Both Encouraged and Restricted by Laws

Important federal legislation pertains to land application of wastes. The federal law which has been responsible for the renewed interest in land application of wastes is PL 92-500, the Federal

Water Pollution Control Act Amendments of 1972. This Act places emphasis on waste management alternatives which are cost-effective and long range, and which emphasize reuse and recycling of waste products. The use of waste management sites for expansion of open space, recreation, and wildlife resources is also important in the law. Land application of wastes, more than any other treatment alternative, can meet the recommendations of PL 92-500.

PL 92-500 emphasizes waste management alternatives which are cost-effective and long range and which reuse and recycle waste products. Land application of wastes meets these recommendations more than any other treatment alternative.

Other laws which pertain to the practice of land application are the National Environmental Policy Act of 1969 (NEPA), the Safe Drinking Water Act, and the Resource Conservation and Recovery Act (RCRA). NEPA requires preparation of an impact statement for all projects involving federal funds. It is likely that as more land application systems are developed, the impact statement may become a routine part of designing these systems.

NEPA requires an environmental impact statement to be filed for any project that uses federal funds.

The Safe Drinking Water Act sets forth National Primary Drinking Water Standards. These Standards apply primarily to groundwater which may be a source of drinking water. In several states, however, all groundwater is viewed as a potential source of drinking water. Land application systems discharging to groundwater will, therefore, be required to meet the standards developed by the federal government under the Safe Drinking Water Act in these states.

Safe Drinking Water Act sets standards for groundwater quality that land application systems must meet, if they discharge to groundwater used for drinking water supplies.

The Resource Conservation and Recovery Act establishes "acceptable" practices for the land disposal of nonhazardous wastes, including sludge from waste treatment systems. It calls for the Environmental Protection Agency (EPA) to develop criteria to determine which disposal facilities are acceptable and which are unacceptable. Implementation of these criteria will rest solely on the state level. EPA is required to draw up public guidelines for the development of state plans and for the provision of financial assistance to state programs. It is also required to publish solid waste management guidelines. It is presently envisioned that the EPA criteria will both establish "environmental limits" where possible, and require the use of the best practicable technology where appropriate.

A glance at any one of these laws will assure the design engineer that there is nothing in the law that will help him with the design procedure. In most cases, the laws stipulate that a commission will be formed to draw up recommendations on a specific point. Often, it may take months or years for these recommendations to be made, commented upon, and completed. In addition, after the recommendations are complete, cases challenging them may be taken to court, and the court decision then becomes the "law" that must be followed. While time will not be spent on the legal ramifications of effluent quality requirements, it is important to be aware of the various stages that requirements generated by federal legislation go through. Additionally, requirements promulgated from one law may be used to fulfill the stipulations of another law. For example, the groundwater requirements drawn up under the Safe Drinking

Water Act are also applicable to PL 92-500. This dual application of a set of requirements is discussed further in Module I-9, "Legal Aspects."

It is important that the design engineer be aware of the requirements which limit or otherwise regulate the practice of land application of wastes on the federal level. If the engineer chooses to keep abreast of legal developments, the *Federal Register* is perhaps the best source of information. Other sources include discussions with state regulatory agencies and EPA regional offices.

> *The engineer must know Federal requirements which limit or otherwise regulate land application.*

More Specific Regulations Found at State Level

More specific regulations and guidelines are found on the state level. In many cases, a federal law will empower the states to draw up their own regulations for a particular issue. For example, the 1948 Water Pollution Control Act gave primary responsibility for controlling water pollution to the states. Each state, in accordance with this law, has established water quality criteria for its waters. These criteria are used to regulate discharges to waters of the state, although the new regulations put less emphasis on this approach. Regulations for land application of wastes are likewise developed by individual states. To date, not all states have chosen to develop such guidelines. States regulate specific aspects of land application, such as application rates, soil characteristics, buffer zones, quality of applied wastewater, storage, monitoring programs, and so on. Trends in state guidelines are discussed in Module I-9, "Legal Aspects." It is important for the design engineer or the legal consultant to contact the state in which he will be working to ascertain the status of regulation of land application of wastes in that particular state.

> *Some states regulate specific aspects of land application, such as application rates, storage, buffer zones, soil characteristics, pretreatment.*

Local Zoning Ordinances Must be Followed

The design engineer must be aware of local restrictions which may affect the design, placement, and operation of a land application system. In most cases, the ordinances which will affect land application systems are those which deal with land use, public health, and nuisances. It should also be remembered that these local laws are changeable, and may be manipulated to eliminate land application as a cost-effective alternative waste management scheme.

> *The engineer must know local laws which will affect land application. These usually deal with land use, public health, and nuisances.*

Good community rapport is a key goal in ensuring that ordinances placing land application at a disadvantage will not be passed. Perhaps most crucial in this respect are the land use ordinances, or zoning laws. Zoning laws regulate where different activities may take place in a community, and determine what kind of tax will be assessed against the different activities. This is important for land application systems, particularly those owned and operated by industry. In one area, a land application system using corn as the cover crop may be deemed agricultural, while the same system may be considered industrial in another area. There is a great difference in the tax rate for agricultural and industrial uses of land. Taxes may be a significant cost in terms of yearly operating expenses. It is essential that the engineer select a site which is zoned agricultural in order to keep taxes as low as possible. In the case of municipal land application systems, this will probably not be a consideration, since municipally owned land is tax free.

> *It is essential for the engineer to know local zoning laws because the land application site should be zoned agricultural in order to be most cost-effective.*

In order to ascertain specific information about the community in which a land application system is to be installed, the design engineer or his legal consultant should meet with the appropriate County Planning Board, Town Clerk, and Village Clerk. Even the smallest of municipalities may have regulations which could affect the planning and design of land application systems.

COMMUNITY PERSPECTIVES

The community in which a land application system is to be located will influence the design and operation of the system to varying degrees. Local ordinances must be complied with. Citizen groups may wish to play a part in the planning of the project. It is important from the very beginning that interested citizens be given the opportunity to participate in the planning of the system. In recent years, citizen groups have gained considerably in their ability to affect planning decisions at the local level. The citizens of a community are the ones who will have to live with the system, and they should rightfully be able to comment and make suggestions about how the system may be modified to make it more acceptable.

> *Public participation in choosing a site fosters public acceptance of the system.*

Public acceptance is a key goal in siting a land application system. The system may be perfectly designed, produce an effluent of drinking-water quality, and also support a golf course, but if the citizens of the community are against it, there will be a problem in getting it from the drawing board to the land.

Community Concerns About Land Application Vary

Several aspects of land application systems may cause citizen groups to fight against siting such a system in their community. The question of public health is of major concern and is treated in detail in Module II-5, "Pathogens."

Briefly, the public health question is this: Will land application of wastes cause an increase in disease in the community where it is located? Disease may be spread directly at the site, from vegetation transported away from the site, from aerosols spread by sprinkler equipment, and from wildlife inhabiting the area.

Land application of wastes is, to many people, a reminder of years past, when improperly handled sewage caused widespread epidemics. These people fear that similar epidemics will result from land application. No incidents of disease have been documented from any planned and properly operated system in the United States.

> *Public fears of epidemics from improperly handled sewage still linger from many years ago. These fears must be allayed by disseminating information about the safety of land application as it is practiced today.*

The public health issue is an emotional one. Careful and accurate explanations, the "kid-glove" treatment, may be needed to convince the community that land application as it is currently practiced is safe and poses no greater threat to the community than does conventional treatment used all over the country. Site visits of interested and influential citizens to locations where land treatment is successful is an effective way of allaying concerns and sustaining interest.

Will Land Application Generate Nuisance Complaints?

Closely related to the question of health problems is the nuisance problem which may result from land application. Odors and appearance are often the factors which prevent the siting of a land application system in a given area. Both of these factors may be controlled by careful management of the system. Odors result primarily from anaerobic conditions. If the site is well managed and kept aerobic, odors should not be a problem. Aerobic conditions can be maintained by scheduling the application of wastewater carefully so that the soil has a chance to dry out between applications. This may require a larger site, but it will result in a more aesthetically pleasing one, and one which is more efficient at degrading organic waste material. Aerobic conditions are generally more desirable for waste application, unless denitrification is necessary. With good management practices of alternating soil aeration and flooding, or physical isolation of continuously flooded denitrification areas, any nuisance conditions can be kept to an absolute minimum.

> *The public may fear that land application will create a nuisance by its odor and unsightly appearance. These fears should also be quelled through information about modern techniques.*

The appearance of the site is largely dependent upon the management scheme. If the wastewater is applied to a forest, there is less likelihood that complaints will arise because it is more difficult to see the equipment. The operator of the system may choose to fence off the area to prevent public access. In fact, many states require that land application sites be fenced to prohibit public entry. A forest site that is inaccessible will only have to look attractive along the perimeter to be acceptable to the public. Open sites not shielded by trees should be carefully managed to avoid any complaints. Factors which make a site look bad include solids deposited on vegetation and ponding of surface water. These factors can be controlled by careful operation of the system. Solids may be removed by adequate screening, so that larger particles are not permitted on the site. If sludge is applied, it may be incorporated directly into the soil, or washed from vegetation with an application of wastewater. Ponding can be controlled by proper drainage and by using application rates which do not exceed the infiltration capacity of the soil. Ponding may cause mosquitoes to propagate and in turn spread disease. See Module II-5, Pathogens" for more on insect control. Thus, ponding should be carefully controlled at land application sites.

> *To avoid an unsightly land application site, operators should minimize deposition of solids on vegetation and surface ponding of water.*

The majority of land application systems are based on a crop of one sort or another. At these sites, harvesting and removal of the crop should help to maintain the appearance of the site. A carefully designed and operated system may provide the only expanse of green in the community, and people may decide to take advantage of the open space provided by the system.

The regular harvest and removal of the cover crop at the land application site will keep it from being unsightly.

Meeting Community Concerns

The community may also resist the idea of land application as a waste management alternative based on economic grounds. If the system is a large one, it may take up many acres. This will have several economic effects on the community:

- Less land will be available for development; land costs may rise.
- Land purchased by the municipality is not taxed; there will be less income from real estate taxes.
- Land application systems may encourage new development not desired by the community.
- Land values may decline because people may not wish to live close to a land treatment system.
- A large farm system on the site may compete with local farming interests.
- If the system is mismanaged and fails, the land may be lost to the community for a long period of time.
- Increased capacity for pollution control may attract additional industry.

These same effects will be felt with smaller land application systems and even with other waste management alternatives. In the case of privately owned systems, such as those owned by industries, several of these problems will be avoided. For example, the land will remain on the tax rolls, and continue to create revenue for the municipality. Economic considerations should be carefully reviewed for the community so that citizens may assess how the land application system will affect them in terms of dollars. Some citizen groups will be more interested in the economic aspects of land application than others.

The effects of land application on the local economy must be carefully reviewed and discussed with the public to avoid fear based on ignorance.

The technical community has the advantage of being able to view all aspects of a pollution control system much more closely than the average citizen. Thus, it is necessary that the technical people explain the meaning of the system to the general population. The economic issue is a good place to start. A small community that is required to install tertiary treatment may read in the newspaper that an engineer has designed a system that costs $5,000,000. This is immediately translated by the taxpayer into cost per family in the community. Such a cost might turn out to be $2,500 per family, and this might not be acceptable. If the general breakdown of costs is shown, and it is emphasized that a large part of the expense is paid for by the federal government, the largest fraction of the remaining costs are for the continuing expenses of operation and maintenance. An interesting possibility of land application systems is the fact that if the site is well managed and a crop is produced, the revenue can offset a large share of the continuing costs of operation and maintenance (EPA, 1976). It is possible that the direct cost to an individual community will be low. For further discussion on crop revenues and the costs they offset, see Module I-5, "Role of Vegetative Cover," and Module II-7, "Crop Selection and Management Alternatives."

The costs of land application should be explained to the community by a technical expert who can compare the costs to those of advanced waste treatment and explain Federal assistance and revenues from crop production.

Several other considerations are important in choosing a land application site. The system must not interfere with established areas of interest in the community. The location of sensitive environmental areas, historic landmarks, and similar places must be pinpointed to assure that they will not be disturbed. For more discussion on how these areas can be located, see Module I-6, "Site Evaluation."

The site for land application must be chosen carefully so as not to interfere with areas of historic or environmental importance.

A community may be interested in improving areas of interest. Wildlife habitats may be enlarged or enhanced using treated wastewater. If the community wants to improve habitat areas, but has hesitated because of the cost involved, the use of wastewater for this purpose may be a dual blessing—the habitat areas will be created, answering the desires of the community, and the wastewater will be properly applied to areas suitable for wildlife. The desires of the community can be incorporated into the management plan for land application. The effect of wastewater on wildlife is discussed in greater detail in Module II-8, "Non-Crop and Forest Systems."

Wastewater may be used in maintenance of wildlife habitats or landscaped areas.

Landscape areas may also use the water for irrigation. In several states, especially Colorado and California, reclaimed wastewater is used to irrigate college campuses, highway shoulders, and other municipally and privately owned green areas. Specific regulations govern the use of wastewater for landscape irrigation. The use of wastewater for these purposes decreases the cost of maintaining large areas of grass, at the same time recycling the wastewater. As long as the soils being irrigated are suitable for waste application, and safety precautions are taken, wastewater can be a useful resource to help keep a community green.

The public reaction to the reuse of wastewater may depend on the ultimate use. A study conducted in California communities indicates that the public is ready for large-scale reuse of renovated water for purposes that do not involve body contact with the renovated water, for instance, golf course irrigation, water for toilets, scenic lakes, garden irrigation, farm irrigation, and factory cooling processes. These results should not be considered indicative of the kind of acceptance that may be encountered elsewhere because Southern California has had positive experiences with wastewater reclamation.

Public reaction to the reuse of wastewater will depend on what the ultimate use of the water will be.

It is important to realize that there are several factions, or groups, within any community. They vary in how vocal they are, how demanding they are on the time of the project engineer, and how successful they are in effecting change in the community. The project engineer should be aware of the groups that are normally active in the community, the issues that are important to them, and the best way to work with them to arrive at compromises acceptable to all concerned.

Although the project engineer will probably not have time to talk with everybody, he should use his contacts in the community as sounding boards to find out specific community concerns. The engineer should be prepared for any questions likely to be raised at public hearings or town meetings.

The project engineer must be aware of the desires of special interest groups in the community and be ready to field any questions at public hearings and meetings.

One source of factual and statistical data is the Census Bureau. The Economic Development Administration may provide community economic profile reports. Regional and local planning authorities have data on land use, recreation, and employment/population projections. The best sources of information, however, are the feedback obtained at public hearings and meetings and from the public advisory board formed on the subject of land application.

Interactions With the Community

A public advisory board is composed of representatives of various interest groups in the community. The group represented on such a board might include:

- farmers representing irrigation districts
- property owners in areas that are being considered for sites of land application
- civic groups interested in community development, including the Chamber of Commerce
- conservation groups, such as the Sierra Club and the Audubon Society

The project engineer may want to form a public advisory group composed of representatives from interest groups in the community.

Public participation can be organized in two ways: reactive or participative. In reactive programs, the major events in the planning process, such as the choice of possible sites, are presented to the public. Reactions to the information presented and the remarks of the participants should be seriously considered in the final screening and selection process.

A participative approach involves the public to a greater extent. The unique involvement of the public at all stages of development generates useful and informative feedback and public support. In the participative approach, there are more meetings and public involvement in the selection of the site. A number of public hearings are held in which the alternatives are presented, and the advantages and disadvantages of each are given. At the next meeting any new alternatives or advantages/disadvantages from the previous meetings are presented. Any rejected alternatives are explained along with the reasons for their rejection. This process is repeated until final site selection is made. See Warner (1971) and Sargent (1972) for further discussion of public participation.

The participative approach involves the public at all stages of development of the project, generating useful and informed feedback and public support.

Most everyone in a community belongs to several groups, whether they identify themselves with these groups or not. For example, families with children are a group, as are families without children, single persons, and families whose children have grown up and moved away. More easily identifiable groups are the ones that represent specific interests such as labor unions, political organizations, special interest groups, and so on. Environmental groups are often in conflict with developers. These groups may be vociferous and can be either positively or negatively oriented.

Purposeful and well organized groups can work for a better environment for the community, incorporating plans for development with plans for environmental enhancement. It is necessary to inform and educate such groups about land application systems.

Land application can be an emotional issue, and a community may be easily aroused to oppose such a system. A detailed explanation of how land application systems utilize resources and recycle nutrients and water should help to convince the public of the worth of such a project in their community. Often, even if a site is not specifically managed for wildlife, it will attract songbirds and small mammals, and will help preserve acres of open space. By keying arguments for land application to the specific interests of the group, the engineer or his representative will have a better chance of gaining acceptance of each group, and finally, of the entire community. Explanations must be, of course, frank and truthful.

The project engineer may key presentations to particular interest groups within the community. However, consistency is important in the overall planning approach.

Each group may have a different view of land application systems, and be concerned with different problems, while the Chamber of Commerce will have questions regarding the effect of the system on the business sector of the community. In working with diverse groups, the engineer or his representative must keep in mind their different interests and work with each group accordingly.

In dealing with groups within a community, it may be helpful to understand the concern of the group to the problems posed by application of wastes to land. For instance, persons who own land adjacent to proposed sites, especially in agricultural areas, will be concerned about drainage and other problems of water management.

The type of waste to be applied to land will greatly affect the operation of the system. Sludge, wastewater, or a combination may be applied. If sludge is applied, several specific problems occur that are not as apparent with wastewater. Sludge has a less attractive appearance. It contains greater concentrations of the constituents which people fear—pathogens, toxic substances, and so on. Aesthetically, sludge incorporated into the surface layers of the soil. This also reduces the odor of sludge. Sludge may receive different treatment processes prior to land application thus resulting in sludges with various amounts of pathogens, toxic substances, and odor potential. Sludge treatment alternatives prior to land application are discussed in Module I-4, "Treatment Systems, Effluent Qualities and Costs."

The type of waste that is applied to the land greatly affects the operation of the site. Sludge application will be more acceptable, aesthetically, if it is incorporated into the surface layers of the soil.

Wastewater causes fewer appearance problems because it is generally screened prior to application, and looks quite clean when it is applied to the site. Application rates should be adjusted for surface ponding. Pathogenic problems are fewer with wastewater application, although there is the potential problem of aerosol transmission of pathogens. Aiming sprinkler heads downward, reducing nozzle pressure, planting a generous buffer zone with hedgerow vegetation, and use of surface methods of application rather than spraying help to reduce the possibility of aerosol transmission of disease.

Sewage and sludge may be perceived as objectionable, disease causing, and dirty. Today few people even think about it. In order to make land application of these wastes more acceptable to the community, it would be wise to change the public's perception of these wastes to a more positive one. The term *pollution* is often dropped in favor of the phrase "misplaced resources." Sewage and sludge may similarly be relabeled misplaced resources. These wastes contain a high percentage of pure water, which in many parts of the country is a scarce resource, as well as nutrients which farmers and gardeners find expensive at the local fertilizer store. If the community can see land application of wastes as a means of recovering precious resources which otherwise would have to be bought and paid for, the system may be more readily accepted.

The project staff should work to change the public's perception of sewage from viewing it as dirty and objectionable to viewing it as a misplaced resource.

The idea of multiple use management has been gaining favor among resource managers. Land application systems may well lend themselves to multiple use management, thereby resulting in several benefits to the community in which it is located. A well-designed system may be operated to dispose of and further treat wastewater, while providing open space for a community, a playing field, and a crop of grain that can be sold to create revenue for the community. The more uses to which a system can be put, the greater will be its appeal to various groups in the community.

The land application site can be used for other purposes besides waste treatment.

Energy is a problem that engineers and communities alike must face in the coming years. Land application is a waste management alternative that can be most efficient in terms of energy use. Some systems can be designed to use practically no "manmade" energy at all, using instead the energy provided by gravity and the sun. For example, the Werribee Farm in Melbourne, Australia, uses electricity only for the primary treatment processes of the more than 150 MGD flow. The water is then distributed through the fields via a series of ditches. The water flows by gravity, and is controlled at dikes which are opened and closed by hand. The cattle raised on the farm are herded by horses, also raised on the farm. Thus, most of the energy used to run the system is provided by gravity, the sun, and animal power. As energy becomes more expensive, land application may prove increasingly cost effective.

Land application can be an efficient waste treatment system in terms of energy use.

Once the concerns of the public are known and the interest groups in the community have been identified, the project engineer or his representative should work closely with those members of the community who show the most interest in the planned land application system. If the system is to be municipally owned, it can be assumed that the local officials feel that it will be acceptable to the public. This may not be the case where the system is privately owned, as in the case of a food processing plant. In either case, the desires of the community should be incorporated into the final design of the system.

The project engineer should work closely with those persons who are most interested in land application.

Even if the system seems to be acceptable to the community, it is necessary to keep in close touch with all community members. Active organizations will be informed through their involvement, but in order to keep everyone in the community aware of the project's progress, a newsletter might be published. A public information program is often necessary, including such diverse activities as newsletters, slide shows, public speaking, and site visits. The program should be designed to appeal to the majority of the community. Close contact between the community and the design group will help to ensure final acceptance of the project.

A public information program may be necessary to insure public acceptance. It might include a newsletter, site visits, transporting people to a successful land treatment site in another area, public speeches, presentations and discussions.

Local Government Has Authority

Because land treatment systems are ultimately located within the bounds of a local government, the regulations and laws of that local government must also be considered. The discussion here is intended to provide a brief overview of how local government is organized, the functions it is mandated to carry out, and the powers it has to carry out these functions.

This discussion focuses on the structure and function of government at the local level, means of enforcing local powers, and the control that the local government has over land use in the area. Land use is of particular interest to those involved in installing land treatment systems, because of the great amounts of land that are usually needed. Planning and zoning powers of the local government, and the way such powers are enforced, namely, through permits, ordinances, and taxes, will be examined.

The local community controls land use through building permits, ordinances, and zoning.

Towns, townships, villages, and counties have their own governments with powers specific to local affairs. The organization of local government varies widely. The New England Town Meeting can be used as a model. This form of local government still functions in some regions of New England, and exists in a modified form in the rest of the Northeast.

Town officials include a moderator or supervisor, and a group of selectmen. These officials are elected. The selectmen, or Town Board, create and change local laws, and authorize work on town property. They create and oversee zoning, health, and nuisance laws, all of which pertain to the design and operation of land treatment sites. A land treatment system must meet the requirements of these local laws. A Town Clerk has access to all local laws and elected officials, and should be contacted for information on the legal requirements in each particular town.

Villages lie within the limits of towns. They can be thought of as miniature cities. In fact their population may grow to a point where they become cities. Village authority usually encompasses fire, water, sewer, police, and highway responsibilities. Government officials generally include a mayor, a board of trustees, and a village clerk. Again, the village clerk is the person to contact for information about the requirements of the village. Villages also have the power to control zoning, nuisance, and health within their boundaries. Figure 1, a political map of Tompkins County, New York, gives an idea of how various sectors of local government are related to each other geographically.

The Town Clerk or Village Clerk should be contacted for information on all local laws and elected officials as well as the legal requirements that land application must satisfy.

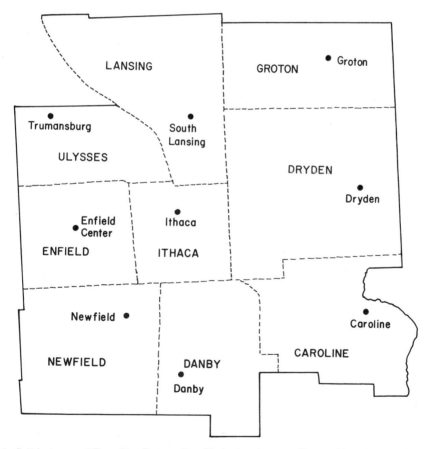

Figure 1. Political map of Tompkins County, New York, showing town lines and location of major cities and villages.

Special districts are often set up to provide a single, specific service to a community. Usually this is a major service, like fire protection or sewage treatment, which single towns or villages cannot afford. School districts are also considered special districts. Except in the case of school districts, the service provided by the special district is paid for only by the recipients of that service.

In some cases, land treatment systems are set up for special districts, just as conventional treatment plants are. The advantage to a special district is that it is administered by a panel of experts, and the administration is centralized.

Instead of serving a village, town or other pre-existing jurisdiction, a land treatment system may serve a special district and be administered by a panel of experts.

A design group must keep in mind the local ordinances and other regulations when planning for the installation of a land treatment system. The focus is on how local governments control land use. In order to carry out its functions, governments are given various powers. One of the powers of the local government is to plan for the future of the community. The device most commonly used to implement this power is zoning. Although many people tend to think of planning and zoning as the same, they clearly are not. Planning is a means of controlling how land within the local government unit—village, town, or county—will be used. Planning implies a well considered scheme for development in the area. Zoning is the method used to control development in the area so as to conform with the plan.

Planning controls how land will be used in a locality; zoning is used to control development so as to conform with the plan.

Why is it necessary for planners of land treatment systems to be familiar with the local regulations and zoning codes? A community that has thought about its future usually has developed a master plan. A master plan is drawn up to form a picture of a community's physical pattern. Control measures are then recommended to direct the community toward that pattern.

In the case of a land treatment system, the master plan can play an important role. Depending on the type of system, it may provide the municipality with the open space, parkland, or lake envisioned in the master plan. Module II-8, "Non-Crop Forest Systems" discusses the alternate ways the land involved in treatment systems can be used for recreation, reclamation, and wildlife habitat. A decision must be made about which alternative sites are most compatible with the master plan. These sites must, of course, also be suitable for land treatment in terms of their soil, drainage, and other pertinent characteristics covered in other modules.

If it is a municipal wastewater system, the design group will work with the local planning board to decide on the best site for the system. Planning boards are set up in towns, villages, and counties in accordance with several state statutes. The function of the planning board is to report, investigate, advise, recommend, monitor performance, offer suggestions, and coordinate all activities in the municipality that will affect its development. The planning board has no real power, it is only an advisory body. Planning is enforced by the zoning officer.

The land application design engineer must work closely with the planning board, an advisory body, which is involved with all activities affecting local development.

Planning is not restricted to regulation of development; it attempts to create a community that is desirable, as well as one that is legally and technically correct in its use of land. Planning proceeds within the framework of laws, the relationship with the local government, the primary concern with the physical development of the community, and community goals and objectives.

Planning is a local concern, and should, therefore, involve local people. Large cities usually have professional planners on their staffs, but in most small municipalities the planning board will not be staffed by professional persons.

Planning boards are usually composed of local lay persons except in large cities where professional planners are on the staff.

Once the master plan has been created, development can be controlled in several ways to conform to that plan. Zoning is the method most commonly used. Zoning divides a municipality into areas for different uses. It establishes regulations to govern land use within each of these areas, or zones. Zoning can channel different kinds of growth into the appropriate area. This leads to preservation of valuable areas for housing, recreation, and open space, and sets aside less desirable areas for industrial and commercial usage. Municipalities may interpret land application of wastes as different uses of the land. One town might consider land application as agricultural in nature, if crops are grown on it. Another town might consider it industrial, if it is used to treat industrial waste, even if crops are grown on it. Zones are taxed at different rates; therefore, the manager of the treatment system should be most interested in how the land will be zoned.

Zoning divides a municipality into areas for different uses and regulates land use in each zone. Because different zones are taxed at different rates, designers of land application sites must seek out a low tax zone, usually an agricultural zone.

Because zoning is the most common way to control land use, it will be discussed in greater depth. The zoning officer enforces zoning laws through the issuance of occupancy permits and building permits. Building permits are of greater concern to those planning to install a land treatment system, since building permits apply to nearly all types of construction, including pipelines, housings for irrigation controls, and so on.

The zoning officer can only decide whether or not a project complies with the zoning laws, and whether or not a building permit can be issued. If the project does not comply with zoning law, it must either be altered, or appeal must be made to the Zoning Board of Appeals (ZBA). The ZBA has the power to (1) correct any errors found in the zoning law, (2) grant a "variance" to the law, or (3) issue a "special permit" for the project. A variance may be a "use variance" or an "area variance," depending on the nature of the appeal. Table 1 summarizes units of local government that exercise authority over land use.

If a land application project does not comply with zoning law, the project engineer can either alter it to comply or appeal to the Zoning Board of Appeals.

Table 1.   Local Political Bodies Relevant to Land Application.

Town Board, Village Board or City Council—a law-making body which passes zoning ordinances that govern land use.

Planning Board—an advisory body with no real enforcement power usually made up of lay persons except in large cities where it is staffed by professional planners. The Planning Board reports, investigates, advises, recommends, monitors performance, offers suggestions, and coordinates all activities in the municipality's development. The Planning Board may create a master plan that describes the community's future development. The purpose of the Planning Board is to make a community that is desirable to live in.

Zoning Officer—the person who enforces the desires of the Planning Board. The zoning officer can decide whether or not a project complies with the zoning laws and therefore whether or not a building permit will be issued. The zoning officer enforces zoning ordinances through the issuance of building permits or occupancy permits.

Zoning Board of Appeals—the decision-making body which has the power to (1) correct any errors found in the zoning law, (2) grant a variance to the law, (3) issue a special permit for the project. A variance may be a use variance or an area variance depending on the nature of the appeal.

BIBLIOGRAPHY

Dunbar, J. O. 1973. Public acceptance—educational and informational needs. *In* Proceedings of a Conference on Recycling Municipal Wastewaters and Sludges to Land. Champaign, Ill.

Felton, P. M. 1968. Citizen action in water—asset or liability. American Water Research Association Proceedings #6.

Frank, J. F., *et al.* 1975. Report of the Illinois Advisory Committee on Sludge and Wastewater Utilization on Agriculture Land.

Porter, K. S. 1975. Nitrogen and phosphorus—food production, waste, and the environment. Ann Arbor Science Publishers Inc. Ann Arbor, Mich.

Sargent, H. L., Jr. 1972. Fishbowl planning immerses Pacific Northwest citizens in Corps projects. *Civil Engineering*, 42:54–56.

Torrence, S. W. 1974. Grass roots government. Robert B. Luce, Inc., Washington, D.C.

U.S. EPA. 1976. Wastewater: Is Muskegon County's solution your Solution? Region V, EPA, Chicago, Ill. 50 p.

Warner, K. P. 1971. A state of the art study of public participation in the water resources planning process. University of Michigan School of Natural Resources, Environmental Simulation Laboratory, Washington, D.C. NWC-SBS-71-013. National Water Commission. 233 pp.

Wilcox, D., A. Taverni, and C. Hamlin, Planning boards and zoning boards of appeal. Local Government Program, NYSSILR, Ithaca, New York. 1975.

APPENDIX

CASE HISTORY—FOOD INDUSTRY LAND APPLICATION PROPOSAL

The case of Clark Foods vegetable canning plant illustrates the importance of involving community officials in plans for land treatment from the outset and keeping lines of communication open throughout the site selection and preparation. It also underlines the importance of answering questions from interested citizens. All representatives of the industry concerned must be aware of this open communication policy because if any information is held back, suspicion may be aroused.

Clark's is located in the Town of Garth, Alabama. Begun in 1966, the plant processes wax beans, green beans, and baked brown beans. Cabbage is fermented and canned as sauerkraut. Clark's employs over 300 seasonal workers from July to November and 80 year-round employees, with an annual payroll of $1.24 million. Clark's is a major buyer of vegetables from local farmers in Sioux County, an agricultural area with 3 out of every 10 jobs related to agriculture. Sioux County ranks first in the nation in the production of sauerkraut; 10,000 tons of raw cabbage were processed at the Clark plant in 1975.

In the mid-1970s, Clark's found that its existing disposal method for washwaters from vegetable processing was inadequate. Its 45-acre spray irrigation field adjoining the factory did not provide sufficient land area to handle the daily flows during the peak canning season and considerable amounts of wastewater were lagooned, leading to complaints from surrounding homeowners of odor, especially from the sauerkraut brine. In December 1975, Clark's applied to the Alabama Department of Environmental Preservation for a permit to process wastewaters via a spray irrigation system of 226 acres in the Towns of Paris, Shawnee, and Garth, all in Sioux County. All three towns are rural:

	Population	Size (sq. mi)
Town of Garth	2780	20.5
Town of Shawnee	2810	48.5
Town of Paris	6330	65.7

Clark's began to take options on land in the proposed spray irrigation area in the mid-1970s. In the spring of 1975 the Town of Garth asked to see Clark's preliminary plans for disposing of wastewaters. Residents of the Town of Paris were curious about the large tracts of land that Clark's showed an interest in and brought the matter to the Town Planning Board. According to town officials in Garth and Paris, Clark's attitude at this time was cordial but close-mouthed.

It was not until July 24, 1975, that Clark's held a formal meeting with the town officials of Paris, Garth, and Shawnee concerning the proposed spray irrigation area. A member of the planning board in Paris told the assembled group that Clark's had options on 465 acres of land. Representing Clark's at the meeting were the vice president of corporate production and engineering, the operations manager of the canned foods division, the company's director of engineering, and one of their soil specialists. Also present were two engineering consultants from the firm they had hired to design their spray irrigation system.

Town officials drew up a list of questions which the Clark's representatives answered. These included questions on the amount of acreage to be used, how much land was to be used in each town, past method of waste disposal, nature of effluent to be sprayed, environmental impact on the land, control of water, type of cover crop, etc. The representatives assured the town officials that there would be no sauerkraut juice sprayed on the land, that the land would be cropped and would not become swampy, and that lagoons would not be used except for storage during heavy rains, heavy production, or during the wintertime.

The representatives of Clark's said that they would dispose of 750,000 gallons per day and that there would be no ponding of water, no pollution of above or underground water, and no runoff. The site would be planted with reed canary grass and harvested three to four times a year. They stressed that Clark's had attained satisfaction through similar facilities in other towns. Company officials said they would make a reasonable agreement with the three towns concerning the limits of the spray irrigation system, but they would not sign any agreement that would control or regulate their future. They also said the plant might be enlarged to process and can beets, as well as increase green bean volume by 50%.

Although this early informational meeting was attended by 5 persons from Shawnee, 7 from Garth, and 11 from Paris as well as 6 high-ranking representatives from Clark's, several town officials described Clark's early attitude as close-mouthed. The representatives invited questions; they gave an informational talk, and showed slides of other spray irrigation projects, including methods of control and monitoring. According to Dick Johnson, the chairman of the planning board in the Town of Garth, Clark's never sat down with Garth officials to present their preliminary plans for the spray irrigation project. The chairman was bitter and opposed to the project.

"Clark's has done it all wrong," he said. "When anyone else—anyone as big as Clark's or anyone with common sense—has a building plan, they approach the town first, the zoning officials, and the planning board, with an informal plan of the site and what they have in mind. The state won't give approval until there is a preliminary approval from the local planning board.

"Two years ago we asked them to explain their plans to us; if you want a wastewater system, discuss it with us. But they wanted Department of Environmental Preservation approval first. They figured that if they got that and other state approval, they would try to make us accept the plan locally without any preliminary knowledge.

"I've been going to their meetings for two years. Clark's should have sat down with us and said at the very beginning, 'What do you think of this? What are your zoning laws? Here are our plans, what do you think?'"

Guy Tindall, the attorney for the Town of Paris had similar observations. "From the very beginning, it was difficult to get specifics out of Clark's. When they first began to buy up large tracts of land in the Town of Paris, surrounding landowners became concerned and asked town officials about it. At that time Clark's plans were not known and the townspeople were assured that they would need a special building permit or use permit in order to go ahead with any plans. But Clark's did not inform us of their plans at this early stage.

"In March 1977, Clark's went before the Town of Paris Zoning Board to get approval of their spray irrigation plan. Their attitude was 'Since our spray irrigation project doesn't violate your zoning ordinances, we don't need to worry. We didn't need to contact you earlier.'"

From the comments of the two town officials, it appears that Clark's did not make an effort to meet with officials of each town at the earliest possible date, to ask them for their suggestions and to assure them that they would comply with the local zoning ordinances. Both town officials received the same impression: Clark's was more concerned with state approval and that once that was received, they felt confident that local approval would follow.

Reactions to the spray irrigation project varied in each of the three towns. Ironically, it was the Town of Paris, in which 90% of the spray irrigation site was to be located, that benefited least from Clark's contributions to the local economy. Farmers in the Town of Shawnee depended on Clark's to buy their snap beans. Residents of the Town of Garth received taxes and employment from the Clark plant. But in Paris, Clark's was not a major buyer of produce, and the town received no taxes from the plant.

From the very beginning the Town of Shawnee welcomed the project because of the town's economic dependence on Clark's and because the portion of the proposed spray irrigation site that was located in Shawnee was to be used only as a buffer zone. The Town of Garth received taxes and employment from Clark's, but the proposed spray irrigation site bordered a residential area in Garth where Dick Johnson, the chairman of the Planning Board, lived. Coincidentally, the chairman of the Paris Planning Board lived contiguous to the western boundary of the proposed spray irrigation site. This Paris official, Wilmer Wood, was a leader in the Civil Liberties Association Against the Dumping of Industrial Wastes on Agricultural Lands, a group of 8 landowners who opposed the spray irrigation project.

What were the objections of the Civil Liberties Association Against the Dumping of Industrial Wastes on Agricultural Land?

- That the washwaters from beans and cabbage to be sprayed on land were industrial in nature and not agricultural. Therefore, Clark's had to seek a zoning use variance from agricultural to industrial. "We all know that Clark's is not in the business of growing grass for cows; Clark's is in the business of canning and selling food to people," a spokesman for the Civil Liberties group said.
- That surrounding property would diminish in value.

- That the soil of the site did not have sufficient permeability to accept 750,000 gallons of water a day.
- That the project would pollute wells and cause nuisance odors.
- That Clark's had not demonstrated that the operation would not adversely affect the environment of the area.
- That the large volumes of water would flood neighboring farmland and disrupt the existing tile drains in the immediate area.
- That the spray irrigation site constituted a private dumping site, not allowed under the Town of Paris zoning ordinances.

Both the Towns of Paris and Garth overruled the objections of the Civil Liberties Association against Dumping on these grounds:

- That Clark's growing of crops in an ordinary farm-like manner, including irrigation of these crops with cabbage washwater and wax and green bean washwater, was an agricultural use. Even though the express purpose of the farming operation was to dispose of wastewater, it was not within the zoning ordinance to question why someone is farming—it may be for profit or for pleasure, the reason is irrelevant.
- In accepting Clark's plan, the chairman of the Garth Zoning Board of Appeals said: "I think a big factor in ruling for Clark's was that the system was approved by the Department of Environmental Conservation and that it is an accepted system by many canneries throughout the country... I can't see any difference between washing beans in your sink and running the washwater into your sewer. To call this industrial wastes is overplaying the word industrial."

What were other objections that arose during the several public hearings on the proposed spray irrigation project?

- That the project would pollute water, land, and air resources.
- That Clark's existing spray irrigation plant adjoining their factory would produce foul odors and deleterious environmental effects.
- That the project would harm an adjoining cemetery, destroying its physical appearance and causing odors. The collection of surface water might cause the coffins to float due to high groundwater elevation.
- That the project would cause nuisance noise in the area.
- That in 20 to 25 years the area would be a swamp.
- That the project was a potential health hazard.
- That the project would adversely affect an adjoining property owner's family, livelihood, property, wildlife refuge, and farm operations.

Although the project was tied up by local zoning boards for more than a year, postponing its summer 1977 start-up date to summer 1978, there were many supporters of the spray irrigation project in all three towns. The primary support groups were the local chambers of commerce, the Farm Bureau, Garth Growth, Inc., C. D. Hoover Farms, Inc., Strong's Nursery, Inc., Farm-It Farms, Inc., individual farmers, and employees of Clark's. The president of the Sioux County Farm Bureau read a prepared statement at public hearings in both the Town of Garth and Town of Paris emphasizing Sioux County's dependence on agriculture in general and on Clark's as a major buyer in particular. "The members of this board have an opportunity, a critical opportunity to assure the continuation of a strong agriculture," she concluded.

Why did Clark's have such difficulties with its 226-arce spray irrigation system? Obviously, the proposal was complicated by the property spanning three towns, tripling the number of approvals needed. Municipalities in this state have stricter zoning ordinances than in other states, being influenced by highly sophisticated zoning ordinances in urban areas, the project manager of Clark's said. He also attributed the difficulties to heightened interest in the environment and residential density of rural areas. "You have people living in rural areas here who work in cities. There is farmland, but there are more homeowners surrounding any proposed irrigation site. Whereas, in the Midwest, farms are larger and homes more spread out—it may be that the owner of a farmhouse on a 160-acre farm will be the only homeowner to deal with in getting a spray irrigation project accepted in the Midwest." Charles Doe, Clark's project manager, said.

A major problem in this particular area was a history of bad experiences with wastes from sauerkraut processing. The Paris Town attorney described the problem in Paris as follows: "For years the two sauerkraut plants dumped their brine into White Creek in town. It was an open sewer. Even now with the new sewage system, when the plants are operating at full capacity, odor in the Town of Paris is bad, especially near the sewage plant. We are now working with the Department of Environmental Preservation and the sewage treatment operators to reduce the odor."

Homeowners near the former spray irrigation field at the Clark factory in the Town of Garth complained of sauerkraut brine odors arising from the lagoons during peak operating season. Another bad experience with spray irrigation had occurred in an adjoining town where another food company sprayed vegetable processing wastewaters onto uncultivated land. The site was poorly managed, anaerobic conditions developed, and strong odors arose. One Clark employee commented: "The only management technique that outfit understood was gravity."

Clark's project manager confirmed this. "People are worried about odor, not about runoff and water pollution. Odor has been the big problem in the past. Problems have arisen in Garth from lagooning of wastewaters from sauerkraut at the Clark plant."

The project manager, who has operated spray irrigation systems for 23 years and set up spray irrigation operations in several other cities, gave the following advice:

- Seek approval of the state agency first, or the federal agency if applicable, and then give the plans to the local government. (*Note:* this was a major objection of the town officials.) Otherwise the local government has nothing to approve.
- Try not to offend any group. Little groups feel jealous if they are not consulted. Keep them all posted. There may be disagreements within the township itself. We had one zoning board chairman who didn't even show the other board members our site plans.
- Try to win endorsement of local farmers and the local Farm Bureau. Farmers should be able to understand the nutrient value of wastewater and the value to crop growth of spray irrigation of wastes.
- Start an educational program on spray irrigation in the local community. Capable, well-educated citizens want to hear experienced experts who have technical knowledge but who can speak in layman's terms.
- Inform all local units of government. Don't bypass them. Make yourself a part of the community and let people know exactly what you are doing. Answer questions. When there is a problem, follow it up, otherwise they will become antagonized and divide up into sides against the project.
- Offer to fly people to a well-operated spray irrigation site. It is definitely worth it. The people who go are impressed.
- Hire a local attorney to interpret the local zoning ordinances. Investigate cases that have been brought through the courts concerning zoning.
- The question of whether to hire outside public relations men depends on how much you want to spend and the reaction of local citizens to outsiders. It is better to settle your own problems with neighbors.
- Cooperate with the press, an important part of any community. You should be fair without revealing any confidential information. Be open to working with various news media, and be able to defend your side of the story.

A Clark official admitted that a local plant employee had repeatedly refused to give information to interested citizens and did not answer questions about the proposed plant. A refusal to communicate by anyone from management can undo much of the good will shown by other company officials.

Clark's has proceeded with construction of its pumphouse and installation of irrigation equipment even though the suit against them by the Civil Liberties Association Against Dumping of Industrial Wastes on Agricultural Land is still pending. They have won the approval of the zoning boards in all three towns. A zoning official in Paris reports that the value of one homeowner's land is being enhanced by the sophisticated drainage that Clark's is installing at the spray irrigation site that adjoins his property. He is a leading member of the Civil Liberties Association group. This town official further reported that Clark's is treating him with "kid gloves" and that all workers at the site listen to his complaints and "hear him out." The official said the drainage installed by Clark's will regulate seasonal flooding that formerly occurred on the land. This natural surface runoff accumulated on the land because it is lower than the land bought by Clark's for its spray irrigation site.

Module I-9

LEGAL ASPECTS

SUMMARY

All waste management systems must meet requirements set by federal, state and local governments. Land treatment systems, just like conventional treatment systems, must meet effluent
limitation standards, cost-effectiveness guidelines, and other legal restrictions.

This module summarizes those laws that are relevant to the land application of wastes, focusing on the applicable federal laws and representative state regulations from different areas of
the country. Local governmental structure is discussed in depth in Module I-8, "Societal
Constraints." That module emphasizes that local regulation of land application proposals is
almost invariably tied to the acceptance they receive from the community, and points out various techniques which the engineer may use to interact with community groups.

"Legal Aspects" describes the 10 points of Public Law 92-500, the Federal Water Pollution
Control Act Amendments of 1972, that relate to land application. It describes the National Environmental Policy Act of 1969 which requires the assessment of the environmental impact
for all projects that receive federal funds.

It describes the Safe Drinking Water Act which establishes national primary drinking water
standards to protect the public health and welfare. This federal law empowers the states to set
these standards. The land treatment project engineer should know the state's drinking water
regulations in order to assess how the system will be affected by these laws. This module also
describes the provisions of the Resource Conservation and Recovery Act of 1976 which
establishes acceptable practices for the land disposal of sludges.

A brief overview of the states which have guidelines for land treatment of wastes is presented. A section focuses on five states, each from a different region of the country, to examine
their regulations more closely: Florida, Texas, Pennsylvania, California, and Minnesota. The
module summarizes water rights laws in the United States as they pertain to land application.

CONTENTS

OBJECTIVES

Upon completion of this module, the reader should be able to:

1. Describe the legislative basis for the renewed interest in land treatment as a waste management alternative.

2. Discuss several of the points in PL 92-500 and relate them to various aspects of the land treatment alternative.
3. Describe what effect NEPA may have on the installation of a land treatment system and RCRA on a sludge application system.
4. Explain why several states have very similar guidelines for land application of wastes.
5. Discuss several nationwide trends in guidelines for land application of wastes.
6. Discuss several of the legal restrictions which directly affect the engineer in the planning and operation of land treatment systems.

INTRODUCTION

Protection of the nation's waterways has long been an interest of the federal government. The earliest anti-water pollution legislation was passed in 1899. Known as the Rivers and Harbors Act, it included a section which prohibited the discharge of refuse into navigable waters. The next important water pollution control legislation was enacted in 1948. The Water Pollution Control Act established the policy of giving primary responsibility for pollution abatement to the states, with support and assistance from the federal government.

The Federal Water Pollution Control Act of 1956 was important to the land treatment area because of three stipulations: (1) the cost of land for sewage treatment was deemed ineligible for grant assistance; (2) no regulations concerning ocean dumping of sludge were provided; and (3) reclaiming and recycling of wastewater were declared ineligible for grant assistance. These stipulations made it very costly to pursue land treatment, since the land area needed is a major cost item. One of the main benefits of this alternative, namely, reclamation of water, was not considered when applications for federal money were reviewed. The lack of regulation of ocean dumping made it convenient for large coastal cities to haul their sludge out to sea. Thus, land treatment was put at a serious disadvantage as a waste treatment alternative (Sullivan, 1973).

The Water Quality Act of 1965 formed the basis of current water quality standards. This Act gave the states the power to implement and enforce water quality criteria for waters of the state (Loehr and Denit, 1975).

The piece of Federal legislation which we will be particularly interested in here is PL 92-500, the Federal Water Pollution Control Act Amendments of 1972. This Act includes several specific goals relevant to waste treatment, including:

- Zero discharge of pollutants into navigable waterways of the U.S. by 1985.
- Control of point sources of waste discharge from industrial and feedlot operations.
- Maximal use of technology within its economic capability.
- Assessment of alternative management techniques to achieve the aforementioned goals.

This module will also review other federal and state regulations pertaining to the land application of wastes, including water rights legislation which affects water movement, particularly in the western United States.

FEDERAL LEGISLATION

Four pieces of federal legislation will be examined in this section: (1) the Federal Water Pollution Control Act Amendments of 1972 (to be referred to as PL 92-500, (2) the National Environmental Policy Act (NEPA), (3) the Safe Drinking Water Act (SDWA) and (4) the Resource Conservation and Recovery Act (RCRA). Primary emphasis will be on PL 92-500.

Federal Water Pollution Control Act Amendments of 1972

This act is a complex program of legislation aimed at cleaning up the waters of the nation. It is long—nearly 100 pages—and so complex that sections of it are still being discussed in the courts.

The present discussion will be limited to those sections and sub-sections which can be directly related to the problem at hand—land application of wastewaters and sludges.

Ten points have been identified as having direct and significant relevance to land application of wastes. A brief interpretation of the ten sections of the law is presented in the text. The original text of the sections appears in Appendix B.

Ten points of PL 92-500 have special relevance to land application of wastes.

The ten points to be discussed are as follows (in order of appearance in PL 92-500):

- Protection of wildlife and recreation resources
- Maximization of technology; Best Practicable Waste Treatment Technology (BPWTT)
- Recycling of pollutants
- Need for cost-effectiveness
- Financing of treatment systems
- Alternative waste management techniques
- Cost of land for treatment systems
- Effluent limitations and the zero-discharge goal
- Monitoring of treatment systems
- Sludge disposal

We are interested in PL 92-500 because it forms the statutory basis for the renewed interest in land treatment of wastes. As noted in the Introduction, water pollution control has been coming under increasing federal regulation.

PL 92-500 not only points the way for increased activity in the field of land treatment technology, it also places emphasis upon effluent control. Pollution control philosophy has evolved from identifying pollutants which have found their way into the environment, and then trying to eliminate them, to controlling the pollutants at their source, and not allowing them to get into the environment in the first place.

This philosophy, aimed at complete elimination of water pollution in the United States, is in keeping with the national policy of environmental protection established by NEPA.

Water pollution control is expanded by the Safe Drinking Water Act (PL 93-523), which establishes requirements for groundwater quality, among other things.

Although PL 92-500 has been called both the best and the worst law ever passed by Congress, there is agreement that it is certainly one of the most complex. The greatest change in pollution control management philosophy is spelled out in Section 301, Effluent Limitations, which describes allowable levels of pollutant discharge. Before the specific requirements are discussed, brief mention should be made of how this law changed historical pollution management practice. For several decades prior to 1972 the degree of pollutant control required for domestic sewage and industrial wastewaters was related to the potential impact of the discharge on receiving waters. It was assumed that all natural surface waters had a natural purification capacity

---

*This and other italicized summaries are intended to highlight key ideas, provide a basis for later review or to aid in skimming sections that are relatively familiar. They can be ignored in a complete reading of the text.

that could be utilized. The question of how much of this purification capacity could or should be used by any specific pollutant determined the degree of treatment required prior to discharge. Thousands of man-years of research led to the development of knowledge needed to understand the impact of pollutants on receiving waters. Many approaches were based on the presence of oxygen in flowing streams, and the resulting decrease in oxygen concentration caused by the addition of organic wastes. The decreasing oxygen concentration below a waste outfall, and the eventual return to a high dissolved oxygen concentration farther downstream was called the "oxygen sag." Nationwide planning was instigated to classify waters in terms of the amount of waste discharge that would be acceptable at all points, both in large river systems and small streams. This classification system was based on the potential use of each surface water resource. For example, if the water body was a source of drinking water, only a small fraction of its purifying capacity could be utilized. On the other hand, some waterways could receive large amounts of pollutant discharge if their use was deemed to be minimal. This was the general situation that existed in water resource planning and engineering prior to the passage of PL 92-500.

PL 92-500 represents a basic philosophical shift in controlling the degradation of the nation's waters. Previous water pollution legislation focused on stream classification, and allowable pollutant discharge based on these standards.

One obvious problem with the historical approach to pollution control planning is that "Mother Nature" may not agree with the arbitrary classification system. Natural flow variations in water bodies and potential of treatment system failure could cause wide fluctuations in the fraction of the purification capacity utilized. This could lead to fish kills and other highly visible evidence of incomplete pollution control. Public concern mounted when individuals began to fear that certain water quality classifications would not provide the desired control. Further disenchantment with this general approach developed as the potential danger from environmental pollutants became manifest. The most common example was the increasing problems of aquatic weed and algal growth caused by pollutants which had no direct effect on the oxygen budget of flowing water, that is, nitrogen and phosphorus. It is extremely difficult to predict the stream assimilation capacity of the plant nutrients in order to avoid nuisance vegetative growth. Finally, the public became aware that widespread distribution of pollutants could not only cause undesired plant growth, but that toxic elements could be concentrated by normal biological activity. The mercury problem illuminated the fact that certain pollutants, discharged at presumably safe levels, could ultimately cause significant damage. Many people became intimately involved with wastewater pollution effects when swordfish was banned due to high mercury concentrations in the flesh of the fish. The ban on phosphorus in household detergents in some areas further emphasized the problem.

Several problems with the pre-1972 pollution control approach led to the development of the effluent limitations of PL 92-500.

The general intent of PL 92-500 to eliminate discharges of pollutants was a reflection of a widely held notion generated by this situation and many other interacting factors. The 1972 amendments indicate that all polluters must take responsibility for their wastes. The receiving waters should not be degraded. Although some have interpreted the law to mean complete elimination of discharge of all matter, a careful reading of the law shows that this is incorrect. In general, the degree of pollutant control required is related to a level proven in full-scale application to be (1) capable of the necessary control and (2) economically acceptable. An alternative which would achieve the greatest control over pollutants and appear to offer the possibility of eliminating the discharge of many pollutants is land application of waste. This technology not only responds to the letter of the laws, but also to the current widely held opinion that maximum control over pollutants is required.

Finally, any pollution control agency's difficulty in controlling discharges when relating them to the vagaries of a receiving water body made a nearly impossible task out of pollutant regulation. By clearly relating the acceptable discharge levels to technically and economically available methods of pollution control, a clear basis of regulation could be developed. The following sections discuss the increasingly strict levels of pollutant control that will be required in two major steps in the near future.

PL 92-500 has been under intensive review since its passage in 1972. One of the provisions that has received a great deal of study is Section 301, dealing with the effluent limitations schedule intended to remove as many pollutants as possible from navigable waterways.

Several recommended changes to PL 92-500 were submitted by the National Commission on Water Quality, chaired by Vice President Rockefeller, on March 2, 1976. This commission was charged with a review of PL 92-500 to determine what changes should be considered by Congress. In general, the recommendations supported all major components of PL 92-500. The text of the Commission's recommendations appears in Appendix A.

PL 92-500, passed in 1972, is still undergoing intensive review.

Following are interpretations of several sections and sub-sections of PL 92-500 which are particularly applicable to the land application of wastes. The text of the law appears in Appendix B.

Section 102(a); 201 (f): Protection of Wildlife and Recreation Resources. In developing water pollution control programs, consideration must be given to the protection and propagation of fish, aquatic life and other wildlife, and to recreational resources and open space preservation.

Land treatment systems, by their very nature, require large amounts of open land, and thereby automatically enhance a given area by keeping this acreage as open, undeveloped space. Additionally, these systems can be designed and managed to provide planned open space, as well as areas for recreation and wildlife habitat. Several alternate management schemes are described in Module II-8, "Non-Crop and Forest Systems."

Section 201 (b): Best Practicable Waste Treatment Technology. This is one of the more important sections of the law. It deals with the requirement for best practicable waste treatment technology (BPWTT). BPWTT must be used on all discharges to receiving waters. Thus, water which is renovated through land treatment may be considered to have undergone BPWTT.

"Best Practicable Treatment" has been interpreted as technology that has been demonstrated to be successful in a significant number of full-scale operations. Thus, a strict interpretation would suggest that land treatment could only be used in cases where it has already been shown to be an effective technology. On the other hand, land treatment is often cited as a viable treatment alternative. Recommendations for cost effectiveness, preservation of open space, and enhancement of recreation and wildlife resources are satisfied by the land treatment alternative.

The waste management alternative chosen for a particular site must be shown to be the best practicable treatment technology, in order for the project to be eligible for Federal funds.

Section 201 (d) (1); 201 (g) (2) (B): Recycling of Pollutants.   Treatment works proposed for grant assistance are, whenever possible, to take into account the possibility of recycling or reclaiming the water, or otherwise eliminating the discharge of pollutants.

> *Waste management alternatives should seek to recycle the resources in the wastes being treated.*

The use of wastewater for irrigation at the land treatment site is one method of recycling pollutants. Not only are the pollutants recycled to produce a benefit (the crop), but the crop may in turn be sold to help pay the cost of operating the system. Module I-3, "Waste Characteristics," discusses the constituents of wastes.

Section 201 (e): Cost Effectiveness.   Waste treatment plants shall be designed and operated in such a manner as to produce revenue. Harvesting a crop from a land treatment site is perhaps the most common method of generating revenue. The site may also be managed as a recreational area, with user fees collected to pay for the system and other area improvements. Managing a crop on a land treatment site is discussed in Module II-7, "Crop Selection and Management Alternatives."

> *Waste management alternatives which are cost-effective are most desirable and should be utilized.*

The need for cost effectiveness is noted in several other sections of the law. Clearly, this is an area where a large amount of information remains to be developed by researchers and pollution control system managers. Costing land treatment systems is discussed in Module II-7 and compared with conventional alternatives in Module I-4, "Treatment Systems, Effluent Qualities and Costs."

Section 201 (g) (1): Financing.   Publicly owned treatment works, including land treatment systems, are eligible for grant assistance from the federal government. Section 202 (a) stipulates that the federal government will authorize grants of 75% of the construction costs of projects that meet all the requirements of PL 92-500. In some areas, a significant portion of the remaining non-federal portion is paid by the state, and only a small portion is paid by the community.

> *The Federal government may offer grant assistance to projects meeting the requirements of PL 92-500.*

Although space does not allow a detailed consideration of financing, two details are worth noting. First, this law clearly specifies that industry should pay for its share of the cost of the waste management system. Thus, industry would also be interested in identifying the most cost-effective alternatives. The second point to note is that in light of the financing obtainable through federal sources the most significant financial burden for the community is the continuing cost for operation and maintenance of the system. Any system that produces a salable by-product can reduce this continuing cost.

Section 201 (g) (2) (A); 304 (d) (2): Alternative Techniques.   EPA is authorized to make grants to any state, municipal, or cooperative governmental agency for the construction of publicly owned waste treatment facilities. This applies to the construction of land treatment sites as well as conventional plants.

All possible alternatives for waste management must be explored in order for a project to be eligible for grant assistance.

However, grants cannot be authorized unless the municipality or agency involved has shown EPA that all waste management alternatives have been explored. The grant must be requested for that management alternative which is deemed to be the cost effective Best Practicable Waste Treatment Technology. Land treatment must, therefore, be evaluated as one of the existing treatment technologies. THIS PART OF THE LAW IS ONE OF THE PRINCIPAL DIRECTIVES FROM THE FEDERAL GOVERNMENT TO EXPLORE THE USE OF THE LAND TREATMENT ALTERNATIVE. Subsequent directives from EPA have reiterated the importance of evaluating land treatment as a viable alternative.

Section 212: Definitions.   This section stipulates that acquisition of land that will be an integral part of the treatment process, or is used for ultimate disposal of treatment residues, will be eligible for grant assistance. This reverses the situation created by the Federal Water Pollution Control Act of 1956, which did not allow federal grant assistance for land acquisition for treatment plants in any case. However, the land on which a conventional treatment plant is located is not eligible for grant assistance. This gives a financial boost to the land treatment alternative, as land costs are often the largest cost item for these systems.

Cities or towns buying land that is specifically for the land application of wastes are eligible for Federal grants to assist in this purchase.

Section 301: Effluent Limitations.   This section describes the timetable to be used to reach the goal of zero discharge of pollutants to waters of the nation by 1985.
By July 1, 1977: Effluent limitations for point sources other than publicly owned treatment works, or publicly owned treatment works in existence on that date, shall meet the standards for secondary treatment as defined by EPA. The best practicable control technology currently available, as defined by EPA, shall be utilized in reaching this goal.
By July 1, 1983: Effluent limitations for point sources shall use the best available technology economically achievable to make reasonable progress toward the national goal of elimination of all pollution discharges by 1985.
All publicly owned treatment works shall have adopted the best practicable waste treatment alternative as defined by EPA.

A schedule is established to work toward the goal of zero discharge of pollutants by 1985.

Section 308: Monitoring.   This section of the law describes monitoring requirements for point sources of pollution. Monitoring is required to carry out the objective of the law (attainment of zero discharge) and will be used in developing effluent limitations and standards. The owner of any point source of pollution shall establish and maintain records, make reports, install monitoring equipment, sample effluents, and provide any other required information, as specified by EPA.

Specific monitoring requirements for point sources of pollution are prescribed by the EPA.

The section also describes the rights of access to monitoring information by EPA.

While PL 92-500 requires monitoring only for point sources of pollution, most states require a monitoring program for land treatment systems. State requirements for monitoring are described on pp. 207–228 of this module. Module II-11, "Monitoring," describes monitoring techniques for land treatment systems.

Section 405; 201 (d) (4): Disposal of Sewage Sludge.   Conventional treatment processes yield both sludges and liquid effluents. This section deals specifically with the sludge component of sewage wastes, and stipulates that sludge must be disposed of in such a way that no pollutants from the sludge will enter a navigable waterway, unless a permit for such discharge has been obtained from EPA. The question of ocean dumping of sludge must now be addressed in light of this section.

> *The disposal of sewage sludge in a manner which will lead to the discharge of pollutants to navigable waterways is prohibited. This is especially pertinent to the question of ocean dumping of sludge.*

The section is also relevant to land application of sludges, since such application may result in runoff of pollutants to the surface waters if the sludge is not handled properly. A common method of controlling runoff from sludge application to land is to inject or otherwise incorporate the sludge into the surface layer of the soil. Application systems are addressed in Module II-9, "Waste Application Systems."

Position of EPA on Land Treatment

The position of the Environmental Protection Agency toward the land treatment alternative is clearly stated in a memorandum from Deputy Administrator John Quarles, dated November 1, 1974. In the memo, Mr. Quarles expresses concern that EPA must do a better job to ensure that land treatment is given an adequate chance as a viable treatment alternative in accordance with the mandate of PL 92-500. In addition, Mr. Quarles suggests that Regional Administrators attempt to heighten public awareness of the land treatment alternative within their region. The complete text of Mr. Quarles' memorandum is reproduced in Appendix C. The EPA position is updated, and stated in even more forceful terms, in an October 3, 1977 memorandum issued by Administrator Douglas Costle (Appendix J).

In addition, Mr. Quarles suggests that Regional Administrators attempt to heighten public awareness of the land treatment alternative within their region. The complete text of Mr. Quarles' memorandum is reproduced in Appendix C. The EPA position is updated, and stated in even more forceful terms, in an October 3, 1977 memorandum issued by Administrator Douglas Costle (Appendix J).

These memoranda are clear indications of the concern of EPA regarding the consideration of land treatment as one of several viable waste treatment technologies available. Where it is cost effective and otherwise meets the requirements of PL 92-500, it must be considered as an alternative. Where a waste treatment method encouraging water conservation is not recommended, permit applicants must justify rejecting land treatment. Also, the EPA will withhold funds from pretreatment facilities required by the states for approval of land application systems, if this pretreatment is deemed unnecessary by EPA.

> *EPA requires consideration of land application in any wastewater treatment feasibility plan. Permit applicants must justify rejection of land application, and states must justify preapplication treatment standards to receive federal funding.*

In the years following the passage of PL 92-500, the requirements which the law stipulates are being developed and published. Criteria for determining the Best Practicable Waste Treatment Technology using land application and land utilization techniques have been set, and include the following:

1. Treatment which results in discharge to a navigable waterway shall meet the requirements for secondary treatment. The engineer should contact his state agency or the regional office of the EPA for the up-to-date definition of secondary treatment.
2. The groundwater under the land treatment site, including the native groundwater, shall be applicable to one of the following three cases:
   Case 1: The groundwater can potentially be used as a drinking water supply.
   Case 2: The groundwater is used as a drinking water supply.
   Case 3: The groundwater is used for purposes other than a drinking water supply.

In each case, groundwater quality criteria are established which must be met by new discharges to the groundwater. These criteria are reproduced in total in Appendix D.

The National Environmental Policy Act of 1969 (NEPA)

The National Environmental Policy Act of 1969 is the cornerstone of federal environmental legislation. Unlike the Water Pollution Control Act Amendments just discussed, NEPA regulates all federally funded projects which have a significant environmental impact. It addresses the need to protect and enhance the quality of the environment for this and future generations. The most important aspect of this law is the requirement to submit formal environmental impact statements for all projects involving federal funding.

Four major goals are defined for this Act:

- To declare a national policy to encourage a productive and enjoyable harmony between man and his environment.
- To promote efforts to reduce damage to the environment.
- To enrich the understanding of the environment.
- To create the Council on Environmental Quality.

A general interpretation of how NEPA relates to the land treatment alternative is presented below. The text of the Introduction and Title I of NEPA appears in Appendix E.

All practicable means and measures shall be used to promote the general welfare, to create and maintain conditions under which man and nature shall exist in harmony, and fulfill the social, economic, and other requirements of present and future generations of Americans. As treatment of our wastes is rapidly becoming a crucial factor in the protection of our environment, this phase of our lifestyle—waste management—is germane to NEPA. Land treatment of wastes is the management alternative which is most closely tied to natural systems. It is crucial, therefore, that the natural systems which allow wastes to be assimilated by the soil continue to function. The philosophy of NEPA is therefore closely tied to the continued success of land treatment systems.

It is the responsibility of the federal government to use all practicable means to improve federal programs and resources to fulfill the objectives of NEPA. One of the stated objectives is to enhance the quality of renewable resources and approach the maximum attainable recycling of depletable resources. Water is a resource which can be recycled and reused. Land treatment is one means of accomplishing this recycling, while also recycling nutrients such as nitrogen, phosphorus, and trace elements through the soil-vegetation system. As land treatment systems will have a definite effect on the surrounding environment, as well as on the waters leaving the treatment site, it can be seen that NEPA may well have a bearing on the development of these systems.

NEPA has been the major piece of legislation used by environmentalists in their efforts to legally question projects which they feel will damage the environment. Therefore, it is well for the design group to keep in mind the requirements of NEPA when it is designing a land treatment system.

Land application systems may fall under the jurisdiction of NEPA insofar as the requirement for impact assessment is concerned.

NEPA is the law which mandates an Environmental Impact Statement for certain projects. The requirement for an impact statement is one which, if not dealt with at the outset of a project, may cause considerable delay and expense in completing the project. It is important for the design group to know when an impact statement is required, and how to go about preparing one which will satisfy the demands of the law (and, if need be, the courts).

All federal agencies are to use a systematic, interdisciplinary approach to ensure integrated use of the natural and social sciences and the environmental design arts in decision-making which will have an impact on the environment. Land treatment system design will require the expertise of soil scientists, engineers, and social scientists to ensure that these systems will have no adverse effect on the community in which they are installed. This is particularly important for large systems which cover several thousand acres, and which may dislocate families, or even entire communities.

Where alternate uses of natural recources are in question, alternate courses of action shall be studied, according to NEPA. Thus, land treatment may be considered a better alternative to tertiary treatment in light of NEPA, as land treatment may allow for reuse of the water and nutrients. Of course, the decision as to alternate courses of action must be made in terms of the requirements of PL 92-500, as well as those of NEPA. While the recycling and reuse of resources is stressed in PL 92-500, we have also seen that cost-effectiveness, preservation of open space, recreation and wildlife areas, and maximization of technology (BPWTT) must be considered before a final decision is made as to which waste treatment technology will be utilized.

The Safe Drinking Water Act (SDWA)—PL 93-523

The Safe Drinking Water Act is a legislative attempt to provide enough good drinking water for everyone now and in the future. The Act calls for EPA to establish national primary drinking water standards to protect the public health and welfare. Water which meets these standards will be safe to drink, without having any unpleasant odor or appearance. SDWA pertains to the land application of wastes insofar as it calls for the protection of underground sources of water which are used for drinking water supplies.

Primary responsibility for water standards implementation and enforcement is given to the states. Once a state has shown that it meets the requirements for primary enforcement responsibility, it is expected to adopt standards, review compliance strategems, and enforce its standards.

Land treatment design engineers must be cognizant of the state's drinking water regulations in order to assess how the effluent from the land treatment system will affect the groundwater, if the groundwater is used as a public drinking water supply.

The Safe Drinking Water Act requires protection of the groundwater as a future source of drinking water.

In accordance with the provisions of SDWA, EPA promulgated National Interim Primary Drinking Water Regulations in December of 1975. These regulations, along with additional ones dealing with radioactivity in drinking water, became effective in June, 1977. The states may propose their own set of standards; however, state standards must be at least as stringent as those proposed by EPA. Since this is the case, individual states must be contacted as to the specific guidelines in force. In addition, different states may use different definitions in deciding whether groundwater is a public drinking water supply. In some cases, all groundwater may be considered to be public drinking water supply, and all effluents which percolate to the groundwater from land treatment systems in those states would be required to meet the groundwater standards established by the state or by EPA in the absence of state criteria. Again, it is emphasized that in evaluating land application as a Best Practicable Waste Treatment Technology in accordance with PL 92-500 the groundwater quality criteria established by the Interim Primary Drinking Water Standards (mandated by SDWA) must be followed.

The Resource Conservation and Recovery Act (RCRA)

Environmental controls are playing an increasingly important role in sludge management. The RCRA of 1976 (PL 94-580) provides for the establishment of three programs:

- A hazardous waste program that provides a "cradle to grave" system for managing hazardous wastes.
- A land disposal program that establishes "acceptable" practices for the land disposal of certain non-hazardous wastes.
- A resource conservation and recovery program.

RCRA regulates sludge land application and sludge disposal in landfills.

RCRA pertains directly to wastewater treatment plant sludge, as it is included in the act's definition of "solid waste," along with garbage, refuse, water treatment plant sludge, and air pollution control sludge. The law encompasses both sludge land application and sludge disposal in landfills. Most relevant to land application is the establishment of acceptable practices for the land disposal of nonhazardous wastes. EPA is to develop criteria to determine which disposal facilities are acceptable and which are unacceptable. These criteria are extremely important because any unacceptable solid waste practice is prohibited by the RCRA unless it is covered by a schedule of compliance that has been approved by the EPA.

RCRA regulates sludge land application and calls for the EPA to develop criteria to determine which disposal facilities are acceptable and which are unacceptable.

Implementation of these criteria would rest solely with each individual state. The state agency may issue permits to control implementation of the EPA criteria, and require that records be kept at the treatment plant to insure that the criteria are met.

It is up to the individual states to implement the EPA criteria for acceptable disposal facilities.

EPA is also required to publish guidelines for the development of state plans and the provision of financial assistance to state programs. To be approved for financial assistance, the RCRA requires that state plans must: (1) prohibit the establishment of unacceptable facilities, (2) provide for the closing or upgrading of existing unacceptable facilities, and (3) provide a schedule for compliance with the criteria within a reasonable time, not to exceed five years from the publication of an inventory of unacceptable disposal facilities that EPA will publish one year after the promulgation of the criteria.

EPA is also required to publish solid waste management guidelines. These will include guidelines which describe disposal practices that can be used to meet the disposal facility criteria. These guidelines are not mandatory for the states; they are advisory only. They are mandatory for all federal facilities and certain grantees under the RCRA.

It is now envisioned that the EPA criteria will both establish "environmental limits" where possible, and require the use of best practicable technology where appropriate. Toward this end descriptive operating methods will be covered in the guidelines describing ways of protecting health and the environment, or best management practices, and they will be waste specific. Initially, the EPA is expected to write guidelines on municipal solid waste land disposal, and municipal sludge land disposal.

The RCRA assures enforcement of the hazardous waste program at state and federal levels. However, there is no federal enforcement for the land disposal program. Sludges which are hazardous will be covered under the hazardous wastes control program. In determining a hazardous waste, RCRA states that one should take into account "toxicity, persistence, and degradability in nature, potential for accumulation in tissue. . ." Although most wastewater sludges contain some amount of such substances as cadmium, mercury, and PCB, it is expected that only a small percentage of municipal sludges would fall under the hazardous wastes provisions of the RCRA (Claussen, 1977).

> Sludges which are deemed "hazardous" will be regulated by the separate hazardous waste control program under the RCRA. Only a small percentage of municipal sludges will fall under the "hazardous" category.

STATE REGULATIONS AND GUIDELINES

Introduction

Congress, in passing PL 92-500, gave the nation a clear mandate to reassess conventional waste management alternatives. Emphasis was placed on alternatives which are cost effective, utilize the best practicable treatment technology, and consider reuse and recycling of water and nutrient resources which are the major components of sewage wastes.

The states are, of course, cognizant of the increasing interest in the land application alternative. Many have developed regulations and guidelines for this method of waste management for use within their boundaries.

Several studies have attempted to summarize the position of each of the states with respect to land application. Such a study was prepared by Temple University in 1972 (Stevens, et al., 1972).

In preparing this module, a survey was undertaken to gather more current information (Morris and Jewell, 1976). The major objectives of the study were to evaluate the extent to which land application is regulated at the state level and the trends which states are following in developing their guidelines. A familiarity with the requirements of different states should give participants a perspective on the kinds of regulations, the variability in the regulations, and the need to address the design of land application systems in different states on an individual and specific basis. The study involved contacting the pollution control agency of each of the fifty states by mail. A copy of current regulations and guidelines for the practice of applying wastewaters and sludges to land was requested. A space was provided where personnel could indicate if their state has no guidelines.

All fifty states responded to the survey. Several sent information applicable to waste management guidelines in general, but not specific to land application. Only the states which sent guidelines specifically for land application of wastes are included in the following discussion.

Twenty-four states did not have regulations or guidelines for land application in 1976. Of these, 5 states were preparing guidelines. This tabulation was updated in 1977, revealing the situation shown in Figure 1. Only 11 states still had no specific land application guidelines, which indicates the rapid development of this regulatory concern. Two other states have regulations in preparation.

A glance through a selection of state guidelines for land application of wastes indicates that certain aspects of this waste management alternative have received more regulatory attention than others.

It is helpful to categorize regulations and guidelines into three parts: System Design, Pre-Application Water Quality, and General Information.

Guidelines pertaining to System Design include the following:

Loading rate	Cover crop
Application system	Storage
Buffer zone	Public access
Monitoring	Effluent quality

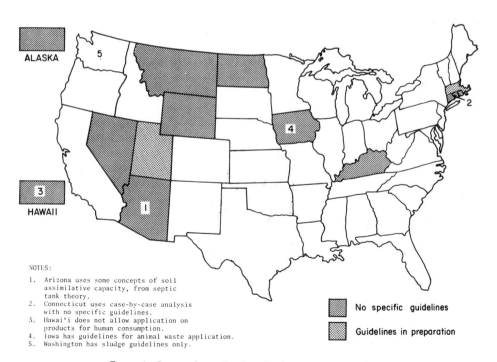

NOTES:
1. Arizona uses some concepts of soil assimilative capacity, from septic tank theory.
2. Connecticut uses case-by-case analysis with no specific guidelines.
3. Hawai'i does not allow application on products for human consumption.
4. Iowa has guidelines for animal waste application.
5. Washington has sludge guidelines only.

No specific guidelines

Guidelines in preparation

Figure 1. Status of state land application regulations—1977.

Pre-application water quality factors include:

Pretreatment requirement	Dissolved oxygen (DO)
Five-day biochemical oxygen demand (BOD_5)	Nitrates
Solids	Organics
Toxic elements	Chlorine residual
pH	Coliform concentration

General information on regulations and guidelines includes:

Type of waste applied	Factors which prevent land application
Philosophy and major concern of state	Weather restrictions
Site characteristics	

Information on state regulations and guidelines was categorized as to system design, preapplication water quality, and general information.

There is a wide range in the number of areas states choose to regulate. In some cases emphasis may be placed on only one or a few areas. For example, Michigan has very specific monitoring guidelines which are relied on to protect the groundwater. On the other hand, some states such as Florida have regulations or guidelines for nearly all the factors listed above.

Relatively few states had legislated regulations for land application systems as of 1977. In most cases, the states issued guidelines which must be used when designing a land application system. The design is then submitted to the appropriate agency in the state. That agency then evaluates the design on a case-by-case basis in terms of the guidelines developed by the state.

Most states have issued guidelines rather than regulations set by law.

The guidelines and regulations of several states are either in draft form or have been updated. It is important, therefore, to check with the appropriate state agency (in most cases the health or environmental protection agency) to get the most recent state regulations and guidelines. See Appendix G for the agency to contact in each particular state.

Several states have based their guidelines either wholly or in part on the standards developed by the Great Lakes–Upper Mississippi River Board of State Sanitary Engineers. Originally known as the Ten State Standards, these guidelines were developed to be used as a guide for design and preparation of plans for sewage treatment works. They represent an attempt at establishing an amount of uniformity of practice among the participating states. The text of the pertinent material is included in Appendix H.

The Ten State Standards are used by several states as the basis for their guidelines for land application of wastes.

The GLUMRB standards place a great deal of emphasis on the design report. This report allows the agency to evaluate the proposed site for suitability to land application. In many cases, a consultant should be engaged to fulfill the requirements for detailed geology, hydrology, and soils information.

Information on adjacent land use is important in evaluating the impact of the land application site on the surrounding community. The site should be compatible with both existing land use and with planned future development.

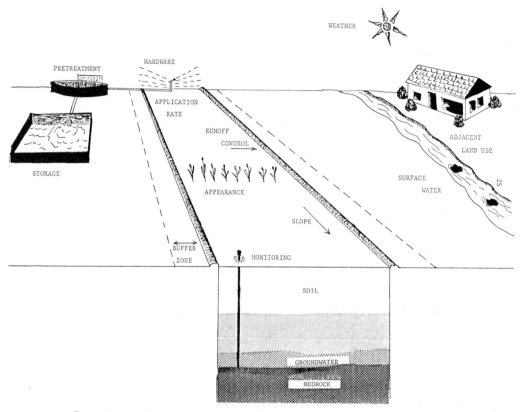

WEATHER

PRETREATMENT

HARDWARE

APPLICATION
RATE

RUNOFF
CONTROL

STORAGE

APPEARANCE

ADJACENT
LAND USE

SURFACE
WATER

SLOPE

BUFFER
ZONE

MONITORING

SOIL

GROUNDWATER

BEDROCK

Figure 2. Several aspects of land application systems are regulated by many states.

The GLUMRB standards require the equivalent of secondary pretreatment in most cases. As we shall see, this is required by nearly all the states which have issued guidelines or regulations for land application of wastes.

Figure 2 shows several aspects of land application systems which are addressed by many of the states. In designing these systems, the engineer should be aware of requirements for pretreatment, storage capacity, type of hardware, extent of buffer zone, application rate for waste, appearance of the site, runoff control, slope of the site, soil, bedrock, hydrology of the site, monitoring program, and adjacent surface water and land use. Several states prohibit waste application during certain weather events or certain times of the year.

Trends in State Guidelines

In reviewing state guidelines for land application, several trends can be observed. This is in part due to the fact that many of the states which have developed guidelines have used similar reference materials. The Great Lakes-Upper Mississippi River Board Addendum #2 is one such widely used reference. A second is the EPA publication entitled *Evaluation of Land Application Systems* (EPA, 1975). This publication presents information on preparing wastewater management plans, design plans and specifications, and operation and maintenance manuals.

Table 1.   States that Required Secondary Treatment Prior to Land Application.[a]

California[b]	Missouri	South Carolina
Colorado	New Hampshire	South Dakota
Delaware	New Jersey	Texas
Florida	New York	Vermont
Georgia	Ohio	Virginia
Illinois	Oregon[c]	West Virginia
Minnesota	Pennsylvania	Wisconsin

[a]Morris and Jewell, 1976.
[b]Pretreatment requirement depends on intended use of water.
[c]Requires water quality of 20 mg/1 BOD_5 and 20 mg/1 suspended solids.

Most states require that wastewater or sludge receive secondary treatment prior to land application. This requirement has a large influence on how cost-effective land application will be as waste treatment alternative.

One nationwide trend has special significance to the future of the land application alternative. This is the requirement which 18 out of 26 states mandate secondary treatment of waste prior to application to land. The states which require pretreatment of or equal to secondary treatment are shown in Table 1. The importance of the secondary treatment requirement to the future of land application lies in the emphasis placed by EPA on treatment alternatives which are cost effective. It is difficult to design a land application system with a secondary plant for pretreatment, while remaining within the bounds of cost effectiveness.

The requirement for secondary treatment stems from the differing views held among waste management personnel toward land application as a waste treatment mechanism. *The states which require secondary treatment tend to view land application as a means of disposing of wastewater. The states which do not require pretreatment consider the soil itself to be a treatment medium, recognizing the renovation capabilities of the soil.*

In a memorandum dated October 3, 1977, EPA Administrator Douglas Costle announced an EPA policy directive which may change the states' position on pretreatment requirements. The memo reads, in part, "Imposition of stringent wastewater treatment requirements prior to land application has quite often nullified the cost-effectiveness of land treatment processes in the past . . . Whenever states insist upon placing unnecessarily stringent preapplication treatment requirements upon land treatment, such as requiring EPA secondary effluent quality in all cases prior to application to the land, the unnecessary wastewater treatment facilities will not be funded by EPA." The full text of Mr. Costle's statement appears as Appendix J of this module.

New EPA policy will deny funding to states for "Unnecessary" pretreatment requirements for municipal land application projects.

In evaluating land application sites, several factors automatically eliminate a site from consideration in most states (Figure 3). These factors include:

1. Possibility of creating a groundwater mound close to the soil surface.
2. Excessive slope of land.
3. Proximity of site to surface waters or drainage ditches which could be contaminated by runoff.

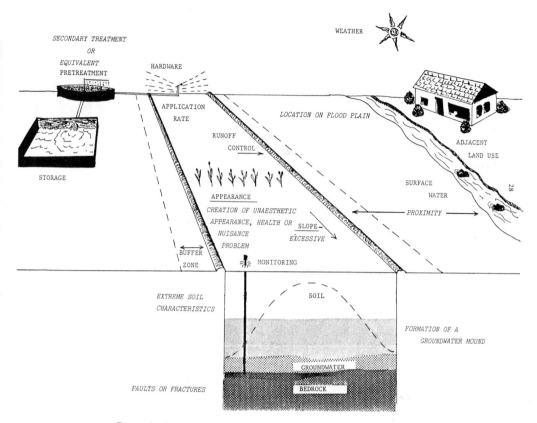

Figure 3. Several factors preclude land application in many states.

4. Location of site on a flood plain.
5. Extreme soil characteristics, such as a very high rate of permeability.
6. Faults or fractures in the underlying bedrock.
7. Creation of an eyesore, health problem, or nuisance on the site or on adjacent property.

Several factors may eliminate land application as an option at a particular site in many states.

Four other areas of land application receive attention from a majority of states (Figure 4). Nearly 50% of the states require that land application sites incorporate methods to control surface runoff, and to prevent off-site runoff from flowing onto the site. Ditches and berms are the most commonly used method of runoff control. Additionally, erosion from these sites must be controlled.

The slope of the site is an important consideration in land application. Generally the slope for cultivated fields which are irrigated with wastewater should be no greater than 4%. For sodded fields, up to 8% slope is typically suggested. For year-round application to forested slopes, some states require a slope no greater than 8%, while others allow this operation on slopes up to 20%. Seasonal operation on terraced, forested land is allowed on slopes of up to 25% in New Jersey, although most other states limit this practice to slopes under 15%. (Table 2).

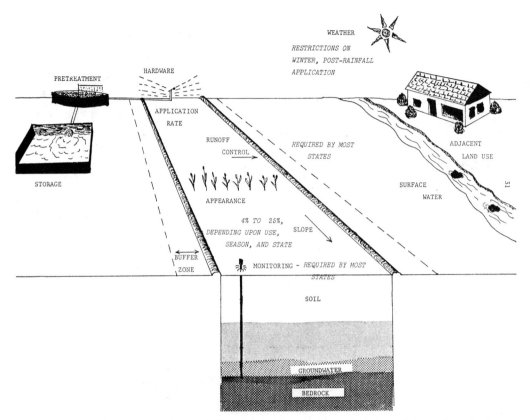

Figure 4. A majority of states have guidelines for runoff control, weather, slope of site, and monitoring.

Operation of land application systems is required to cease under severe weather conditions in several states. In these states, irrigation should not be carried out during or after heavy rain-storms. Irrigation must cease in winter in Missouri and Nebraska. New York, Minnesota, New Hampshire, and South Dakota limit the irrigation season to 18–20 weeks per year, effectively eliminating the option of winter irrigation. States which allow a winter irrigation often require that (1) pipes be capable of being drained to prevent freeze-up, (2) runoff from snow or ice build-up be controlled, and (3) irrigation is stopped when the land is frozen or snow-covered. This last requirement pertains to Maine, Virginia, and West Virginia.

Monitoring guidelines are set by 85% of the states. The majority of these stipulate that at least one monitoring well be placed in each direction of major groundwater flow. Several states, however, specify which parameters are to be analyzed, where wells are to be located, frequency of sampling, and equipment checks.

Runoff control, slope of site, weather restrictions, and monitoring programs are specified by a majority of the states.

The majority of states stipulate that land application systems must be monitored with at least one monitoring well to be placed in each direction of major ground-water flow.

When states develop guidelines and regulations for land application, they may base sections on existing guidelines or regulations for other aspects of environmental protection. For example, water quality criteria established for flowing surface waters of the state may be used when determining the level of effluent quality required from a land application system. It is therefore necessary for the design engineer to consult with officials of the state pollution control agency to identify existing regulations which may affect land application system design.

> *Regulations or guidelines for land application of wastes may coincide with other pollution controls or health regulations of the state.*

Whereas most states have issued guidelines for the design and operation of land application systems, other states have published formal regulations. The states which have regulations rather than the more informal set of guidelines include California, Delaware, Idaho, Kansas, Missouri, Oregon, and Vermont. In several cases, these regulations are part of the health legislation of the state. In states which have guidelines, the design engineer is expected to use the guidelines when developing the system design. He then submits the design to the appropriate agency, which approves or denies it. Several states, including those which have neither regulations nor guidelines, stress that permits for land application systems will be granted on a case-by-case basis. In light of the realities of the land application alternative this is the most sensible approach, since each land application site will be essentially unique in terms of soils, underlying bedrock, geology, hydrology, and so forth.

Representative Guidelines

It would be unwieldy to attempt to present all the guidelines which states across the country have developed to regulate land application of wastes (Table 3). Thus, the following discussion of guidelines and regulations will proceed by examining the guidelines or regulations of one state from each of the five climatic zones of the contiguous United States. These zones are used here for two reasons: (1) land application of wastes is directly affected by climate, and therefore regulations can be expected to vary from region to region; and (2), because these climatic zones are also used in Module I-10, "Case Studies," to discuss individual projects in terms of their geographic and climatic location.

Figure 5 is a map indicating the Climatic Zones as delineated by Pound and Crites (1973, p. 128). The representative states which will be discussed are as follows:

> Region A: California
> Region B: Texas
> Region C: Florida
> Region D: Pennsylvania
> Region E: Minnesota

These states were chosen as representative examples because they have the most comprehensive guidelines or regulations within their regions. The guidelines and regulations described below are those that were obtained in the 1976 survey by Morris and Jewell.

Region A: California.   In California the Board of Health is responsible for regulations controlling the use of reclaimed wastewater for irrigation. Regulations for the use of sewage sludge on agricultural land are in preparation.

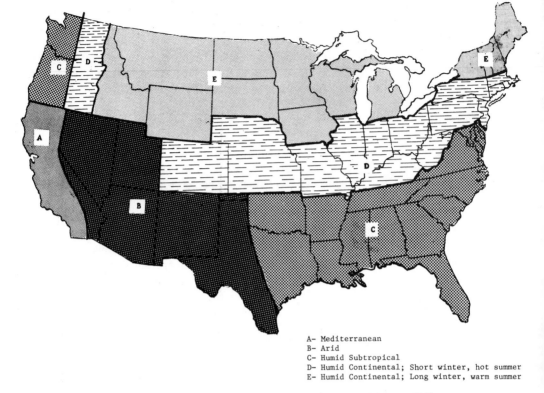

A- Mediterranean
B- Arid
C- Humid Subtropical
D- Humid Continental; Short winter, hot summer
E- Humid Continental; Long winter, warm summer

Figure 5. Climatic zones for land application (Pound and Crites, 1973).

Waste discharge requirements for wastewater or sludge applied to land are determined on a case-by-case basis. These regulations, which take into account existing pertinent legislation, are oriented toward protecting the waters of the state.

Two pieces of legislation form the basis for California's regulations for land application of wastes. The Porter-Cologne Water Quality Control Act of 1974 establishes the waste discharge requirements for land application of wastes. Wastewater Reclamation Criteria (California, 1975) describe allowable uses for primary and secondary wastewater. In addition, the Department of Health has issued a document entitled *Guidelines for the use of Reclaimed Water for Spray Irrigation of Crops* (California, 1974).

Surface irrigation of food crops may utilize water that has been disinfected and oxidized. Disinfection is considered adequate if at some point in the process the median number of coliform bacteria does not exceed 2.2 per 100 ml for the last 7 days for which analyses have been completed.

Reclaimed water with quality equivalent to that of primary treated effluent may be used for surface irrigation of orchards and vineyards as long as the fruit does not come in contact with the irrigating water on the ground.

The guidelines for land application of wastes in California are particularly interesting because of the extensive use of primary-treated wastewater in that state for irrigation.

Table 2.   Recommended Site Characteristics Required by Various States for
           Land Application of Wastes as of 1976.

	Slope Guidelines			Minimum Depth to Groundwater in Feet (Not Underdrained)
	None Given	Dependent on Cover Crop	Maximum Allowable Slope (%)	
California	X			
Colorado	X			
Delaware	X			2
Florida			5	5[b]
Georgia		Yes	20	10
Idaho	X			
Illinois		Yes[a]	14	5–10[c]
Kansas	X			
Maine			8	
Michigan	X			
Minnesota			2	10[d]
Missouri			2	
Nebraska		Yes		5
New Hampshire			10	
New Jersey		Yes	25	
New York		Yes	14	
Ohio			12	
Oregon	X			
Pennsylvania		Yes[a]	14	10
South Carolina		Yes	20	5
South Dakota	X			6[d]
Texas	X			
Vermont			25	
Virginia			15	5
West Virginia		Yes[a]	14	
Wisconsin	X			

[a]Slope guidelines are 4% for irrigation of cultivated fields, 8% for irritation of sodded fields, 8% year-round
irrigation of forested areas, and 14% on seasonal irrigation of forested areas.
[b]Except for recharge basins where a minimum depth of 18 inches is required.
[c]Dependent on infiltration rate of soil.
[d]Where underdrains are installed, minimum depth to groundwater 4 feet.

Food crops which are processed in such a way as to destroy pathogens before consumption
may also be irrigated with primary effluent. Before such irrigation commences, however, permission must be granted by the Department of Health. To date, the Public Health Department
has discouraged all such uses. Table 4 summarizes water quality required for various uses in
California. Figure 6 and Table 5 indicate the design criteria established in California.

In designing the system, water lines for domestic water and reclaimed water should have
maximum attainable separation. Valves and outlets on the reclaimed water lines should be operated only by authorized personnel.

The discharge resulting from irrigation must be confined to the site. Runoff must be contained

Table 3.   Summary of Several Common Aspects of State Guidelines for Land Application of Wastewater Which Have Major Impact on the Final Design. (Results of 1976 Survey) (NI-No Information Given)

State	Storage Requirement	Buffer Zone Requirement	Cover Crop	Hardware	Loading Rate (Max. in./acre-wk)
California	NI	500 ft to water supply wells	NI	Maximum attainable separation	NI
Colorado	NI	NI	NI	NI	NI
Delaware	Reserve area required	200 ft	Crop planted before irrigation begins	Minimize aerosol formation	Not to exceed infiltration rate
Florida	7-day flow plus 3 ft freeboard	150 ft to houses; 200 ft to water wells	Crop planted before irrigation begins	Minimize aerosol formation	4
Georgia	30 days design flow	At least 300 ft	Woodlands or non-food crop	Fixed distribution system	1
Idaho	NI	NI	NI	NI	NI
Illinois	To accommodate flows in excess of irrigation	150 ft to water supplies; 200 ft to surface water	NI	Stationary systems capable of being drained	NI
Kansas	NI	NI	NI	NI	NI
Maine	NI	300 ft for spray irrigation	No application on bare soil	NI	NI
Michigan	NI	NI	NI	NI	NI
Minnesota	210 days	To extent possible	Acceptable vegetative cover	Minimize aerosol drift; automatic shutoff during rain	2 (4 during July and August)
Missouri	Winter flow plus allowance for wet Spring	NI	Reed canary grass, tall fescue	Drains to prevent freeze-up	NI
Nebraska	180 days	50 ft	NI	No cross connections between potable and reclaimed water pipes	3
New Hampshire	$\frac{2}{3}$ yearly flow	Site dependent	NI	NI	2
New Jersey	Site dependent	200 ft	No application on bare soil	Portable systems unacceptable	2

New York	To handle maximum reasonable variation in flow	NI	Cover crop required; harvest when necessary	Station systems preferred	NI
Ohio	NI	NI	No application on root crops, leafy vegetables	NI	NI
Oregon	Adequate storage	NI	No irrigation of crops for human or dairy cattle consumption	NI	NI
Pennsylvania	To handle maximum reasonable variation in flow	200 ft	Few restrictions	Fixed lines for winter irrigation; low spray trajectory	2
S. Carolina	3 days flow	100 ft	No application on bare soil or crops for human or grazing animal consumption	Drains to prevent freeze-up	2
S. Dakota	210 day flow	To extent possible	"Suitable"	Minimize wind drift and aerosol formation	2
Texas	NI	500 ft to water supplies	No irrigation of food crops for raw consumption	No cross connections between potable and reclaimed water pipes	NI
Vermont	April–May flows	100 ft to surface waters	NI	Pump system must deliver daily flow within 8 hours	2
Virginia	60 days	200 ft for forested site; 600 ft for open site	No irrigation of food crops for raw consumption	Permanent spray system	2
W. Virginia	60 days	400 ft	NI	Permanent spray system, drains to prevent freeze-up	1
Wisconsin	NI	1,000 ft from public water supplies	NI	Minimize runoff, incorporate sludge	NI

Table 4.   Water Quality Criteria for Reclaimed Wastewater in California
are Dependent Upon Ultimate Use of the Water.

Water Quality Requirement	Ultimate Use
Equivalent to primary treated	1. Surface irrigation of orchards, vineyards 2. Food crops which are to be processed[a] 3. Surface or spray irrigation of fodder, fiber and seed crops
Disinfected, oxidized	1. Surface irrigation of food crops[b] 2. Irrigation of pasture for dairy animals[c] 3. Restricted recreational impoundment (non-contact water sports)[b] 4. Landscape impoundments
Disinfected, oxidized, clarified, filtered	1. Spray irrigation of food crops[d] 2. Non-restricted recreational impoundments (contact water sports)[d]

[a]Requires permission from Department of Health.
[b]Requires median of 2.2 coliform organisms per 100 ml.
[c]Requires median of 23 coliform organisms per 100 ml.
[d]Requires median of 2.2 coliform organisms per 100 ml; no more than 23 coliform organisms per 100 ml in any 30-day period.

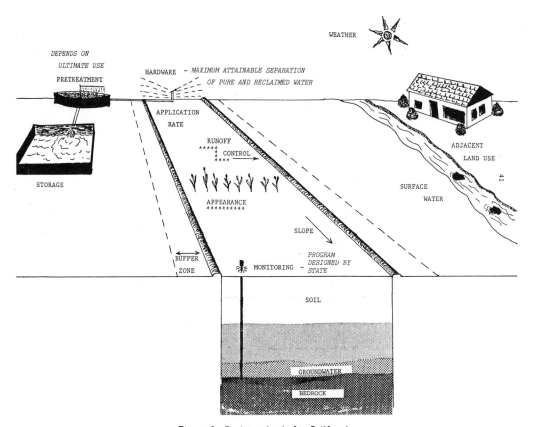

Figure 6. Design criteria for California.

Table 5.   Summary of Design Criteria for Land Application of Wastes in California.

Parameter	Guidelines
Major concern	Protection of waters of state
Pretreatment	Depends on ultimate use
Runoff control	Discharge confined to site
Hardware	Maximum attainable separation of reclaimed and domestic waterlines
Buffer zone	At least 500 ft from water wells, reservoirs
Monitoring	Dependent on water quality
Cover crop	Dependent on water quality
Public access	Dependent on water quality

and properly disposed of. The system shall not lead to the creation of unappealing slimes or odors. Ponding should be minimized, and the breeding of insect disease vectors controlled.

The monitoring regimen is decided by the state. In most cases, samples for suspended solids and coliform are to be collected daily. For uses which require secondarily treated wastewater, analysis for coliform and turbidity, using a continuous recording turbidometer, is required.

> *Guidelines for the use of wastewater differ depending on the ultimate use of the water.*

Where primary wastewater is used, the site should be fenced. For spray sites, windblown spray should not be allowed to reach areas which are accessible to the public. Drinking fountains must be protected from windblown spray. If wastewater is used at golf courses, notice of its use shall be given on scorecards and at water hazards. Qualified supervision is required at recreational impoundments. Wastewater is not to be spread on roads, walkways, picnic tables, or other areas not under control of the user.

When wastewater is used for irrigation, enough time should pass between the final irrigation and harvesting to allow the crops and soil to dry. Irrigated areas should be thoroughly dry before grazing animals, particularly dairy animals, are released on them. Measures to prevent direct contact between edible portions of the crop and the reclaimed water shall be taken.

California has been using reclaimed wastewater for a comparatively long time. Several projects in the state are of particular interest. Three of these, at Bakersfield, Fresno, and Santee, are examined in Module I-10, "Case Studies." The latter project utilizes wastewater for extensive recreational facilities including swimming. Bakersfield and Fresno apply the wastewater to crops.

Region B: Texas.   Although only the Western part of Texas falls within Climatic Zone B, it will be discussed here, as none of the other states of Region B—Utah, Arizona, or New Mexico—have guidelines or regulations specifically for land application of wastes. Indeed, Region B also includes the southeastern part of California, although the majority of California takes up the entire area of Region A. Figure 7 indicates design criteria for Texas.

The main concern in Texas is protection of public health. Secondary treated wastewater is often used for irrigation of isolated pastures. Crops not used for human consumption may be irrigated with water that has received secondary treatment; in this case chlorination is recommended. Crops used for human consumption may not be irrigated with reclaimed wastewater. Golf courses and other areas where public access is controlled may use wastewater for irrigation; however, irrigation should be practiced only when these areas are closed to the public.

> *The guidelines of Texas are aimed at protecting the public health.*

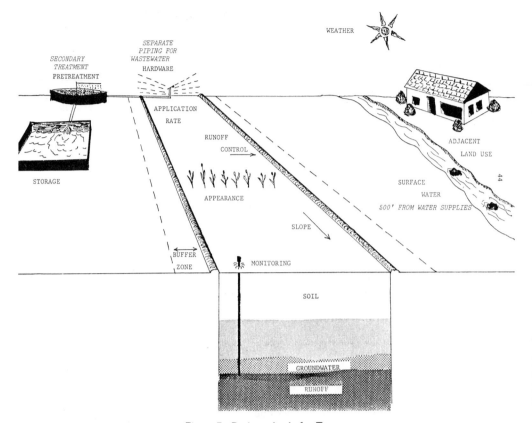

Figure 7. Design criteria for Texas.

The pipes carrying treated wastewater may have no physical contact with pipes carrying drinking water. Additionally, all outlets, pipes, and valves on the wastewater lines must be identified. Wastewater to be used for irrigation at areas accessible to the public should achieve the quality criteria presented in Table 6.

Digested sludges may be applied to pastureland if public health nuisances have been eliminated.

Wastewater and sludge application sites must be at least 500 feet from drinking water wells or water supply treatment plants.

Table 6.   Wastewater used for Irrigation in Public Access Areas in Texas Must Meet Strict Secondary-Treatment Standards.

Constituent	Concentration
BOD_5	20 ppm
SS	20 ppm
Fecal coliform	50 MPN/100 ml
Cl residual	2.0–5.0 ppm for 20 minutes at peak flow

Region C: Florida. The draft guidelines established by Florida for the application of municipal wastewaters to land attempt to protect the water in receiving streams and safeguard the health, safety, and welfare of the public. Florida is one of the few states which views land application as a treatment means, rather than merely as a disposal method. The effluent from the land application site must be compatible with that of local ground and surface waters.

Although Florida considers land application to provide some amount of treatment for the waste, the state still requires that wastewater receive secondary pretreatment prior to land application.

Figure 8 indicates design criteria for Florida. Land application systems in Florida are viewed as a long-term, cost-effective, and viable alternative method for meeting discharge limitations and water quality standards and should be designed as such.

Florida prohibits the use of wastewater for the irrigation of food crops for human consumption which may be eaten raw or without processing that is sufficient to destroy any associated pathogens.

The requirement for secondary treatment is applicable to all land application projects. Other criteria listed in Table 7 may be altered by the state, depending on site-specific considerations. Pre-application effluent quality required is dependent upon the application rate and the use of the water. This information is presented in Table 8.

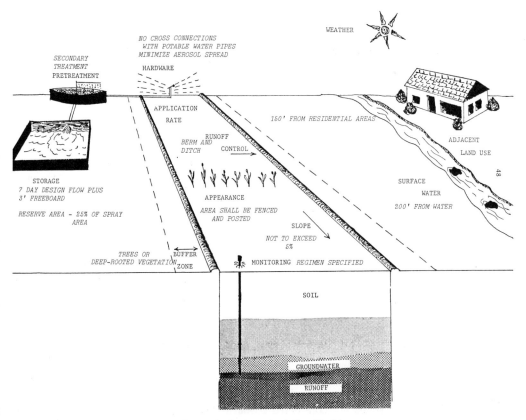

Figure 8. Design criteria for Florida.

Table 7.   Guidelines for Land Application of Municipal Wastewater in Florida.

Parameter	Guidelines
Slope	Not to exceed 5%.
Runoff	A berm and perimeter ditch built to contain storm runoff, prevent direct discharge to surface water.
Cover crop	To be planted before irrigation begins.
Buffer zone	Site must be 150 feet from existing or potential residential areas, 200 ft from water. A peripheral buffer zone of trees or deep-rooted vegetation shall enclose the site.
Storage	7-day design flow plus 3 feet freeboard.
Reserve area	25% of required spray area excluding buffer zone.
Spray technique	Minimize aerosol formation.
Monitoring	Require background quality. Test for pH, BOD, coliform, N, NO_3-N, P, TDS, hardness, chloride at least one groundwater monitoring well in each major direction of groundwater flow. Samples to be collected from different depths of water table.
Piping	No cross connections with potable water supply. Irrigation system, drains, dikes, and storage basin to be designed according to applicable engineering standards.
Public access	Fences to keep out livestock and trespassers; post warning signs; areas with public access to be irrigated at night.

Table 8.   Pretreatment Requirements in Florida are Dependent on
Application Rate and Use of Water.

Type of Dispersal or Recharge	Pretreatment Before Holding Basin
Low rate land spreading (irrigation and crop harvesting)	Secondary treatment & chlorination. $BOD_5 \leqslant 20$ ppm. SS $\leqslant 20$ ppm. Total N $\leqslant 25$ ppm. Total P $\leqslant 10$ ppm.
High rate land spreading (irrigation and crop harvesting)	Secondary treatment and mixed media filtration. BOD_5 & SS $\leqslant 10$ ppm. Total N $\leqslant 10$ ppm. Total P $\leqslant 10$ ppm. Breakpoint chlorination. Free residual chlorine of 1.0 ppm after 15 min. contact at maximum flow.
Recharge Basins	Advanced waste treatment BOD_5 & SS $\leqslant 5$ ppm. Total N $\leqslant 3$ ppm. Total P $\leqslant 1$ ppm[a]. Breakpoint chlorination. Free chlorine of 1 ppm after 15 min. contact or maximum flow.

[a]Phosphate removal may not be required if there is no likelihood of phosphorus enrichment of surface waters in the vicinity.

Note: Groundwater monitoring is required for all projects.

Region D: Pennsylvania.   Pennsylvania has produced the *Spray Irrigation Manual* (Pennsylvania, 1972) which describes guidelines for locating and designing spray irrigation sites. It also includes a handbook which, upon completion by the engineer, becomes part of the required design report. The design criteria are summarized in Figure 9.

All spray irrigation systems are considered to be discharges to waters of the state. Therefore, such systems will require a permit from the Pennsylvania Department of Environmental Resources.

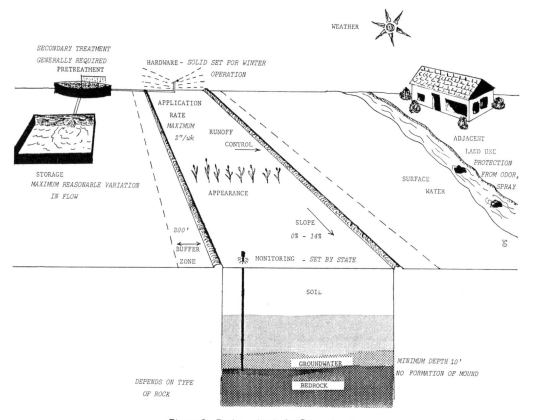

Figure 9. Design criteria for Pennsylvania.

The soil mantle is viewed as a treatment mechanism. Only waste constituents which can be treated successfully by the soil may be applied. Even so, secondary treatment is generally required prior to land application.

Pennsylvania views the soil as a treatment mechanism, but still requires secondary pretreatment of wastewater.

Irrigation should be restricted to a once-per-week application to allow the soil to dry out and re-aerate, thereby promoting the conditions necessary to continue waste degradation. The soil itself should provide for a slow but continuous downward movement of wastewater. This slow percolation allows adequate detention time in the soil matrix needed for the waste-degrading reactions to occur. The Hublersburg clay loam at the Penn State research site is typical of this type of slowly-permeable soil.

Pennsylvania has developed the recommendations indicated in Table 9 for application rates for spray irrigation of secondarily treated wastewater. The state has also issued guidelines pertaining to the underlying geology of the land application site. These guidelines appear in Table 10.

The extent of the required buffer zone is often a factor in design of land application systems. In Pennsylvania, a 200 foot buffer zone is required. In some cases the cost of land for buffer zones may be considerable.

Table 9.   Pennsylvania Has Varied Recommendations for Spray Irrigation of Wastewater.

Site Characteristics	Recommended Maximum Application Rates (in./wk)			
	Spring	Summer	Fall	Winter
Soil rapidly to moderately permeable; deep to well-drained	2	2	2	2
Soils rapidly to moderately permeable; moderately deep, well-drained	1.5	1.5	1.5	1.5
Moderately to very slowly permeable soils, moderately well drained with seasonal high water table	*Unacceptable*	2	2	*Unacceptable*
Bedrock at or near surface	Up to 2 in./wk may be approved upon submission of relevant supporting data			
Flood plain soils		1.5	1.5	

The condition of the groundwater is also important in selecting a site for spray irrigation of wastewater. Usually, the maximum groundwater elevation should not exceed 10 feet, and the formation of a groundwater mound should be avoided. Monitoring wells should be placed in each direction of major groundwater movement away from the site. In addition, one well should monitor the background quality of groundwater entering the site. Groundwater monitoring points may be natural springs or wells; in either case these monitoring points must provide adequate access and water flow for sampling at all times.

Pennsylvania requires a 200 foot buffer zone around the entire spray field. This may be a costly requirement for larger systems.

Chemical analyses from monitoring points are to be submitted quarterly. Required tests include phosphates, ammonia-nitrogen, nitrate-nitrogen, and methylene blue active substance. Other tests may be required by the Department of Environmental Resources.

Table 10.   Suitability of Underlying Rock for Land Application of Wastes in Pennsylvania.

Rock	Suitability
Sandstones	Poorly consolidated sandstones and deeply weathered greywackes and arkoses are most suitable.
Shales	Usually a poor choice. While some are deeply weathered and provide adequate renovation, others may have open fractures that will allow flow of wastewater directly to groundwater, others are so tight they reject infiltrating water, form a perched water table and eventually lead to ponding.
Limestone	Sites are preferred where the soil cover is thick and bedrock ledges or pinnacles are well below surface. Where soils are thin and bedrock occurs near surface, addition of wastewater may cause accelerated sinkhole development and surface collapse.
Perched water table	An experienced geologist should supervise drilling in areas where these are known to occur.
Glacial deposits	Extremely variable, but generally only marginally acceptable for spray irrigation. Some soils on moraine materials may be acceptable for seasonal operation at low application rates. Sands and gravels of outwash plains and valley fills generally unacceptable due to high permeability.

Table 11. Summary of Design Criteria for Land Application of Wastes in Pennsylvania.

Parameter	Guidelines
Philosophy	Considers soil to be a treatment medium.
Pretreatment	Secondary treatment.
Runoff control	Control runoff from ice build-up.
Hardware	Fixed irrigation lines for winter operation. Drains to prevent pipe freeze-up. Trajectory of spray as low as possible.
Buffer zone	200 ft around spray field.
Monitoring	One well in each direction of major underground flow; determine quality of groundwater entering site.
Cover crop	Idle fields, forests, grasslands, crop areas.
Storage	To handle maximum reasonable variation in flow.
Slope	0-14% depending on cover crop.
Application rate	Maximum 2 in./wk.
Groundwater depth	At least 10 ft to groundwater. No formation of groundwater mound.

Few limitations are placed on the choice of cover for the land application system. Idle fields, forests, grassland, and crop areas are acceptable. The cover chosen should provide a high rate of evapotranspiration, and should prevent erosion from runoff. A crop should be harvested and removed at least once a year, and more often if large amounts of nitrogen are applied. Standard agricultural practices for land application sites are acceptable for fields with slopes up to 4%. If a sod is the cover crop, fields with up to 8% slope may be used. For year-round application to forested areas, slopes up to 8% are acceptable. Seasonal irrigation may be practiced on forested slopes up to 14%.

If the land treatment facilities are not designed to handle surge flows or to operate during the winter, storage must be provided. The storage facilities should be able to handle the maximum reasonable variation in flow.

For year-round sprinkler operation, solid-set piping is recommended. Year-round irrigation may only be conducted in areas of permanent vegetation, preferably forest areas. Pipes should have drains to prevent freeze-up. Runoff from ice accumulation must be controlled. Adjacent land use should be protected from spray odor and degradation of groundwater. Trajectory of spray should be as low as possible to prevent aerosol spread. Table 11 summarizes the Pennsylvania guidelines for the design of a land treatment system.

Region E: Minnesota. Minnesota has published recommended design criteria for land application of wastewater. Municipal effluents must receive secondary treatment prior to application on land. Industrial effluents may be exempted from this requirement. The design criteria for Minnesota are schematically indicated in Figure 10. The water quality prior to land application must be as follows:

BOD_5	25 mg/1
SS	30 mg/1
Fecal coliform	200 MPN/100 ml

A storage lagoon with a minimum 210-day capacity must be built in accordance with criteria for waste stabilization ponds.

Land application systems must be located 1 mile from municipal water supplies, and 0.25 mile from a private water supply, human residence, state park or other recreation area, and crop irrigation area.

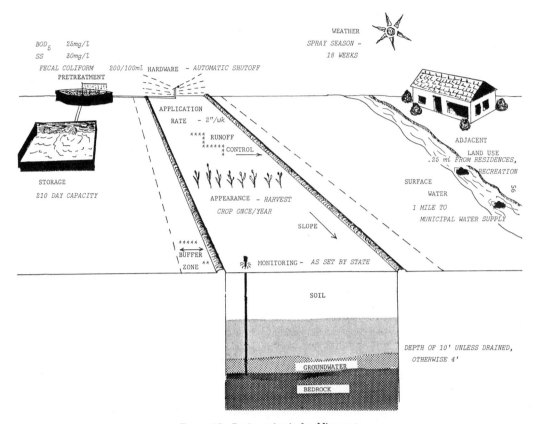

Figure 10. Design criteria for Minnesota.

Minnesota requires a storage lagoon with a 210 day capacity. This is a very large storage requirement, and may affect the decision to choose the land application alternative.

Buffer zones should be developed by purchase of adjacent land, or control of land use in adjacent area.

The site should be diked to (1) prevent runoff from leaving the site, (2) aid in recapture of effluent, and (3) prevent extra surface water from entering the site.

Overall application should not exceed 52 in./acre-yr. This figure is used in calculating required acreage. Maximum application rate is set at 2 in./acre-wk except for July and August, when up to 4 in./acre-wk may be allowed. Maximum application rate is 0.5 in./hr, with a maximum total application of 0.25 in./hr. The spray season is limited to 18 weeks. No part of the field may be sprayed continuously for more than 6 days.

Spray equipment should minimize wind drift and aerosol formation. There should be provision for automatic shutoff of irrigation during precipitation.

Slopes of 2% are recommended for broad field or ridge-and-furrow systems. The latter systems should utilize trenches 1 foot deep, and 8 inches apart.

The site should be fenced to prevent entrance by livestock, wild animals, or humans. Warning

Table 12.   Summary of Design Criteria for Land Application of Wastes in Minnesota.

Parameter	Guidelines
Pretreatment	BOD$_5$ 25 mg/1 suspended solids 30 mg/1 fecal coliform 200 MPN/100 ml
Runoff control	Dikes to prevent runoff
Hardware	Automatic shutoff capability during precipitation
Buffer zone	To extent possible through purchase or control of adjacent land
Monitoring	One well in each direction of major underground flow. Wells 200 ft beyond perimeter, 500 ft apart, no deeper than 5 feet below low water table. Baseline data before operation; test for conductivity, chlorine residual, total dissolved solids, Nitrate-, nitrite-, and ammonia-nitrogen, phosphorus, fecal coliform, methylene blue active substance
Cover crop	Harvest once per year
Storage	210 days
Spray season	18 weeks
Application rate	2 in./wk
Groundwater	At least 10 ft to groundwater; at least 4 ft if underdrained

signs should be posted. Monitoring wells are required 200 feet beyond the site perimeter, 500 feet apart, and should extend no deeper than 5 feet below the seasonal low water table. Separate wells are to be used to sample water from deeper strata. The quality and quantity of effluent discharged to the field, and the static water level of the wells, should also be measured. Routine tests required include:

Conductivity	Ammonia
Chlorides	Methylene blue
Dissolved salts	active substance
Nitrates	Fecal coliform
Nitrites	BOD$_5$
	Phosphorus

Acceptable vegetative cover is required which should be harvested and disposed of at least once a year. The wastewater applied to land should conform as much as possible to drinking water standards.

The guidelines for Minnesota are summarized in Table 12.

Site abandonment may be required if there is significant change in the groundwater quality or effluent quality from the spray field. Additional treatment and/or site abandonment may be required if there is a significant change in groundwater quality or effluent quality from the spray field.

Conclusions

The states of the nation, empowered by Congress to regulate waste management activities within their boundaries, have taken varying approaches to the land application alternative. As of 1977, 37 of 50 states had issued regulations or guidelines for this practice. Two states were preparing guidelines. Of the remaining 11 states, most approve design plans on a case-by-case basis. Existing pollution control legislation of the state, as well as existing guidelines for land application developed by other states or agencies are frequently used for reference.

Regulations and guidelines vary according to geography, demography, and economy of the states. The states that have issued guidelines are primarily those with larger populations and more industrialized. The popularity of land application in the state has also affected the promptness with which guidelines have been issued in the past. Since land application must be considered in order to receive federal funding under the provisions of Section 201 of PL 92-500, it is anticipated that all states will have guidelines within a few years.

Several regulations may severely affect the viability of land application as an alternative. The cost of land is a major portion of the system cost, and requirements for storage and buffer zones may impinge on the cost effectiveness of the system. For example, using Minnesota's requirement for a 210-day storage capacity, and assuming a 1 MGD flow, an additional 92 acres would be required for a storage lagoon 7 feet deep. Using Pennsylvania's requirement for a 200 foot buffer zone all around the irrigation area, a spray field 1 mile square would require nearly 100 additional acres for the buffer zone.

The requirement that the wastewater receive secondary treatment prior to land application also severely restricts the viability of land application as a practicable treatment technology. Most of the states require secondary treatment or its equivalent prior to land application. For a 1 MGD flow, secondary treatment involves about a $50,000 annual operating cost. This additional cost could eliminate land application from the ranks of cost effective alternatives.

> *Several guidelines issued by the states may prove severely restrictive to land application as a cost-effective alternative. The requirements for secondary pretreatment, extensive storage, and buffer zones make these systems much less competitive in cost.*

The secondary treatment requirement regulates the BOD_5, suspended solids, and fecal coliform allowed in wastewater used for irrigation. However, other waste constituents which may cause problems, particularly nitrate, phosphorus, and toxic substances, are not regulated by the majority of states.

Land application can be a viable, cost effective waste treatment alternative at appropriate sites. It should be remembered that land application systems are specific to each site, and it is often difficult to generate guidelines that are applicable to all systems. In developing guidelines, states should allow sufficient latitude in order to take full advantage of the potential of land application.

Requirements for secondary treatment should depend on the ability of the site to remove waste constituents, and the management scheme to be used at the site. Loading rates should take into account nitrogen, phosphorus, and toxic substances, as well as BOD_5, suspended solids, and the concentration of fecal coliforms. In most instances, land application system designs are approved or denied on the basis of careful, site specific evaluations. As long as this continues to be the case, land application can remain a viable waste management alternative.

> *Attention must be paid to loading rates for nitrate, phosphorous, and toxic substances, as well as BOD_5, suspended solids, and fecal coliform concentrations. Most states do not have guidelines for these waste constituents, which, if applied in excess, could cause system problems.*

Water Doctrines in U.S.-Either Riparian or Appropriative

The major water doctrines in the United States—riparian or appropriative—qualify surface water rights apart from other types of real property. The difference lies in the fact that the use of the water, not the water itself, is the subject of the property right involved. The riparian doctrine recognizes a property right to the water only when the use of it is reasonable in terms of allowing others who share ownership of stream bank property to have an equal right to the water. Under the appropriative doctrine, a property right does not even arise until the water has been put to beneficial use. There is general agreement that beneficial use and reasonable use both carry economic as well as legal connotations (Wallace and Cox, 1973).

> *The major U.S. water doctrines make the use of water, not the water itself, the subject of the property involved.*

Land Application Constitutes an Additional Use. Application of municipal sludges and effluents to land constitutes an additional water use. Although this recycling has most of the attributes of irrigation, the rate of application and other parameters are defined not in terms of optimum irrigation but obtaining improved water quality. Therefore, the question must be asked: Is this recycling of wastewater a beneficial or reasonable use under current water law doctrines? While improved water quality may well be accepted as a national goal, should it be obtained at the expense of property rights established by state water laws?

> *Land application constitutes a use of water in addition to "normal" consumptive uses.*

Appropriative Rights Are Not Tied to Land Ownership. Appropriative rights tended to be enacted by statute and defined in the courts on a case-by-case basis. As a result, wide variations exist among the 19 western states that recognize such rights. In general, the basic principles of appropriative rights theory are: (1) first in time, first in right for the water, and (2) subsequent appropriations cannot diminish the quantity or quality of a senior right. Usually, permits are required to establish the right to appropriative water, and the water thus appropriated must also be put to a beneficial use. Rights to appropriated water are not connected with land ownership. They may be bought, sold, exchanged, or transferred wholly or in part (Powell, 1975).

> *Appropriative water rights are based on first in time, first in right of water, and on the belief that subsequent appropriations of water cannot diminish the quantity or quality of a senior water right.*

The general rule in those western, mostly arid states following the appropriative doctrine, is that once established, water use will remain substantially unchanged unless change can be accomplished without detriment to other appropriators—including those with junior rights. Thus a conflict arises where a proposed modification in use involves a change from nonconsumptive to a consumptive use, since the latter depletes the source of flow by not returning the water to its original channel. This is the case when a large percentage of the stream flow is effluent discharge.

Land application of municipal wastewater would appear to fall into this category of change. Irrigation is a greater consumer of water than traditional municipal use. In fact, the appropriator located immediately downstream from the previous point of waste discharge may be denied all use of the return flow that existed before irrigation was started.

> *Land application of wastewater may involve a change from nonconsumptive to a consumptive use, depleting the source of flow by not returning the water to its original channel.*

Many states recognize a combination of riparian and appropriative rights. This dual-rights system has developed in states that have water-short and water-surplus areas within their borders. In such cases, the appropriative theory is usually the predominant one (Large, no date).

Knowledge of Water Rights Law is Needed.   On the basis of water rights, the operation of a land treatment system may involve a change in water use from nonconsumptive (passing flow through a plant for treatment and subsequently discharging it to the same stream used for water supply) to consumptive. This change can interfere with the water rights of downstream or senior claims to the water because the source of flow is depleted when the discharge is not returned to its original channel. Because this potential for legal problems exists, a knowledge of water rights law is both desirable and necessary. Water rights problems tend to arise in areas where water is in short supply or where it has been fully allocated. Yet the existence of a market for reclaimed water in these areas will aid in the cost effectiveness and acceptability of land treatment. On a national level, these areas are shown in Figure 11.

Most riparian or land ownership rights are in effect east of the Mississippi River and most appropriative or permit system rights are in effect west of the Mississippi. A legal distinction is made between discharges to a receiving water in a well-defined channel or basin (natural watercourse), superficial waters not in a channel or basin (surface waters), and underground waters

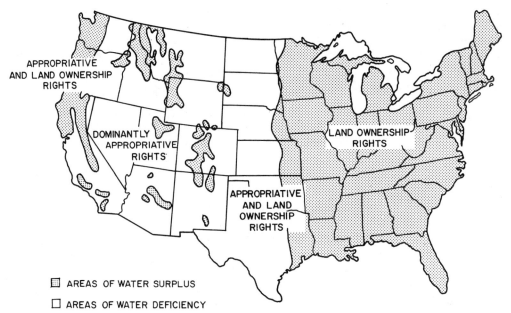

☒ AREAS OF WATER SURPLUS

☐ AREAS OF WATER DEFICIENCY

Figure 11. Dominant water rights doctrines and areas of water surplus or deficiency (Metcalf and Eddy, 1977, from Large).

Table 13. Potential Water Rights Problems for Land Treatment Alternatives.[a]
(After Metcalf and Eddy, 1977)

Water Definition and Water Rights Theory	Land Treatment Process		
	Slow Rate	Rapid Infiltration	Overland Flow
Natural watercourses			
Riparian	Unlikely	Unlikely	Unlikely
Appropriative	Likely[b]	Likely[b]	Depends on location of discharge from collection ditch
Combination	Likely[b]	Likely[b]	Depends on location of discharge from collection ditch
Surface waters			
Riparian	Unlikely	Unlikely	Likely[c]
Appropriative	Unlikely	Unlikely	Likely[c]
Combination	Unlikely	Unlikely	Likely[c]
Percolating or groundwaters			
Riparian	Unlikely	Possible	Unlikely
Appropriate	Likely	Likely	Unlikely
Combination	Likely	Likely	Unlikely

[a]For existing conditions and alternatives formulation stage of the planning process only. It is also assumed that the appropriative situations are water-short or over-appropriated.
[b]If effluent was formerly discharged to stream.
[c]If collection/discharge ditch crosses other properties to natural watercourse.

not in a well-defined channel or basin (percolating or groundwaters). Table 13 is a guide to determine whether certain land treatment alternatives will present water rights problems.

Most States Operate Under Riparian Rights.   Most states operate under the riparian doctrine. This is based on the simple premise that whoever owns land traversed by or bordering a flowing stream may make reasonable uses of its waters that do not interfere with other property owners having similar rights. After making a reasonable use of the water for his own purposes, a riparian owner must return all the surplus to its natural channel before it reaches downstream riparian owners.

> *Most states follow riparian doctrine, requiring landowners adjacent to streams to return all surplus water to its natural channel after making a reasonable use of the water.*

The amount of acreage required for land disposal makes it unlikely that land so used would be situated so that return flows would reach the stream of origin at a point above the property lines of all lower riparians. Therefore, land application is likely to violate the rights of other water users on the stream.

The situation is complicated further when the return flows ultimately find their way to a different stream. Such interbasin transfers generally are not recognized under the riparian doctrine. There is no cause for legal action if no actual injury has occurred to another landowner's rights. Therefore, legal obstacles may not exist where there is water surplus. Where a surplus does not exist, land application could be excluded in some riparian situations unless special provisions are made to either acquire the water rights of those affected or to return the used effluent to a point above the lower riparian properties.

Land application is likely to violate the rights of other water users of the stream only if there is no surplus, and legal obstacles may arise in areas where water is in short supply.

Since the riparian doctrine protects the quantity and the quality of the flow on behalf of abutting landowners, it automatically protects the natural watercourse itself. Included in this protection are the stream's scenic attributes, associated wildlife habitats, and instream uses, such as fishing and recreation. Where the recycling of waste effluents significantly modifies the stream regimen, these other attributes may become the basis of a legal action by any affected citizen.

Surface water problems must be carefully considered when designing land application systems in light of today's more liberal court interpretations on such questions as the right to sue and class actions on behalf of groups possessing a common interest. Opening the courtroom doors to such actions greatly expands the liability potential.

More liberal court interpretations on the right to sue and class action suits increase the liability of land application operators for violation of water rights.

Natural Watercourses Flow in Defined Channels.   A natural watercourse is one in which water flows in a defined channel either on or below the earth's surface. It includes lakes, estuaries, and intermittent and perennial streams. The major legal problem with natural watercourses in both riparian and appropriative states is the reduced discharge which may result from diversion, of what was a direct discharge, through a land application site to the watercourse. If the watercourse is near or at overappropriation, junior water users who feel that a reduction in flow may impair their reasonable use of the water may seek administrative or judicial relief. In a riparian state, the diversion of a discharge that was not originally part of a stream should not be cause for legal action by downstream users under natural flow theory.

The major problem with natural watercourses is the diversion of what was a direct discharge through a land application site to the natural watercourse.

For appropriative rights states, the risk of legal action against the diversion is easier to analyze. If the conditions of the stream are such that the diversion would threaten the quality or quantity of the appropriated water of a downstream user, the damaged party has cause for legal action against the diverter. This action may be injunctive, in which the diverter is prevented from affecting the diversion, or monetary, in which the diverter would be required to compensate for damages caused by his diversion. If the stream in dispute is not already over-appropriated as is the case in many western streams, or if the area is not short of water, it is unlikely that damages could be proved as a result of the diversion.

If the diversion threatens the quality or quantity of the appropriated water of a downstream user, the damaged party can sue the diverter. This is more likely to happen in areas short of water.

Surface Waters Are Not Contained in Basins or Channels.   Surface waters are not contained in a well-defined basin or channel. Examples are rainfall or snowmelt directly on a parcel of land. Such waters belong to the landowner, but he cannot collect or discharge them across adjoining properties without the consent of the owners of those lands. This is true in both riparian and appropriative states.

If any of the land treatment alternatives under consideration require that the renovated water cross another's property, the granting of a drainage or utility easement across the land to the natural watercourse or final user is necessary in all cases. The cost of such an easement must be considered in the cost-effectiveness analysis.

> *If land treatment requires that the renovated water cross another's property, the granting of a drainage or utility easement across the land to the natural watercourse or final user is necessary.*

Some Cases Uphold Right to Pure Groundwater.   Land application of wastewater may be legally constrained by private rights to groundwater in cases where alteration of water quality or natural flow patterns result in adverse effects. Although land treatment is intended to reduce overall water pollution, any degradation of groundwater quality may subject the operator to legal action by the users of that water. Groundwater discharge may also damage other users by artificially raising their water table.

> *Any artificial rise in the water table or any degradation of groundwater quality by the land treatment site operator may be grounds for a suit.*

In riparian states, the claim of damages would require that a landowner prove that he overlies the same source of groundwater as the land treatment operator. If the alleged damages are not caused by negligent operation of the land treatment site, or operation that is deliberately harmful to the adjoining land owners, it would be doubtful that there would be sufficient cause for legal action. In appropriative states, the question of an increase in the level or volume of a groundwater should cause no problems because no one's appropriative right would be threatened.

The right of the landowner to uncontaminated groundwater has not always been recognized. In some cases the courts have been reluctant to impose liability where the pollution resulted from lawful uses of adjoining land. The justification for this attitude has been that such property injury could not have been anticipated. In other cases, however, the right to uncontaminated water has been upheld and those responsible for contamination have been held liable. In these cases, the right to pure groundwater has been viewed as absolute. Liability has been imposed on the party responsible for degradation of the water without regard to the reasonableness of the activity or the care with which the operation was conducted.

> *The courts have wavered in establishing the right to uncontaminated groundwater and have been reluctant to impose liability where the pollution resulted from lawful uses of adjoining land. In other cases, the right to pure groundwater has been viewed as absolute.*

Other Water Rights to Consider.   In some states, basin authorities or water irrigation districts have regulations against the transfer of water outside their jurisdictional boundaries. In the western states particularly, the right to divert or use water does not carry with it the right to store such water. The right to water salvaged from imported water that has run off irrigated lands is not automatic either. The rights in both cases must be specifically obtained or at least must be assured by precedent legal action.

A brief overview of water rights law may be sufficient for the operation of small land treatment systems, but for larger systems and in problem areas the watermaster or water rights engineer at the state or local level should be consulted. Some states either have no records or carry unenforceable rights in their records, so that further investigation will be necessary if doubt remains.

> *The watermaster or a water rights engineer at the state or local level should be consulted when designing large land treatment sites or in problem areas.*

An excellent reference, *A Summary-Digest of State Water Laws* by R. L. Dewsnup and D. W. Jensen (1973), is available from the National Water Commission in Washington, D.C. Although summaries of precedent rulings are not guarantees, they may clarify the situation if similar cases can be found. Finally, if problems arise, a water rights attorney should be consulted.

> *If legal problems arise over water, a water rights attorney should be consulted.*

Water Rights Problems Can Be Resolved.   To resolve water rights problems, the project engineer should do the following:

- Try to define the water rights setting that could affect the fate of any renovated water.
- Be aware of the quantity and priority of all water rights in the district or basin.
- Define the water rights constraints for all alternatives.
- Once the candidate sites have been selected, examine the point of discharge, availability and quantity of discharge, and modifications to existing practices.
- If there are problems with any of the feasible alternatives, consult a water rights attorney to define more closely the legal constraints on the alternatives and to define the land treatment operator's rights and responsibilities.

If the land treatment operator's rights to the renovated water can be established, he can now trade those rights with any potentially damaged senior rights or use the revenues from sale of the water to offset possible damage claims, (Metcalf and Eddy, 1977).

BIBLIOGRAPHY

Anderson, F. R. 1973. NEPA in the courts. John Hopkins University Press, Baltimore, Md. 324 p.

California, 1975. Wastewater reclamation criteria. Title 22, Division 4, California Administrative Code Chapter 4.

California. 1974. Guidelines for the use of reclaimed water for spray irrigation of crops. Department of Health. Mimeo.

Claussen, Eileen. 1977. New federal perspectives on the land application of sludge. (Presented at ninth annual Waste Management Conference, Cornell University.) 9 p.

Committee on Merchant Marine and Fisheries. 1973. Federal laws relating to conservation and development of our nation's fish and wildlife resources. Environmental Quality and Oceanography. U.S. Govt. Print. Office, Washington, D.C.

Dewsnup, R. L. and D. W. Jensen, (ed). 1973. A summary-digest of state water laws. National Water Commission. Washington, D.C. 826 p.

EPA. 1975. Evaluation of land application systems. EPA-430/9-75-001. Office of Water Program Operations. Washington, D.C. 182 pp.

EPA. 1976. National interim primary drinking water regulations. EPA-570/9-76-003. Office of Water Supply. Washington, D.C. 159 p.

Florida. 1973. Guidelines for treatment and/or disposal of wastewaters by irrigation on land. Dept. of Pollution Control. Division of Operations. Memo No. 49. Mimeo.

Large, D. W. (no date) Legal constraints imposed on land application of wastewater by private water rights law.

Loehr, R. C., and J. D. Denit. 1975. Effluent regulations for animal feedlots. Presented at the International Seminar on Animal Wastes, Bratislava, Czechoslovakia, Sept. 28-Oct. 5, 1973.

Metcalf and Eddy. 1977. Process design manual for land treatment of municipal wastewater. EPA-625/1-77-008. U.S. Environmental Protection Agency, U.S. Army Corps of Engineers, U.S. Dept. of Agriculture. Washington, D.C. pp. 3-32 to 3-37.

Miller, S. S. 1975. Environmental law—1974 style. *Environ. Sci. Technol.*, 9(3):194-195.

Minnesota. 1972. Recommended design criteria for disposal of effluent by land application. Minnesota Pollution Control Agency. Division of Water Quality. Mimeo.

Morris, C. E. and W. J. Jewell. 1976. Regulations and guidelines for land application of wastes—a 50 state overview. *In* Loehr, R. C. (ed). Land as a waste management alternative. (Proc. 8th Waste Management Conf., Cornell University). Ann Arbor, Mich., Ann Arbor Science. pp. 9-28.

Pennsylvania. 1972. Spray Irrigation Manual. Bureau of Water Quality Management, Department of Environmental Resources. Publication No. 31, Harrisburg, PA 49 p.

Powell, G. M. 1975. Design seminar for land treatment of municipal wastewater effluents. EPA Technology Transfer Program. (Presented at Technology Transfer Seminar.) 75 p.

Pound, C. E. and R. W. Crites. 1973. Wastewater treatment and reuse by land application, volume II. EPA-660/2-73-006b. Office of Research and Development, U.S. EPA. Washington, D.C. 249 p.

Stevens, R. M. 1972. Green land—clean streams. Center for the Study of Federalism. Temple University, Philadelphia, PA. 330 p.

Sullivan, R. H. 1973. Federal and state legislative history and provisions for land treatment of municipal wastewater effluents and sludges. *In* Proc. Joint Conf. on Recycling Municipal Sludges and Effluents on Land. EPA, USDA, Nat'l. Assn. State Univ. Land-Grant Coll. Champaign, Ill. July 9-13. pp. 1-8.

Texas. 1972. Recommendations from the staff of the division of wastewater technology and surveillance when the domestic wastewater effluent is to be used for irrigation of areas accessible to the public. Mimeo.

Torrence, S. W. 1974. Grass roots government. Robert B. Luce, Inc., Washington, D.C. 225 p.

Walker, W. R. and W. E. Cox. 1973. Meandering Water Rights. *Water Spectrum*, 5 (No. 1). 37.

Wilcox, D. A., A. Taverni, and C. Hamlin. 1975. Planning boards and zoning boards of appeal. Local Government Program. NYSSILR. Cornell University, Ithaca, N.Y.

APPENDIX A

Recommendations of the National Commission on Water Quality

(1) Maintaining the July 1, 1977, compliance date with "uniform treatment requirements by both industry and publicly owned treatment works, but provide some flexibility to grant extensions, and even waivers, on a case-by-case and category-by-category basis;" (2) maintaining the 1983 interim water quality goal, but "postponing the 1983 requirements for application of uniform technologies 5 to 10 years, pending an assessment of progress in water quality improvement and review of these results by a new National Commission on Water Quality by 1985;" (3) meeting the 1983 Interim water quality goal by "application of the 1977 requirements to all dischargers, revisions of 1977 limitations, effluent limitations for the elimination of the discharge of toxic pollutants in toxic amounts beginning immediately, new source performance standards for all new point source discharges, periodic upgrading of permits for discharges into water quality limited waters, and application of control measures to combined sewer overflows, stormwater runoff, agricultural and nonpoint sources;" (4) the decentralization of regulatory and administrative "functions of the national program by selective certification of states, based on satisfactory state plans and programs to control both point and nonpoint sources (including irrigated agriculture);" (5) stabilization of the Federal construction grants program "by assuring 75% federal financing for priority treatment made at a fixed amount (not less than $5 billion nor more than $10 billion per year) for a specified number of years (5 to 10);" (6) redefining the "goal of elimination of discharge of pollutants with one stressing conservation and reuse of resources;" (7) authorizing flexibility in applying control or treatment measures to irrigated agriculture after an inventory of the problem, and support salinity alleviation projects to reduce salt loads from sources other than man's activities.

APPENDIX B

Text of Pertinent Sections of PL 92-500 Discussed
Under Federal Legislation

Section 102(a)–Comprehensive programs for water pollution control:

(a) The Administrator shall, after careful investigation, and in cooperation with other Federal agencies, State water pollution control agencies, interstate agencies, and the municipalities and industries involved, prepare or develop comprehensive programs for preventing, reducing, or eliminating the pollution of the navigable waters and groundwaters and improving the sanitary condition of surface and underground waters. In the development of such comprehensive programs due regard shall be given to the improvements which are necessary to conserve such waters for the protection and propagation of fish and aquatic life and wildlife, recreational purposes, and the withdrawal of such waters for public water supply, agricultural, industrial, and other purposes. For the purpose of this section, the Administrator is authorized to make joint investigations with any such agencies of the conditions of any waters in any State or States, and of the discharges of any sewage, industrial wastes, or substance which may adversely affect such waters.

Sec. 201(f)–"(f) The Administrator shall encourage waste treatment management which combines 'open space' and recreational consideration with such management.

Section 201 (b)–Best practicable waste treatment technology:

"(b) Waste treatment management plans and practices shall provide for the application of the best practicable waste treatment technology before any discharge into receiving waters, including reclaiming and recycling of water, and confined disposal of pollutants so they will not migrate to cause water or other environmental pollution and shall provide for consideration of advanced waste treatment techniques.

Section 201 (d)–Recycling of Pollutants:

"(d) The administrator shall encourage waste treatment management which results in the construction of revenue providing facilities providing for–

"(1) the recycling of potential sewage pollutants through the production of agriculture, silviculture, or aquaculture products, or any combination thereof;

"(B) as appropriate, the works proposed for grant assistance will take into account and allow to the extent practicable the application of technology at a later date which will provide for the reclaiming or recycling of water or otherwise eliminate the discharge of pollutants.

Section 201 (e)–Cost-effectiveness:

"(e) The Administrator shall encourage waste treatment management which results in integrating facilities for sewage treatment and recycling with facilities to treat, dispose of, or utilize other industrial and municipal wastes, including but not limited to solid waste and waste heat and thermal discharges. Such integrated facilities shall be designed and operated to produce revenues in excess of capital and operation and maintenance costs and such revenues shall be used by the designated regional management agency to aid in financing other environmental improvement programs.

Section 201 (g) (1)–Financing:

"(g) (1) The Administrator is authorized to make grants to any State, municipality, or intermunicipal or interstate agency for the construction of publicly owned treatment works.

Section 201 (g)(2)(A)–Alternative Techniques:

"(2) The Administrator shall not make grants from funds authorized for any fiscal year beginning after June 30, 1974, to any State, municipality, or intermunicipal or interstate agency for the erection, building, acquisition, alteration, remodeling, improvement, or extension of treatment works unless the grant applicant has satisfactorily demonstrated to the Administrator that—

"(A) alternative waste management techniques have been studied and evaluated and the works proposed for grant assistance will provide for the application of the best practicable waste treatment technology over the life of the works consistent with the purposes of this title;

"(2) The Administrator, after consultation with appropriate Federal and State agencies and other interested persons, shall publish within nine months after the date of enactment of this title (and from time to time thereafter) information on alternative waste treatment management techniques and systems available to implement section 201 of this Act.

Section 212—Definitions:

"Sec. 212. As used in this title—

"(1) The term 'construction' means any one or more of the following: preliminary planning to determine the feasibility of treatment works, engineering, architectural, legal, fiscal, or economic investigations or studies, surveys, designs, plans, working drawings, specifications, procedures, or other necessary actions, erection, building, acquisition, alternation, remodeling, improvement, or extension of treatment works or the inspection or supervision of any of the foregoing items.

"(2) (A) The terms 'treatment works' means any devices and systems used in the storage, treatment, recycling, and reclamation of municipal sewage or industrial wastes of a liquid nature to implement section 201 of this Act, or necessary to recycle or reuse water at the most economical cost over the estimated life of the works, including intercepting sewers, outfall sewers, sewage collection systems, pumping, power, and other equipment, and their appurtenances; extensions, improvements, remodeling, additions, and alterations thereof; elements essentail to provide a reliable recycled supply such as standby treatment units and clear well facilities; and any works, including site acquisition of the land that will be an integral part of the treatment process or is used for ultimate disposal of residues resulting from such treatment.

"(B) In addition to the definition contained in subparagraph (A) of this paragraph, 'treatment works' means any other method or system for preventing, abating, reducing, storing, treating, separating, or disposing of municipal waste, including storm water runoff, or industrial waste, including waste in combined storm water and sanitary sewer systems. Any application for construction grants which includes wholly or in part such methods or systems shall, in accordance with guidelines published by the Administrator pursuant to sub-paragraph (C) of this paragraph, contain adequate data and analysis demonstrating such proposal to be, over the life of such works, the most cost efficient alternative to comply with sections 301 or 302 of this Act, or the requirements of section 201 of this Act.

Section 301—Effluent Limitations:

"Sec. 301. (a) Except as in compliance with this section and sections 302, 306, 307, 318, 402, and 404 of this Act, the discharge of any pollutant by any person shall be unlawful.

"(b) In order to carry out the objective of this Act there shall be achieved—

"(1) (A) not later than July 1, 1977, effluent limitations for point sources, other than publicly owned treatment works, (i) which shall require the application of the best practicable control technology currently available as defined by the Administrator pursuant to section 304(b) of this Act, or (ii) in the case of a discharge into a publicly owned treatment works which meets the requirements of sub-paragraph (B) of this paragraph, which shall require compliance with any applicable pretreatment requirements and any requirements under section 307 of this Act; and

"(B) for publicly owned treatment works in existence on July 1, 1977, or approved pursuant to section 203 of this Act prior to June 30, 1974 (for which construction must be completed within four years of approval), effluent limitations based upon secondary treatment as defined by the Administrator pursuant to section 304(d)(1) of this Act; or,

"(C) not later than July 1, 1977, any more stringent limitation, including those necessary to meet water quality standards, treatment standards, or schedules of compliance, established pursuant to any State law or regulation (under authority preserved by section 510) or any other Federal law or regulation, or required to implement any applicable water quality standard established pursuant to this Act.

"(2) (A) not later than July 1, 1983, effluent limitations for categories and classes of point sources, other than publicly owned treatment works, which (i) shall require application of the best available technology economically achievable for such category or class, which will result in reasonable further progress toward the national goal of eliminating the discharge of all pollutants, as determined in accordance with regulations issued by the Administrator pursuant to section 304(b)(2) of this Act, which such effluent limitations shall require the elimination of discharges of all pollutants if the Administrator finds, on the basis of information available to him (including information developed pursuant to section 315), that such elimination is technologically and economically achievable for a category or class of point sources as determined in accordance with regulations issued by the Administrator pursuant to section 304(b)(2) of this Act, or (ii) in the case of the introduction of a pollutant into a publicly owned treatment works which meets the requirements of subparagraph (B) of this paragraph, shall require compliance with any applicable pretreatment requirements and any other requirement under section 307 of this Act; and

"(B) not later than July 1, 1983, compliance by all publicly owned treatment works with the requirements set forth in section 201(g)(2)(A) of this Act.

"(c) The Administrator may modify the requirements of subsection (b)(2)(A) of this section with respect to any point source for which a permit application is filed after July 1, 1977, upon a showing by the owner or operator of such point source satisfactory to the Administrator that such modified requirements (1) will represent the maximum use of technology within the economic capability of the owner or operator; and (2) will result in reasonable further progress toward the elimination of the discharge of pollutants.

"(d) Any effluent limitation required by paragraph (2) of subsection (b) of this section shall be reviewed at least every five years and if appropriate, revised pursuant to the procedure established under such paragraph.

"(e) Effluent limitations established pursuant to this section or section 302 of this Act shall be applied to all point sources of discharge of pollutants in accordance with the provisions of this Act.

"(f) Notwithstanding any other provisions of this Act it shall be unlawful to discharge any radiological, chemical, or biological warfare agent or high-level radioactive waste into the navigable waters.

Section 308—Monitoring:

"Sec. 308. (a) Whenever required to carry out the objective of this Act, including but not limited to (1) developing or assisting in the development of any effluent limitation, or other limitation, prohibition, or effluent standard, pretreatment standard, or standard of performance; (2) determining whether any person is in violation of any such effluent limitation, or other limitation, prohibition or effluent standard, pretreatment standard or standard of performance; (3) any requirement established under this section; or (4) carrying out sections 305, 311, 402, and 504 of this Act—

"(A) The Administrator shall require the owner or operator of any point source to (i) establish and maintain such records, (ii) make such reports, (iii) install, use, and maintain such monitoring equipment or methods (including where appropriate, biological monitoring methods), (iv) sample such effluents (in accordance with such methods, at such locations, at such intervals, and in such manner as the Administrator shall prescribe), and (v) provide such other information as he may reasonably require; and

"(B) The Administrator or his authorized representative, upon presentation of his credentials—
"(i) shall have a right of entry to, upon, or through any premises in which an effluent

source is located or in which any records required to be maintained under clause (A) of this subsection are located, and

"(ii) may at reasonable times have access to and copy any records, inspect any monitoring equipment or method required under clause (A), and sample any effluents which the owner or operator of such source is required to sample under such clause.

"(b) Any records, reports, or information obtained under this section (1) shall, in the case, of effluent data be related to any applicable effluent limitations, toxic, pretreatment, or new source performance standards, and (2) shall be available to the public, except that upon a showing satisfactory to the Administrator by any person that records, reports, or information, or particular part thereof (other than effluent data), to which the Administrator has access under this section, if made public would divulge methods or processes entitled to protection as trade secrets of such person, the Administrator shall consider such record, report, or information, or particular portion thereof confidential in accordance with the purposes of section 1905 of title 18 of the United States Code, except that such record, report, or information may be disclosed to other officers, employees, or authorized representatives of the United States concerned with carrying out this Act or when relevant in any proceeding under this Act.

"(c) Each State may develop and submit to the Administrator procedures under State law for inspection, monitoring, and entry with respect to point sources located in such State. If the Administrator finds that the procedures and the law of any State relating to inspection, monitoring, and entry are applicable to at least the same extent as those required by this section, such State is authorized to apply and enforce its procedures for inspection, monitoring and entry with respect to point sources located in such State (except with respect to point sources owned or operated by the United States).

Section 405 – Disposal of sewage sludge:

"Sec. 405 (a) Notwithstanding any other provision of this Act or of any other law, in any case where the disposal of sewage sludge resulting from the operation of a treatment works as defined in section 212, of this Act (including the removal of in-place sewage sludge from one location and its deposit at another location) would result in any pollutant from such sewage entering the navigable waters, such disposal is prohibited except in accordance with a permit issued by the Administrator under this section.

"(b) The Administrator shall issue regulations governing the issuance of permits for the disposal of sewage sludge subject to this section. Such regulations shall require the application to such disposal of each criterion, factor, procedure, and requirement applicable to a permit issued under section 402 of this title, as the Administrator determines necessary to carry out the objective of this Act.

"(c) Each State desiring to administer its own permit program for disposal of sewage sludge within its jurisdiction may do so if upon submission of such program the Administrator determines such program is adequate to carry out the objective of this Act."

APPENDIX C

Text of Memo From John Quarles

UNITED STATES ENVIRONMENTAL PROTECTION AGENCY

SUBJECT: Land Treatment   DATE: November 1, 1974
FROM: Deputy Administrator /s/ John Quarles
TO: Regional Administrators

The purpose of this memorandum is to express my concern that EPA must do a better job in assuming that land treatment is given full and adequate consideration as a possible method for municipal sewage disposal in projects funded with Federal grants.

Land application of wastewaters is practiced successfully and extensively in the United States. Many land treatment systems have been in continuous use since 1900. It is apparent from this long-term experience and documented research work that land treatment technology is a viable alternative to be considered as part of waste management systems.

In section 201 of the Federal Water Pollution Control Act Amendments of 1972, it declares that:

"Waste treatment management plans and practices shall provide for the application of the best practicable waste treatment technology before any discharge into receiving waters, including reclaiming and recycling of water, and confined disposal of pollutants so they will not migrate to cause water or other environmental pollution and shall provide for consideration of advance waste treatment techniques."

Pursuant to section 304(d)(2), which directs EPA to publish information on alternative treatment management techniques and systems available to implement section 201, the document "Alternative Waste Management Techniques for Best Practicable Waste Treatment" was published. Therein it considers land application as a viable alternative for best practicable waste treatment.

In addition, the Cost-Effectiveness Analysis Regulations which apply to all projects subject to best practicable treatment state that:

"All feasible alternative waste management systems shall be initially identified. These alternatives should include systems discharging to receiving waters, systems using land or surface disposal techniques, and systems employing the reuse of wastewater."

The above requirements shall be met for all projects awarded after June 30, 1974. This means that land treatment must be considered in the basic selection of method for waste treatment.

I urge that you ascertain that your regional review of application for construction of publicly-owned treatment works require that land application be considered as an alternative waste management system. If it can be demonstrated that land treatment is the most cost-effective alternative, is consistent with the environmental assessment, and in other aspects satisfies applicable tests, the Region should insist that land treatment be used and should refuse to fund projects using other systems of waste treatment.

Your director of Water Programs Division has received the draft document "Evaluation of Land Application Systems." This document should be utilized during the review process. Additional assistance can be obtained by contacting the Municipal Construction Division (OWPO), the Municipal Technology Division (ORD), or the Robert S. Kerr Laboratory (RD).

In order to promulgate proper consideration of land treatment systems by future grant applicants I suggest that the Regional Office provide opportunity for public awareness of land treatment technology. As an example, Region III is planning a two day symposium November 20-31, 1974, at the University of Delaware to highlight land application technology. The idea for the symposium originated in the Regional Office and was planned cooperatively between the regional staff and Office of Water Program Operations headquarters staff. The objective of the symposium is to clarify the technical and policy issues involved and to chart directions for future decisions on land treatment techniques. The symposium will provide useful information to over 300 engineers, scientists, public officials and private citizens. This technique or a similar one could be used by your region to emphasize consideration of land treatment.

APPENDIX D

National Interim Primary Drinking Water Regulations for Groundwater

Case 1: The groundwater can potentially be used for drinking water supply.

(1) The maximum contaminant levels for inorganic chemicals and organic chemicals specified

in the National Interim Primary Drinking Water Regulations (40 CFR 141) (Appendix D) for drinking water supply systems should not be exceeded except as indicated below (see Note 1).

(2) If the existing concentration of a parameter exceeds the maximum contaminant levels for inorganic chemicals or organic chemicals, there should not be an increase in the concentration of that parameter due to land application of wastewater.

Case II: The groundwater is used for drinking water supply.

(1) The criteria for Case I should be met.

(2) The maximum microbiological contaminant levels for drinking water supply systems specified in the National Interim Primary Drinking Water Regulations (40 CFR 141) (Appendix D) should not be exceeded in cases where the groundwater is used without disinfection (see Note 1).

Case III: Uses other than drinking water supply.

(1) Groundwater criteria should be established by the Regional Administrator based on the present or potential use of the groundwater.

The Regional Administrator in conjunction with the appropriate State officials and the grantee shall determine on a site-by-site basis the areas in the vicinity of a specific land application site where the criteria in Case I, II, and III shall apply. Specifically determined shall be the monitoring requirements appropriate for the project site. This determination shall be made with the objective of protecting the groundwater for use as a drinking water supply and/or other designated uses as appropriate and preventing irrevocable damage to groundwater. Requirements shall include provisions for monitoring the effect on the native groundwater.

(C) Alternatives Employing Reuse. The total quantity of any pollutant in the effluent from a reuse project which is directly attributable to the effluent from a publicly-owned treatment works shall not exceed that which would have been allowed under Paragraphs (A) and (B) above.

Note 1.—Any amendments of the National Interim Primary Drinking Water Regulations and National Revised Primary Drinking Water Regulations hereafter issued by EPA prescribing standards for public water system relating to inorganic chemicals, organic chemicals or microbiological contamination shall automatically apply in the same manner as the National Interim Primary Drinking Water Regulations.

Groundwater Requirements

The following maximum contaminant levels contained in the National Interim Primary Drinking Water Regulations (40 CFR 141) are reprinted for convenience and clarity. The National Interim Primary Drinking Water Regulations were published in final form in the Federal Register on December 24, 1975. In accordance with the criteria for best practicable waste treatment, 40 CFR 141 should be consulted in its entirety when applying the standards contained therein to wastewater treatment systems employing land application techniques and land utilization practices.

Maximum Contaminant levels for inorganic chemicals. The following are the maximum levels of inorganic chemicals other than fluoride:

Contaminant:	Level (milligrams per liter)
Arsenic	0.05
Barium	1.
Cadmium	0.010
Chromium	0.05
Lead	0.05
Mercury	0.002
Nitrate (as N)	10.
Selenium	0.01
Silver	0.05

The maximum contaminant levels for fluoride are:

Temperature degrees Fahrenheit[1]	Degrees Celsius	Level (milligrams per liter)
53.7 and below	12 and below	2.4
53.8 to 58.3	12.1 to 14.6	2.2
58.4 to 63.8	14.7 to 17.6	2.0
63.9 to 70.6	17.7 to 21.4	1.8
70.7 to 79.2	21.5 to 26.2	1.6
79.3 to 90.5	26.3 to 32.5	1.4

[1] Annual average of the maximum daily air temperature.

Maximum contaminant levels for organic chemicals. The following are the maximum contaminant levels for organic chemicals:

	Level (milligram per liter)
(a) Chlorinated hydrocarbons:	
Endrin (1,2,3,4,10,10-Hexachloro 6,7- epoxy- 1,4,4a,5,6,7,8,8a-octahydro-1,4,-endo, endo-5,8,-dimethano naphthalene)	0.0002
Lindane (1,2,3,4,5,6,-Hexachlorocyclohexane, gamma isomer)	0.004
Methoxychlor (1,1,1-Trichloro-2, 2-bis [p-methoxyphenyl] ethane	0.1
Toxaphene ($C_{10}H_{10}Cl_8$-Technical chlorinated Technical chlorinated camphene, 67 to 69 percent chlorine	0.005
(b) Chlorophenoxys:	
2,4-D (2,4-Dichlorophenoxyacetic acid	0.1
2,4,5-TP Silve (2,4,5-Trichlorophenoxypropionic acid)	0.01

Maximum microbiological contaminant levels. The maximum contaminant levels for coliform bacteria, applicable to community water systems and non-community water systems are as follows:

(a) When the membrane filter technique pursuant to 141.21(a) is used, the number of coliform bacteria shall not exceed any of the following:

(1) One per 100 milliliters as the arithmetic mean of all samples examined per month pursuant to 141.21(b) or (c):

(2) Four per 100 milliliters in more than one sample when less than 20 are examined per month; or

(3) Four per 100 milliliters to more than five percent of the samples when 20 or more are examined per month.

(b)(1) When the fermentation tube method and 10 milliliter standard portions pursuant to 141.21(a) are used, coliform bacteria shall not be present in any of the following:

(i) More than 10 percent of the portions in any month pursuant to 141.21 (b) or (c):

(ii) Three or more portions in more than one sample when less than 20 samples are examined per month; or

(iii) Three or more portions in more than five percent of the samples when 20 or more samples are examined per month.

(2) When the fermentation tube method and 100 milliliter standard portions pursuant to 141.21(a) are used coliform bacteria shall not be present in any of the following:

(i) More than 60 percent of the portions in any month pursuant to 141.21(b) or (c):

(ii) Five portions in more than one sample when less than five samples are examined per month; or

(iii) Five portions in more than 20 percent of the samples when five or more samples are examined per month.

(c) For community or non-community systems that are required to sample at a rate of less than 4 per month, compliance with Paragraphs (a), (b)(1), or (2) shall be based upon sampling during a 3 month period, except that, at the discretion of the State compliance may be based upon sampling during a one month period.

Source: Federal Register 41(29): 6190–6191

APPENDIX E

The National Environmental Policy Act of 1969
Introduction and Title 1

An act to establish a national policy for the environment, to provide for the establishment of a Council on Environmental Quality, and for other purposes.

Be it enacted by the Senate and House of Representatives of the United States of America in Congress assembled, that this Act may be cited as the "National Environmental Policy Act of 1969."

PURPOSE

Sec. 2. The purposes of this Act are: To declare a national policy which will encourage productive and enjoyable harmony between man and his environment; to promote efforts which will prevent or eliminate damage to the environment and biosphere and stimulate the health and welfare of man; to enrich the understanding of the ecological systems and natural resources important to the Nation; and to establish a Council on Environmental Quality.

TITLE I

Declaration of National Environmental Policy

Sec. 101. (a) The Congress, recognizing the profound impact of man's activity on the interrelations of all components of the natural growth, high-density urbanization, industrial expansion, resource exploitation, and new and expanding technological advances and recognizing further the critical importance of restoring and maintaining environmental quality to the overall welfare and development of man, declares that it is the continuing policy of the Federal Government, in cooperation with State and local governments, and other concerned public and private organizations, to use all practicable means and measures, including financial and technical assistance, in a manner calculated to foster and promote the general welfare, to create and maintain conditions under which man and nature can exist in productive harmony, and fulfill the social, economic, and other requirements of present and future generations of Americans.

(b) In order to carry out the policy set forth in this Act, it is the continuing responsibility of the Federal Government to use all practicable means, consistent with other essential considerations of national policy, to improve and coordinate Federal plans, functions, programs, and resources to the end that the Nation may—

(1) Fulfill the responsibilities of each generation as trustee of the environment for succeeding generations;

(2) Assure for all Americans safe, healthful, productive, and esthetically and culturally pleasing surroundings;

(3) Attain the widest range of beneficial uses of the environment without degradation, risk to health or safety, or other undesirable and unintended consequences;

(4) Preserve important historic, cultural, and natural aspects of our national heritage, and maintain, wherever possible, an environment which supports diversity, and variety of individual choice:

(5) Achieve a balance between population and resource use which will permit high standards of living and a wide sharing of life's amenities; and

(6) Enhance the quality of renewable resources and approach the maximum attainable recycling of depletable resources.

(c) The Congress recognizes that each person should enjoy a healthful environment and that each person has a responsibility to contribute to the preservation and enhancement of the environment.

Sec. 102. The Congress authorizes and directs that, to the fullest extent possible: (1) the policies, regulations, and public laws of the United States shall be interpreted and administered in accordance with the policies set forth in this Act, and (2) all agencies of the Federal Government shall—

(A) Utilize a systematic interdisciplinary approach which will insure the integrated use of the natural and social sciences and the environmental design arts in planning and in decision-making which may have an impact on man's environment;

(B) Identify and develop methods and procedures, in consultation with the Council on Environmental Quality established by Title II of this Act, which will insure that presently unquantified environmental amenities and values may be given appropriate consideration in decision-making along with economic and technical considerations;

(C) Include in every recommendation or report on proposals for legislation and other major Federal actions significantly affecting the quality of the human environment, a detailed statement by the responsible official on—

(i) The environmental impact of the proposed action,

(ii) Any adverse environmental effects which cannot be avoided should the proposal be implemented,

(iii) Alternatives to the proposed action,

(iv) The relationship between local short-term uses of man's environment and the maintenance and enhancement of long-term productivity, and

(v) Any irreversible and irretrievable commitments of resources which would be involved in the proposed action should it be implemented. Prior to making any detailed statement, the responsible Federal official shall consult with and obtain the comments of any Federal agency which has jurisdiction by law or special expertise with respect to any environmental impact involved. Copies of such statements and the comments and views of the appropriate Federal, State, and local agencies, which are authorized to develop and enforce environmental standards, shall be made available to the President, the Council on Environmental Quality and to the public as provided by section 552 of Title 5, United States Code, and shall accompany the proposal through the existing agency review processes;

(D) Study, develop, and describe appropriate alternatives to recommended courses of action in any proposal which involves unresolved conflicts concerning alternative uses of available resources;

(E) Recognize the worldwide and long-range character of environmental problems and, where consistent with the foreign policy of the United States, lend appropriate support to initiatives, resolutions, and programs designed to maximize international cooperation in anticipating and preventing a decline in the quality of mankind's world environment;

(F) Make available to States, counties, municipalities, institutions, and individuals, advice and information useful in restoring, maintaining, and enhancing the quality of the environment;

(G) Initiate and utilize ecological information in the planning and development of resource-oriented projects; and

(H) Assist the Council on Environmental Quality established by Title II of this Act.

APPENDIX F

Resource Conservation and Recovery Act of 1976

OBJECTIVES:

Sec. 1003. The objectives of this Act are to promote the protection of health and the environment and to conserve valuable material and energy resources by—

"(1) providing technical and financial assistance to State and local governments and interstate agencies for the development of solid waste management plans (including resource recovery and resource conservation systems) which will promote improved solid waste management techniques (including more effective organizational arrangements), new and improved methods of collection, separation, and recovery of solid waste, and the environmentally safe disposal of nonrecoverable residues;

"(2) providing training grants in occupations involving the design, operation, and maintenance of solid waste disposal systems;

"(3) prohibiting future open dumping on the land and requiring the conversion of existing open dumps to facilities which do not pose a danger to the environment or to health;

"(4) regulating the treatment, storage, transportation, and disposal of hazardous wastes which have adverse effects on health and the environment;

"(5) providing for the promulgation of guidelines for solid waste collection, transport, separation, recovery, and disposal practices and systems;

"(6) promoting a national research and development program for improved solid waste management and resource conservation techniques, more effective organizational arrangements, and new and improved methods of collection, separation, and recovery, and recycling of solid wastes and environmentally safe disposal of nonrecoverable residues;

"(7) promoting the demonstration, construction, and application of solid waste management, resource recovery, and resource conservation systems which perserve and enhance the quality of air, water, and land resources; and

"(8) establishing a cooperative effort among the Federal, State, and local governments and private enterprise in order to recover valuable materials and energy from solid waste.

DEFINITIONS:
Sec. 1004. As used in this Act:

"(3) The term 'disposal' means the discharge, deposit, injection, dumping, spilling, leaking, or placing of any solid waste or hazardous waste into or on any land or water so that such solid waste or hazardous waste or any constituent thereof may enter the environment or be emitted into the air or discharged into any waters, including groundwaters.

"(5) The term 'hazardous waste' means a solid waste, or combination of solid wastes, which because of its quantity, concentration, or physical, chemical, or infectious characteristics may—

"(A) cause, or significantly contribute to an increase in mortality or an increase in serious irreversible, or incapacitating reversible, illness; or

"(B) pose a substantial present or potential hazard to human health or the environment when improperly treated, stored, transported, or disposed of, or otherwise managed.

"(26A) The term 'sludge' means any solid, semisolid or liquid waste generated from a municipal, commercial, or industrial wastewater treatment plant, water supply treatment plant, or air pollution control facility or any other such waste having similar characteristics and effects.

"(27) The term 'solid waste' means any garbage, refuse, sludge from a waste treatment plant, water supply treatment plant, or air pollution control facility and other discarded material, including solid, liquid, semisolid, or contained gaseous material resulting from industrial, commercial, mining, and agricultural operations, and from community activities, but does not include solid or dissolved material in domestic sewage, or solid or dissolved materials in irrigation return flows or industrial discharges which are point sources subject to permits under section 402 of the Federal Water Pollution Control Act, as amended (86 Stat. 880), or source, special nuclear, or byproduct material as defined by the Atomic Energy Act of 1954, as amended (68 Stat. 923).

"(29) The term 'solid waste management facility' includes (A) any resource recovery system or component thereof, (B) any system, program, of facility for resource conservation, and (C) any facility for the treatment of solid wastes, including hazardous wastes, whether such facility is associated with facilities generating such wastes or otherwise.

IDENTIFICATION AND LISTING OF HAZARDOUS WASTE:

"Sec. 3001. (a) CRITERIA FOR IDENTIFICATION OR LISTING.—Not later than eighteen months after the date of the enactment of this Act, the Administrator shall, after notice and opportunity for public hearing and after consultation with appropriate Federal and State agencies, develop and promulgate criteria for identifying the characteristics of hazardous waste, and for listing hazardous waste, which should be subject to the provisions of this subtitle, taking into account toxicity, persistence, and degradability in nature, potential for accumulation in tissue, and other related factors such as flammability, corrosiveness, and other hazardous characteristics. Such criteria shall be revised from time to time as may be appropriate.

"(b) IDENTIFICATION AND LISTING.—Not later than eighteen months after the date of enactment of this section, and after notice and opportunity for public hearing, the Administrator shall promulgate regulations identifying the characteristics of hazardous waste, and listing particular hazardous wastes (within the meaning of section 1004(5)), which shall be subject to the provisions of this subtitle. Such regulations shall be based on the criteria promulgated under subsection (a) and shall be revised from time to time thereafter as may be appropriate.

RESEARCH, DEMONSTRATIONS, TRAINING, AND OTHER ACTIVITIES:

"Sec. 8001.   (a) GENERAL AUTHORITY.—The Administrator, alone or after consultation with the Administrator of the Federal Energy Administration, the Administrator of the Energy Research and Development Administration, or the Chairman of the Federal Power Commission, shall conduct, and encourage, cooperate with, and render financial and other assistance to appropriate public (whether Federal, State, interstate, or local) authorities, agencies, and institutions, private agencies and institution, and individuals in the conduct of, and promote the coordination of, research, investigations, experiments, training, demonstrations, surveys, public education programs, and studies relating to—

"(1) any adverse health and welfare effects of the release into the environment of material present in solid waste, and methods to eliminate such effects;

"(2) the operation and financing of solid waste disposal programs;

"(10) improvements in land disposal practices for solid waste (including sludge) which may reduce the adverse environmental effects of such disposal and other aspects of solid waste disposal on land, including means for reducing the harmful environmental effects of earlier and existing landfills, means for restoring areas damaged by such earlier or existing landfills, means for rendering landfills safe for purposes of construction and other uses, and techniques of recovering materials and energy from landfills.

SPECIAL STUDIES; PLANS FOR RESEARCH, DEVELOPMENT, AND DEMONSTRATIONS:

"Sec. 8002. (g) SLUDGE.—The Administrator shall undertake a comprehensive study and publish a report on sludge. Such study shall include an analysis of—

"(1) what types of solid waste (including but not limited to sewage and pollution treatment residues and other residues from industrial operations such as extraction of oil from shale liquefaction and gasification of coal and coal slurry pipeline operations) shall be classified as sludge;

"(2) the effects of air and water pollution legislation on the creation of large volumes of sludge;

"(3) the amounts of sludge originating in each State and in each industry producing sludge.

"(4) methods of disposal of such sludge, including the cost, efficiency, and effectiveness of such methods;

"(5) alternative methods for the use of sludge, including agricultural applications of sludge and energy recovery from sludge."

APPENDIX G

Addresses for State Guidelines on Land Treatment

Guidelines for land application of wastes vary from one state to another. For the most up-to-date information about guidelines and regulations on land treatment of wastes in each particular state, the following agencies should be contacted. It may be useful to compare your state's guidelines with those of another. Examining other states' guidelines may be especially helpful if your state has no specific guidelines.

This list of names and addresses is current as of September, 1977. (States and the appropriate agency will be listed in alphabetical order)

Alabama

James W. Warr
Chief Administrative Officer
Water Improvement Commission
State of Alabama
Perry Hill Office Park
3815 Interstate Court
Montgomery, AL 36109

Alaska

Johnathan W. Scribner, Dir.
Water Programs, Department of Environ-
   mental Conservation
Pouch O
Juneau, AK 99811

Arizona

Wm. H. Shafer, Assistant Chief
Technical Services & Support
Dept. of Health Services
Bureau of Water Quality Control
1740 West Adams
Phoenix, AZ 85007

Arkansas

Vel Deguzman, P. F.
Arkansas Dept. Pollution Control & Ecology
P.O. Box 9853
Little Rock, AR 72219

California

W. R. Attwater, Chief Coun.
State Water Resources
Control Board
P.O. Box 100
Sacramento, CA 95801

Colorado

Felix L. Sparks, Director
Water Conservation Board
102 Columbine Bldg.
1845 Sherman Street
Denver, CO 80203

Connecticut

Robert B. Taylor
Director of Water Compliance & Hazardous
   Substances
State Office Building
Hartford, CT 06115

Delaware

Robert J. Zimmerman
Resource Engineer
Water Resources Section
Division of Environmental Control
Tatnall Building
Dover, DE 19901

Florida

G. J. Thabaraj, Ph.D.
Dept. of Environ. Regulation
2562 Executive Center Circle, East
Tallahassee, FL 32301

Georgia

Mr. Harold Reheis
Section Chief
Water Quality Control Section
Environmental Protection Div.
Ga. Dept. of Natural Resources
Trinity-Washington Bldg.
Atlanta, GA 30334

Hawaii

George Yuen
Director of Health
Department of Health
P.O. Box 3378
Honolulu, HI 96801

Idaho

Darrel Clapp, Supervisor
Environmental Studies
Department of Water Resources
State House
Boise, ID 83720

Illinois

Darryll Bauer, P. E.
Chairman, Committee on Sludge
Illinois Envir. Protection Agen.
2200 Churchill Road
Springfield, IL 62706

Indiana

Steve W. Kim, Chief
Division of Water Pollution Con.
State Board of Health
1330 West Michigan Street
Indianapolis, IN 46206

Iowa

Larry E. Crane
Executive Director
3920 Delaware Avenue
P.O. Box 3326
Des Moines, IA 50316

Kansas

H. A. Janzen, Chief
W. P. C. Section
Kansas Dept. of Health & Environment
Topeka, KA 66620

Kentucky

William S. Forester, Director
Dept. for Natural Resources & Environ-
   mental Protection
Bureau of Env. Protection
Frankfort, KY 40601

Louisiana

James F. Coerver, Head
Bureau of Environmental Services
Louisiana Health & Human Res.
   Administration

Division of Health
P.O. Box 60630
New Orleans, LA 70160

Maine

Frank W. Ricker
Executive Director
Soil & Water Conser. Commis.
State Office Building
Augusta, ME 04330

Maryland

Peter S. Tinsley, Hydrologist
Groundwater Permits Section
Department of Natural Resources
Tawes State Office Bldg.
Annapolis, MD 21401

Massachusetts

John R. Elwood, Supv. San. Engr.
Mass. Division of Water Poll. Control
P.O. Box 545
Westboro, MA 01581

Michigan

Paul A. Blakeslee
Water Quality Division
Mich. Dept. of Natural Res.
P.O. Box 30028
Lansing, MI 48909

Minnesota

Dale L. Wikre, Geologist
Division of Water Quality
Minnesota Poll. Control Agency
1935 West County Road B2
Roseville, MN 55113

Mississippi

Charles Chisolm
P.O. Box 827
Jackson, MS 39205

Missouri

University of Missouri Publications
B-9 Whitten Hall
Columbia, MO 65201

Montana

D. G. Willen, Chief
Water Quality Bureau
State Dept. of Health & Env. Science
Helena, MT 59601

Nebraska

Nate Beezley, P. E.
Water Pollution Control Div.
Nebraska Dept. of Environ. Con. Control
Box 94653 State House Station
Office 301 Centennial Mall South
Lincoln, NB 68509

Nevada

James B. Williams, Jr. P. E.
Department of Human Resources
Environmental Protection Ser.
Capitol Complex
Carson City, NV 89710

New Hampshire

Russell S. Bowie, Assoc. San. Eng.
N. H. WS. & P. C. C.
P.O. Box 95 105 Loudon Rd.
Concord, NH 03301

New Jersey

Haig F. Kasabach
Division of Water Resources
Dept. of Envir. Protection
P.O. Box 2809
Trenton, NJ 08625

New Mexico

Maxine S. Goad
New Mexico Environmental Improvement
    Agency
P.O. Box 2348
Santa Fe, NM 87503

New York

Frank O. Bogedain, P.E.
Division of Pure Waters
NY Department of Envir. Con.
50 Wolf Road
Albany, NY 12233

North Carolina

M. W. Puette, Enforcement Administrator
Division of Envir. Manage.
Dept. of Natural Resources
P.O. Box 27687
Raleigh, NC 27611

North Dakota

Norman L. Peterson, Director
Div. of Water Sup. & Poll. Con.
State Capitol Bldg.
Bismarck, ND 58505

Ohio

Division of Hazardous Waste Control
Ohio EPA
Box 1049
361 E. Broad St.
Columbus, OH 43216

Oklahoma

Mark S. Coleman, Director
Water Quality Man. & Research
Oklahoma State Dept. of Health
P.O. Box 53551
Oklahoma City, OK 73105

Oregon

Diarmuid F. O'Scannlain, Dir.
Dept. of Environmental Quality
1234 S.W. Morrison
Portland, OR 97205

Pennsylvania

William D. LaCour
Planning Analyst
Div. of Solid Waste Management
P.O. Box 2063
Harrisburg, PA 17120

Rhode Island

J. S. Quinn, Jr.
Room 204 Health Dept.
Providence, RI 02908

South Carolina

Roger E. Davis, P.E.
Bureau of Wastewater & Stream Quality
    Control
J. Marion Sims Bldg.
2600 Bull St.
Columbia, SC 29201

South Dakota

Tom Becker
Public Info. Specialist
Dept. of Environmental Protection
Pierre, SD 57501

Tennessee

Water Quality Control Board
Dept. of Public Health
621 Cordell Hull Bldg.
Nashville, TN 37219

Texas

Henry L. Dabney, P.E., Director
Div. of Wastewater Tech. & Surveillance
Texas Dept. of Health Resources
Austin, TX 78756

Utah

Don A. Ostler
44 Medical Drive
Salt Lake City, UT 84113

Vermont

William J. Siok, Hydrogeologist
Env. Eng. Div.
Vermont Agency of Envir. Conservation
State Office Bldg.
Montpelier, VT 05602

Virginia

William L. Magette, Engineer
State Water Control Board
2111 North Hamilton Street
P.O. Box 11143
Richmond, VA 23230

Washington

LaVerne DeNike
State of Washington
Department of Ecology
Solid Waste/Resource Recov. Div.
Olympia, WA 98504

West Virginia

William W. Bradford, P.E.
Asst. Chief, Sewage Program
Division of Sanitary Engineering
Department of Health
Charleston, WV 25305

Wisconsin

Robert W. Schaefer
Box 7921
Madison, WI 53711

Wyoming

William L. Garland, Administrator
Dept. Environmental Quality
Water Quality Division
Basement, Hathaway Building
Cheyenne, WY 82002

APPENDIX H

Addendum No. 2

To Recommended Standards for Sewage Works

Great Lakes–Upper Mississippi River Board of State Sanitary Engineers (GLUMRB)
(1968 Edition)

April 1971
Ground Disposal of Wastewaters

Interest has been expressed in the development of guidelines for engineering review of proposed projects for ground disposal of wastewaters.

There are apparently relatively few known large-scale installations of spray irrigation systems and very limited data available within the ten GLUMRB states.

The protection of groundwater and surface resources is the major concern in the development of guidelines. However, quality of groundwater discharged to surface waters also must be considered in the water quality criteria.

Practices must be established which will help prevent wastes of any nature from being introduced into the fresh groundwaters which will so change their characteristics as to make them unsuitable for potable water supply or other present and future usage.

The priority of the water usage is subject to the jurisdiction of the appropriate state and local regulatory agencies.

Preliminary Considerations

Ground disposal installations are normally used where the waste contains pollutants which can successfully be removed through distribution to the soil mantle. These pollutants can be removed through organic decomposition in the vegetation-soil complex and by adsorptive, physical, and chemical reactions with earth materials. Preliminary considerations of a site for ground disposal should be the compatibility of the waste with the organic and earth materials and the percolation rates and exchange capacity of the soils. The ground disposal of wastewater will eventually recharge the local groundwater; therefore, the quality, direction and rate of movement and local use of the groundwater, present and potential, are prime considerations in evaluating a proposed site.

It is essential to maintain an aerated zone of at least five feet and preferably more, to provide good vegetation growth conditions and removal of nutrients. It must be realized a groundwater mound will develop below after it is in use. The major factors in design of ground disposal fields are topography, soils, geology, hydrology, weather, agricultural practice, adjacent land use and equipment selection and installation.

Design Report

The design report shall include maps and diagrams as noted below. It shall also include any additional material that is pertinent about the location, geology, topography, hydrology, soils, areas for future expansion and adjacent land use.

Location

(1) A copy of the U.S.G.S. topographic map of the area ($7\frac{1}{2}$-minute series where published) showing the exact boundaries of the spray field.

(2) A topographic map of the total area owned by the applicant at a scale of approximately one inch to 50 feet. It should show all buildings, the waste disposal system, the spray field boundaries and buffer zone. An additional map should show the spray field topography in detail with a contour interval of two feet, and include buildings and land use on adjacent lands within $\frac{1}{4}$ mile of the project boundary.

(3) All water supply wells which might be affected shall be located and identified as to uses; e.g., potable, industrial, agricultural, and class of ownership; e.g., public, private, etc.

(4) All abandoned wells, shafts, etc., shall be located and identified. Pertinent information thereon shall be furnished.

Geology

(1) The geologic formations (name) and the rock types at the site.

(2) The degree of weathering of the bedrock.

(3) The local bedrock structure including the presence of faults, fractures and joints.

(4) The character and thickness of the surficial deposits (residual soils and glacial deposit).

(5) In limestone terrain, additional information about solution openings and sinkholes is required.

(6) The source of the above information must be indicated.

Hydrology

(1) The depth to seasonal high water table (perched and/or regional) must be given, including an indication of seasonal variations. Static water levels must be determined at each depth for each aquifer in the depth under concern. Critical slope evaluation must be given to any differences in such levels.

(2) The direction of groundwater movement and the point(s) of discharge must be shown on one of the attached maps.

(3) Chemical analyses indicating the quality of groundwater at the site must be included.

(4) Indicate the source of the above data.

(5) The following information shall be provided from existing wells and from such test wells as may be necessary:

(a) Construction details—where available: Depth, well log, pump capacity, static levels, pumping water levels, casing, grout material and such other information as may be pertinent.

(b) Groundwater quality: E.g., Nitrates, total nitrogen, chlorides, sulphates, pH, alkalinities, total hardness, coliform bacteria, etc.

(6) A minimum of one (1) groundwater monitoring well must be drilled in each dominant direction of groundwater movement and between the project site and public well(s) and/or high capacity private wells with provision for sampling at the surface of the water table and at five (5) feet below the water table at each monitoring site. The location and construction of the monitoring well(s) must be approved. These may include one or more of the test wells where appropriate.

Soils

(1) A soils map should be furnished of the spray field, indicating the various soil types. This may be included on the large-scale topographic map. Soils information can normally be secured through the USDA Soil Conservation Service.

(2) The soils should be named and their texture described.

(3) Slopes and agricultural practice on the spray field are closely related. Slopes on cultivated fields should be limited to 4% or less. Slopes on sodded fields should be limited to 8% or less. Forested slopes should be limited to 8% for year-round operation, but some seasonal operation slopes up to 14% may be acceptable.

(4) The thickness of soils should be indicated. Indicate how determined:

(5) Data should be furnished on the exchange capacity of the soils. In case of industrial wastes particularly, this information must be related to special characteristics of the wastes.

(6) Information must be furnished on the internal and surface drainage characteristics of the soil materials.

(7) Proposed application rates should take into consideration the drainage and permeability of the soils, the discharge capacity, and the distance to the water table.

Agricultural Practice

(1) The present and intended soil-crop management practices, including forestation, shall be stated.

(2) Pertinent information shall be furnished on existing drainage systems.

(3) When cultivated crops are anticipated, the kinds used and the harvesting frequency should be given; the ultimate use of the crop should also be given.

Adjacent Land Use

(1) Present and anticipated use of the adjoining lands must be indicated. This information can be provided on one of the maps and may be supplemented with notes.

(2) The plan shall show existing and proposed screens, barriers, or buffer zones to prevent blowing spray from entering adjacent land areas.

(3) If expansion of the facility is anticipated, the lands which are likely to be used for expanded spray fields must be shown on the map.

Treatment Before Land Disposal

In general, the equivalent of secondary treatment will be required. All wastes must be amenable to treatment by the soil prior to application. All wastes to be spray irrigated shall be disinfected. Disinfection may be required for other types of irrigation. Screening shall be provided in all cases where solids are expected of a size equal to or greater than the nozzle hole diameter.

Storage shall be provided to the maximum capacity required to accommodate flows in excess of quantities to be irrigated.

Piping to Sprinklers

The piping should be so arranged to allow the irrigation pattern to be varied easily. Stationary systems are preferred; but if a moveable system is proposed, one main header must be provided with individual connections for each field and sufficient spare equipment must be available to assure non-interrupted irrigation. Facilities must be provided to allow the pipes to be completely drained at suitable points to prevent pollution and freezing.

Sprinkling System

Sprinklers must be so located as to give a non-irrigated buffer zone around the irrigated area and design of the buffer zone must consider wind transport of the wastewaters. The system shall be designed to provide an even distribution over the entire field.

The application rate must be selected low enough to allow the waters to percolate into the soil and to assure proper residency within the soil mantle. Proposed application rates will not be accepted without substantiating data.

In general, sufficient monitoring controls should be provided to indicate the degree of efficiency with which the sprinklers are working. A pressure gauge and flow meter should be provided.

Runoff

The system shall be designed to prevent surface runoff from entering or leaving the project site.

Fencing

The project area shall be enclosed with a suitable fence to preclude livestock and discourage trespassing. A vehicle access gate of sufficient width to accommodate mowing equipment should be provided. All access gates should be provided with locks.

Warning Signs

Appropriate signs should be provided along the fence around the project boundaries to designate the nature of the facility and advise against trespassing.

Bibliography

Agricultural Utilization of Sewage Effluent and Sludge, an Annotated Bibliography, Federal Water Pollution Control Administration, U.S. Department of the Interior, Jan., 1968.

APPENDIX J

Text of Memo From Douglas Costle

UNITED STATES ENVIRONMENTAL PROTECTION AGENCY

SUBJECT: Land Treatment   DATE: October 3, 1977
FROM: The administrator /s/ Douglas Costle
TO: Assistant Administrators (Regions I–X)
         Regional Administrators (Regions I–X)

President Carter's recent Environmental Message to the Congress emphasized the design and construction of cost-effective publicly owned wastewater treatment facilities that encourage water conservation as well as adequately treat wastewater. This serves to strengthen the encouragement under the Federal Water Pollution Control Act Amendments of 1972 (P.L. 92-500) to consider wastewater reclamation and recycling by land treatment processes.

At the time P.L. 92-500 was enacted, it was the intent of Congress to encourage to the extent possible the development of wastewater management policies that are consistent with the fundamental ecological principle that all materials should be returned to the cycles from which they were generated. Particular attention should be given to wastewater treatment processes which renovate and reuse wastewater as well as recycle the organic matter and nutrients in a beneficial manner. *Therefore, the Agency will press vigorously for publicly owned treatment works to utilize land treatment processes to reclaim and recycle municipal wastewater.*

RATIONALE

Land treatment systems involve the use of plants and the soil to remove previously unwanted contaminants from wastewaters. Land treatment is capable of achieving removal levels comparable to the best available advanced wastewater treatment technologies while achieving additional benefits. The recovery and beneficial reuse of wastewater and its nutrient resources through crop production, as well as wastewater treatment and reclamation, allow land treatment systems to accomplish far more than most conventional treatment and discharge alternatives.

The application of wastewater on land is a practice that has been used for many decades; however, recycling and reclaiming wastewater that may involve the planned recovery of nutrient resources as part of a designed wastewater treatment facility is a relatively new technique. One of the first such projects was the large scale Muskegon, Michigan, land treatment demonstration project funded under the Federal Water Pollution Control Act Amendments of 1966 (P.L. 84-660), which began operations in May 1974.

Reliable wastewater treatment processes that utilize land treatment concepts to recycle resources through agriculture, silviculture and aquaculture practices are available. The technology for planning, designing, constructing and operating land treatment facilities is adequate to meet both 1983 and 1985 requirements and goals of P.L. 92-500.

Land treatment is also presently in extensive use for treatment of many industrial wastewaters, particularly those with easily degraded organics such as food processing. Adoption of suitable in-plant pretreatment for the removal of excessive metals and toxic substances would expand the potential for land treatment of industrial wastewater and further enhance the potential for utilization of municipal wastewater and sludges for agricultural purposes.

APPROACH

Because land treatment processes contribute to the reclamation and recycling requirements of P.L. 92-500, they should be preferentially considered as an alternative wastewater management technology. Such consideration is particularly critical for smaller communities. While it is recognized that acceptance is not universal, the utilization of land treatment systems has the potential for saving billions of dollars. This will benefit not only the nationwide water pollution control program, but will also provide an additional mechanism for the recovery and recycling of wastewater as a resource.

EPA currently requires each applicant for construction grant funds to make a conscientious analysis of wastewater management alternatives with the burden upon the applicant to examine all available alternative technologies. *Therefore, if a method that encourages water conservation, wastewater reclamation and reuse is not recommended, the applicant should be required to provide complete justification for the rejection of land treatment.*

Imposition of stringent wastewater treatment requirements prior to land application has quite often nullified the cost-effectiveness of land treatment processes in the past. We must ensure that appropriate Federal, State and local requirements and regulations are imposed at the proper point in the treatment system and are not used in a manner that may arbitrarily block land treatment projects. *Whenever States insist upon placing unnecessarily stringent preapplication treatment requirements upon land treatment, such as requiring EPA secondary effluent quality in all cases prior to application on the land, the unnecessary wastewater treatment facilities will not be funded by EPA.* This should encourage the States to re-examine and revise their criteria, and so reduce the cost burden, especially to small communities, for construction and operation of unnecessary or too costly facilities. The reduction of potentially toxic metals and organics in industrial discharges to municipal systems often is critical to the success of land treatment. The development and enforcement at the local level of pretreatment standards that are consistent with national pretreatment standards should be required as an integral part of any consideration or final selection of land treatment alternatives. In addition, land treatment alternatives must be fully coordinated with on-going areawide planning under section 208 of the Act. Section 208 agencies should be involved in the review and development of land treatment options.

Research will be continued to further improve criteria for preapplication treatment and other aspects of land treatment processes. This will add to our knowledge and reduce the uncertainties about health and environmental factors. I am confident, however, that land treatment of municipal wastewaters can be accomplished without adverse effects on human health if proper consideration is given to design and management of the system.

INTER-OFFICE COORDINATION

The implementation of more recent mandates from the Safe Drinking Water Act (P.L. 93-532), the Toxic Substances Control Act (P.L. 94-469), and the Resource Conservation and Recovery Act of 1976 (P.L. 94-580) must be closely coordinated with the earlier mandate to recycle wastes and fully evaluate land treatment in P.L. 92-500. Agencywide coordination is especially important to the proper management of section 201 of P.L. 92-500, because the construction and operation of thousands of POTW's involve such a broad spectrum of environmental issues. A concerted effort must be made to avoid unilateral actions, or even the appearance of unilateral actions, which satisfy a particular mandate of one Act while inadvertently conflicting with a major Agency policy based upon another Act. The intention of P.L. 92-500, as it concerns land treatment, is compatible with the pertinent aspects of more recent environmental legislation.

ACTION REQUIRED

Each of you must exert maximum effort to ensure that the actions of your staffs reflect clearly visible encouragement of wastewater reclamation and recycling of pollutants through land treatment processes in order to move toward the national goals of conserving water and eliminating the discharge of pollutants in navigable waters by 1985.

This policy will apply to all future municipal construction grant activities, as well as all current grant applications in the Step 1 category that have not been approved as of this date. Detailed information and guidance for implementation of this policy is under preparation and will be issued in the near future.

Module I-10

CASE STUDIES REVIEWED

SUMMARY

This module provides information about 14 existing land application systems. References are cited which may be used to examine 100 or more other sites.

CONTENTS

OBJECTIVES

Upon completion of this module the reader should be able to:

1. Use the information given in this module or in the referenced literature to supplement the ideas and insights expanded on in other modules.
2. Use the basic format of this module to build up a private library of abstracts of land application systems.

3. Arrive at a number of specific, pertinent questions that should appear in every report of land application systems, and evaluate reports in terms of the adequacy or inadequacy of each report.

INTRODUCTION

This module is a compendium of descriptions of 14 land application sites in the United States and abroad. It is designed as background information and as a reference of specific examples to illustrate basic concepts of land treatment.

It is not always easy for readers to determine how various ideas blend together and work in a real system. Therefore, this module is designed to review real land application systems and to give the readers an opportunity to evaluate these systems in relation to the information given in other modules.

As shown in Figure 1, there are more than 360 land application systems in the United States and many more are in the planning stage. This is a conservative estimate. This module documents 14 of those sites, each site exemplifying a unique problem. Abstracts of those cases appear in this module. The bibliography gives sources of information for compiling similar abstracts on more than 100 land application sites. The reader may wish to expand this file of actual systems by consulting these references.

Probably the best single source of information on long-term use of land application technology is the publication *Land Application of Sewage Effluents and Sludges: Selected Abstracts*, compiled and published by the EPA. The abstracts are arranged in chronological groupings and cross-referenced. This reference contains a large number of interesting systems built prior to 1974. A short summary of systems built between 1973 and 1976 entitled "Selected Recent Reports on Land Application of Municipal Wastewaters," is available from the EPA. The 1973 report *Survey of Facilities Using Land Application of Wastewater* is also useful.

Figure 1. Locations of the more than 360 land application sites in the United States.

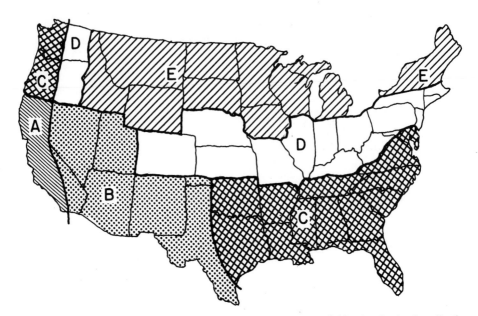

Figure 2. The United States is divided into five general climate zones useful in planning land application systems (after Pound and Crites, 1973).

It contains some general discussion of the techniques involved as well as case histories of domestic and industrial applications.

Figure 2 illustrates the general climatic zones of the United States which are used in each case history description in this module. Reference to this climatic data is included in the "Case Study Cover Sheet" which introduces each of the 14 examples. Where foreign sites are documented, an attempt has been made to relate these sites to the domestic climatic zones of Figure 2.

Werribee Farm System Melbourne, Australia

The Werribee Farm System is one of seven sewage treatment facilities serving Melbourne, Australia. It is widely known as a large-scale land application system that has handled raw municipal sewage for more than 75 years. Until the mid 1970s, 95% of the sewered effluent of Melbourne went to the Werribee Farm. Melbourne officials are very satisfied and seek to use land application in connection with as many of their facilities as possible. Urban sprawl, however, is decreasing available lands so secondary pretreatment is used to decrease needed acreage for other sites. Of the 27,000 acres, 17,000 acres are used for some form of waste treatment. The facility is predominantly permanent pastures with some three quarters of its land doubling as wild bird preserves. The remaining 10,000 acres are used for roads, houses, animal and machinery shelter, dry grazing, yards and other purposes.

> *The land application system serving Melbourne, Australia covers over 17,000 acres. Although highly successful for more than 75 years, the system is being encroached upon by urban development. Pretreatment and lagooning of some waste flow is now being employed to decrease the land area required for treatment.*

*This and other italicized summaries are intended to highlight key ideas, provide a basis for later review or to aid in skimming sections that are relatively familiar. They can be ignored in a complete reading of the text.

CASE STUDY COVER SHEET

SYSTEM Werribee Farm System   1897
              (Name)   (Date started)

LOCATION Melbourne, Australia
                                                          (Person involved)

FACILITY DESCRIPTION raw sewage   flood irrigation & overland flow
                          (waste classification)   (application system(s))

APPLICATION 4 in./day; Total 44 in/yr; 1 day apply, 17-19 day rest
                  (rate)   (schedule)

CROP(S) Pastureland grasses: Cattle, sheep, some horses

PRETREATMENT Screening

VOLUME TREATED 150 mgd
                                        similar to
WORKING YEAR 12 mo. CLIMATE ZONE   D

SOIL Silt-clay loam

COST U.S. $1.53 (per capita) per year

LAND AREA 27,000 acre

STORAGE CAPACITY

COMMENT: Old and very successful land application system handling large volumes

          of raw sewage. No health problems to animals or 17 families residing

          in area. Animal sales bring good income. Odor problems are encoun-

          tered as system suffers urban encroachment. Not a research project

          but has 31 test wells and specific monitoring schedule for water and

          livestock. Soils and vegetation are monitored occasionally. Operates

          as flood irrigation in summer, overland flow in winter. Increasing

          use of aerobic and anaerobic lagoons for wastewater treatment in

          recent years due to limitation in available land area, and encroaching

          urbanization.

REFERENCES: Seabrook, B.L. 1975. Land application of wastewater in
              Australia. The Werribee farm system. Prepared for U.S. EPA
              Municipal Construction Division, Office of Water Program Opera-
              tions (May). 27 p.

              Johnson, R. D., R. L. Jones, T. D. Hinesly, D. J. David.
              1974. Selected chemical characteristics of soil, forage
              and drainage water from the sewage farm serving Melbourne,
              Australia. Prepared for the Dept. of Army Corps of
              Engineers. 54 p.

              Searle, S. S. and C. F. Kirby. 1972 (fall). Waste into
              wealth. Water Spectrum, U.S. Army Corps of Engineers.
              15-21.

Each pasture is 20 acres and is divided into 50 bays by low check banks, subsoiled, graded, and sown with selected grasses (Johnson, *et al.*, 1974). The grasses are grazed by 20,000 cattle and 10,000 sheep. Summer application consists of flooding 600 acres of bays daily to 4 inches, then allowing a 17-19 day "rest" period. The organic load averages about 30 lb/acre-day BOD. The Werribee Farm System is underdrained, with the effluent (high in K) discharged into Port Phillip Bay. Shallow lagoon storage is being phased out. Winter treatment is by overland flow over 3,472 acres with excess being treated in 3,393 acres of anaerobic and aerobic lagoons. A schematic presentation of the system is given in Figure 3.

Surface soil is slightly acid red-brown silty clay. Soil becomes calcareous at about 12 inches with clay:silt:sand being about 35:45:20. The C.E.C. of the 1-7 inch layer of control soil is 15 meq/100 g and 10-25 meq/100 g for sewage amended soil. Infiltration capacity is about 2 in./day. About 144 mgd (peak flows up to 300 mgd) arrive at the Werribee Farm. Annual rainfall averages 19 inches of which 12.5 inches fall during the irrigation season. Evapotranspiration accounts for about 35.6 inches in the same period, suggesting that about half of the annual application of 44 inches of sewage water is evaporated.

Sales of sheep and beef return $675,000 (U.S.)/year to Werribee. Animals are government inspected before sale and rejection rates are less than or equal to rates of animals grazed on untreated pastures. Families living within the Werribee Farm area exhibit very good health records.

Analyses of soils and vegetation in 1924 and again in 1972 suggest that organic nitrogen in topsoils has increased from roughly 0.36 to 1.12% and phosphorus from roughly 0.08 to 0.175% (normal ranges for agricultural soils are 0.02-0.50% N and 0.01-0.40% P). Carbon content of irrigated topsoils has increased from 3.7 to 10.0%. At the same time the C/N ratio of surface soils has decreased from about 13/1 to 10/1. The average pH of soils has decreased from 7.5 to 6.2 but ranges widely (1.1 to 8.4) in irrigated soils. N, C and P levels in subsoils are "normal." Mn, Fe and Cr concentrations in the surface soil remain low. Pb is tightly bound in surface soils but its accumulated concentration has not exceeded the "normal range" in soils at any but one sampling site. Only at sites subjected to 60 and 73 years of application are Zn levels much above that expected in normal soils, but even there Cu concentrations remain less than the normal maximum range of soil while Ni is well within the normal range. The zinc equivalent load of soils is about 8.5% of C.E.C., exceeding recommended levels (5% at pH > 6.5) even at lower pHs, but clinical symptoms of toxication are not apparent in vegetation.

Vegetation is known to take up N, P and K from the sewage, but there is little or no change in Mg and Ca uptake. The resulting wider ratios (K/Ca and K/Mg) in forage leads to a condition

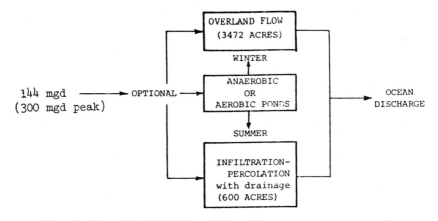

Figure 3. Schematic of the Melbourne, Australia, wastewater treatment system.

known as grass tetany ("staggers" or hypomagnesia) in animals. This requires the addition of MgO to the dry hay fed to the animals. The sodium content of grasses appears to have increased the most, reaching values above those expected in irrigated grasses. Zinc and Cu levels in foliage tissues are at the high end of the normal range, with a few just exceeding that range. Cadmium contents barely exceed levels expected in the grasses and the Zn:Cd ratio values in grasses grown on plots irrigated for 60 and 73 years are 117:1 and 160:1, respectively. Lead content of foliage does not exceed normal values.

Water renovation was intended to reduce suspended solids to < 30 mg/l and BOD to < 20 mg/l to meet Australian standards of the late 19th century, and to this end the Werribee Farm has been successful. It was not intended to achieve renovation equivalent to 1983 standards set for the United States. Nevertheless, 88% of N and 91% of P is removed from raw sewage. High K concentrations remain in the tile effluent, several times greater than the concentration of K in Port Phillip Bay. Nickel concentration is about 0.2 mg/l. From 78 to 91% of Zn, Cd, Cr and Pb is removed and Cu concentrations are reduced to less than that of seawater.

Odors remain a real problem. The odors are not oppressive: The families who chose to live within the Werribee Farm Area testify to that. But modern urbanites make unhappy neighbors for the Werribee Farm, and odor is their objection. Clearly, if raw sewage is to be treated by land application, the site will have to be remote. The alternative is to introduce pretreatment, perhaps even secondary treatment as Melbourne is beginning to do, to eliminate the odors.

As residential development increases near the Werribee Farm overland flow treatment site, odor becomes more of a problem. The system is changing from application of raw sewage to application of pretreated sewage, even up to secondary treatment.

Cape Cod Water Renovation and Retrieval System Otis Air Force Base, Cape Cod

The Otis Air Force Base waste treatment facility was built in 1942 to handle a 4 mgd flow. In 1973 Woods Hole Oceanographic Institute of Massachusetts began a research program centered on the Otis facility. In the original design, secondary effluent from a trickling filter was flooded onto 20 sand filter beds, but present loads require the use of only two filter beds at any one time on a rotational basis. One of the filter beds has been taken out of service and converted to a 0.3 MG capacity storage lagoon. The lagoon is the reservoir used to supply a newly installed spray irrigation system. The intention of the research project is to compare the extent of wastewater renovation by sand filters and spray irrigation of grasses and legume crops.

Secondary effluent from a trickling filter is flooded onto sand filter beds at the Otis Air Force base land application facility.

The waste application site includes a mass of unconsolidated gravel, sand and silt deposited by glacial outwash which is underlain by an impermeable consolidated bedrock roughly 260 feet below the surface. In a north-south direction, the bedrock remains level at an average depth of 170 feet below sea level. East of the site it dips to a depth of 400 feet below sea level.

Precipitation and its ultimate storage in groundwater is the sole source of fresh water on Cape Cod. An annual rainfall of about 2.14 million gallons per day (mgd) per square mile (45 in/yr), following transpiration losses, provides an estimated 1.07 million gallons per day per square mile to form a water table that reaches a maximum height of 60 feet above sea level north of Otis.

CASE STUDY COVER SHEET

SYSTEM Cape Cod Water Renovation and Retrieval System   1973
                        (Name)   (Date started)

LOCATION Otis Air Force Base, Cape Cod   Ralph C. Vaccaro
                                                           (person involved)

FACILITY DESCRIPTION Municipal   Spray irrigation and infiltration
                (waste classification)   (application system)

APPLICATION wide range of experimental variations applying 1-3 in./wk
                (rate)   (schedule)

CROP(S) reed canary grass, alfalfa, timothy

PRETREATMENT Imhoff-trickling filter
                    50,000 gallons per day
VOLUME TREATED (designed to treat 3.7 mgd)

WORKING YEAR 12 months   CLIMATE ZONE D
        unconsolidated gravel, sand and silt
SOIL   deposited by glacial outwash underlain
        by an impermeable consolidated bedrock
        roughly 260 ft below the surface

COST $500,000
                2.6 acres for irrigation
LAND AREA 17 acres for sand filtration

STORAGE CAPACITY 0.3 MG

COMMENT: Objective is to evaluate alternative means of wastewater treatment
          and to develop design criteria for the recharge of water of potable
          quality to the groundwater reservoir of the coastal and outwash plains
          of Cape Cod and the Islands. Features a spray irrigation system
          wherein animal forage crops are used to remove nutrients and trace
          metals from secondary effluent. Additional attention is being
          given to the existing sand filter beds which, over the past 33 years
          have provided the traditional means of disposing of secondary effluent
          from the treatment plant at Otis. Extensive monitoring includes
          seven observation wells, nine groundwater sampling wells, suction
          lysimeters, soil analyses.

REFERENCES: Mann, A.W., R.F Vaccaro, P.L. Deese. Controlled chlorination
             in agricultural systems irrigated with secondary wastewater
             effluents. Journal of Water Pollution Control Federation.
             In press.

             Mead, R. and R.F. Vaccaro. Sewage disposal in Falmouth,
             Massachusetts. III. Predicted effects of inland disposal

(continued on next page)

CASE STUDY COVER SHEET (continued)

and sea outfall on groundwater.   J. Boston Society of
Engineers 58(4): 278-297. 1971.

Kerfoot, W.B. and B.H. Ketchum.   Cape Cod wastewater renovation and retrieval system, a study of water treatment and
conservation.   Technical Report WHOI 74-13, Woods Hole
Oceanographic Institution, Woods Hole, Massachusetts. 1974.

Kerfoot, W.B., B.H. Ketchum, P. Kallio, P. Bowker, A. Mann,
C. Scolieri.   Cape Cod wastewater renovation and retrieval
system, a study of water treatment and conservation, first
year of operation.   Technical Report WHOI 75-32, Woods Hole
Oceanographic Institution, Woods Hole, Massachusetts.   1975.

Ketchum, B.H., R.F. Vaccaro, P. E. Kallio, A. Mann,
P.L. Deese, C. Palmer.   Cape Cod wastewater renovation and
retrieval system: a study in water treatment and conservation.   Technical Interim Report.   WHOI-77-32 Appendix.
Woods Hole Oceanographic Institution, Woods Hole, Massachusetts.
1977.

Ketchum, B.H., R.F. Vaccaro, P.E. Kallio, A. Mann,
P.L. Deese, C. Palmer.   Cape Cod wastewater renovation and
retrieval system: a study of water treatment and conserva-
tion.   Technical Interim Report, June 11, 1975-June 10, 1976.
WHOI-76-93, Woods Hole Oceanographic Institution, Woods Hole,
Massachusetts. 1976.

Ketchum, B.H., R.F. Vaccaro, P.E. Kallio, A. Mann,
P.L. Deese, C. Palmer, M.R. Dennett, P.C. Bowker, N. Corwin.
Cape Cod wastewater renovation and retrieval system: a study
of water treatment and conservation.   Interim Technical
Report, WHOI-77-32, Woods Hole Oceanographic Institution,
Woods Hole, Massachusetts. 1977 .

Spray irrigation plots have a surface layer of loam underlain by roughly a meter of Enfield sandy loam. Below 2 m depths, the topsoil grades from fine sandy loam to medium sand. Deep geological cores indicate a substrate of medium to coarse sand with occasional cobblestone layers to the vicinity of bedrock 258 feet below the surface.

During the history of the sewage treatment plant, in operation since 1942, over 6 billion gallons of water have been discharged onto the sand filter bed system. The area of application which was served by gravity sand filtration totals 17 acres and is divided into 22 beds. At full operation of 3.7 mgd, the application rate was 150,000 gallons per acre per day. Presently the Otis sewage treatment plant treats less than 50,000 gallons per day because of reduced personnel at the Otis base. Effluent is delivered to the filter beds by gravity mains and distributed by large wooden sluiceways. Cores taken from the beds show a layer roughly 1 foot thick of graded sand underlain by natural deposits of Enfield sandy loam, and some silt deposits within the first few feet. At greater depths, 18 to 20 feet of medium sand and cobblestone occur down to groundwater level.

To evaluate a spray irrigation cropping program for wastewater management, the pilot facility was designed to provide year-round irrigation to test the water quality effects of a holding basin, to test prechlorination before irrigation, and to compare the performance of

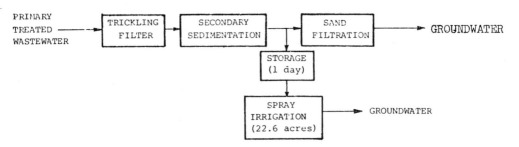

Figure 4. Presentation of the research land application facility for the Otis Air Force Base, Cape Cod, Massachusetts.

fixed versus rotary rigs for wastewater distribution. Two irrigation sites have been seeded with forage crops. Within Site A three subplots provide rates of application of 1, 2 and 3 in./wk of effluent over three equal areas of 0.225 acre. Site B contains a 150-foot rotary irrigator anchored on a center pivot. Six deflection heads 8 feet apart mounted downward and of decreasing opening diameter toward the center deliver at the rate of 2 inches of effluent per week to each of 4 subplots, each encompassing 0.445 acre. Each subplot is equipped with banks of lysimeters which are used to sample interstitial groundwater from the depths of 0.5, 1, 2, 3 and 4 feet. A total of 9 wells have been installed throughout both areas which are oriented according to groundwater flow so that groundwater monitoring can be provided throughout the experimental area. A high capacity retrieval well capable of pumping groundwater from a depth of about 60 feet at a rate of 300 gal./min also has been installed. Figure 4 shows the set-up of this system.

The monitoring program provides information on short- and long-term trends in terms of nitrogen, phosphorus, and trace metals removal after various degrees of treatment. All wells are constructed of PVC plastic which allows sampling for groundwater nutrients, metals and pesticides and many other organic substances without undue contamination. Monitoring within the sand beds is also provided by a series of suction lysimeters along with 7 observation wells to determine the extent of wastewater renovation and the quality of the recharged water.

> *An extensive monitoring program at Otis Air Force Base provides data on long term trends in nitrogen, phosphorus, and trace metal removal after various degrees of treatment.*

The removal of phosphorus from secondary effluent increases with the stage of treatment. The phosphorus concentration in the secondary effluent before lagooning ranged from about 8 to 10 ppm. The concentrations were higher during winter than in summer. Following chlorination and distribution over the irrigation field the phosphorus concentration was reduced to less than 0.5 ppm in the interstitial water recovered from 6 inches below the surface. At successively greater depths, no significant changes in phosphorus were observed down to the depth of groundwater sampling at 50 feet.

Total inorganic nitrogen concentrations in Otis secondary effluent before lagooning range from about 12.5 to 18.5 ppm and show a comparable reduction pattern to that of phosphorus following successive stages of treatment. During the winter-spring period, ammonia is the most abundant form of inorganic nitrogen in secondary effluent. During the summer and fall months, oxidized forms of nitrogen are more abundant than ammonia. The ammonia is almost completely adsorbed in the first foot of soil, but the oxidized forms of nitrogen penetrate at reduced concentrations to the groundwater. The data on inorganic nitrogen distribution suggest that soil nitrification is maintained at all seasons of the year.

The ability of sand filter beds to remove trace metals has been evaluated by sampling the soil at various depths. The heavy metals tend to accumulate within the upper few centimeters of sand. By comparing the integrated amounts of these metals distributed within the upper 52 cm with the heavy metal supply over the past 33 years it is possible to assign removal efficiencies for each of the five metals examined. Data indicate that 86% of the Cu, 49% of the Zn, 113% of Cd, 128% of the Pb and 59% of the Cr supplied are bound in the surface soil. Thus, of the metals examined only Zn and possibly Cr would appear to have a reasonable chance of the groundwater some 640 cm (21 ft) below the surface.

The crops accumulate nitrogen, and phosphorus, as well as calcium, magnesium, copper, chromium and nickel within the plant tissues. There is excess phosphate-phosphorus in the effluent, but like the heavy metals bound on the sand filter beds, this excess phosphorus becomes bound within the upper foot of soil. Significant phosphorus or heavy metal leaching into groundwater is not anticipated within the forseeable future since so much soil above groundwater level remains available for adsorption. Excessive nitrate-nitrogen concentrations (50 ppm) in the wells monitoring the sand filter beds have been found, but the crops grown on the irrigation plots provide adequate control of this contaminant, and only trace amounts of nitrate (about 2 ppm) in the wells monitoring these irrigated plots have been found.

Fort Devens Rapid Infiltration
Fort Devens, Massachusetts

The U.S. Military Installation of Fort Devens utilized the 17 acres of a kame (a beehive-shaped mound of glacial sand and gravel) for the construction of 22 rapid infiltration sand filter beds. Unchlorinated effluent from Imhoff tanks is flooded onto 3 beds for 2 days, then the beds are allowed to rest for 14 days. On a yearly basis, each bed receives effluent for a total of 52 days. Sludge from the Imhoff tanks is withdrawn each April and November and spread on sludge drying beds. Those beds are underdrained with an outfall in an adjacent wetland. Only two full-time employees are needed to carry out normal operation and maintenance of the facility. A schematic of this facility is shown in Figure 5.

Unchlorinated effluent from Imhoff tanks is flooded onto 17 acres of sand filtration beds with rapid infiltration capacities at Fort Devens.

The actual characteristics of this site were not fully defined until studies were begun in 1973. The soil profile is dominated by sand and gravel, with silts and clays accounting for only 10 to 15% of the volume in the upper profile and less than 1% below 1.6 feet. Permeabilities of 4×10^{-4} to 4×10^{-3} in./sec were recorded. Those rates are considered to be rapid to very rapid, and all horizons easily transmit the designed daily flow of 3 mgd. After the 2 days of flood-

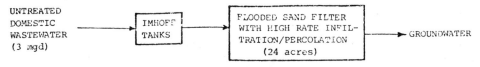

Figure 5. Illustration of the flow sequence followed at the Fort Devens, Massachusetts, wastewater treatment facility.

CASE STUDY COVER SHEET

SYSTEM   Ft. Devens Rapid Infiltration   1942
               (Name)   (Date started)

LOCATION   Ft. Devens, Mass.   M. B. Satterwhite

                                                (Person involved)

FACILITY DESCRIPTION   Municipal   Rapid Infiltration
                       (waste classification)   (application system(s))

APPLICATION   1.1-1.4 ft/day   apply 2 days with 14 days rest
                   (rate)   (schedule)

CROP(S)   local weeds: annual "weedy" grasses, fall panicum, barnyard grass.

                unchlorinated Imhoff
PRETREATMENT tank effluent

VOLUME TREATED   1.3 mgd

WORKING YEAR 12 mo.   CLIMATE ZONE   D

SOIL sands or gravely sands

COST   Annual O&M = $50,000

LAND AREA   16.6 acres

STORAGE CAPACITY   none

COMMENT: Unchlorinated primary effluent from Imhoff tanks has been flooded
          onto sand filters since 1942 with virtually no monitoring system.
          Discharge goes to 22 treatment beds each about 0.8 acre in size
          constructed on an oval, steep sided mound of glacial sand and
          gravel, or kame. Filter beds are cleaned periodically (last time,
          1968) by removing 1 ft of bottom, raking exposed surface, and
          replacing excavate with bank run sand and gravel. First monitoring
          done in 1974-1975. System now uses 14 observation wells.

REFERENCES: Satterwhite, M.B., G.L. Stewart, B.J. Condike, and E. Vlach.
             September 1976. Rapid infiltration of primary sewage effluent
             at Fort Devens, Massachusetts. CRREL Report 76-48, prepared
             for Directorate of Military Construction, Office, Chief of Engineers.

             Satterwhite, M.B., B.J. Condike, and G.L. Stewart.
             Treatment of primary sewage effluent by rapid infiltration.
             CRREL Report 76-49. Prepared for Directorate of Military
             Construction, Office, Chief of Engineers.

ing, effluent has normally accumulated on the surface of the beds to a depth of 0.5 to 1.6 feet.
This standing water infiltrates the beds within the initial 2 to 3 days of the recovery period,
restoring aerobic conditions to the surface of the beds. Winter conditions, while reducing
infiltration rates somewhat, do not interfere with normal operations. The effluent is sufficiently

warm, 46–54°F during the winter, to melt any accumulated ice and snow cover and to infiltrate and move through the sand beds.

Although winter temperatures reduce infiltration rates somewhat, the effluent is sufficiently warm to melt ice and snow cover and to move through the sand beds.

Chemical analyses of soil samples obtained from the upper 3.05 m of the treatment beds showed that levels of organic matter, electrical conductivity, nitrogen, copper, phosphates, calcium, magnesium, potassium, manganese, sodium, iron and zinc were substantially higher than those of background samples, whereas levels of sulfur, chloride, and cation exchange capacities were only slightly higher. Treatment bed soil samples had lower pH levels and boron concentrations than those found in background samples.

The quality of the primary effluent applied to the treatment beds and the groundwater in 14 observation wells was determined by sampling at biweekly intervals.

Groundwater quality in wells located 60 to 100 m from the application area showed that the primary effluent after flowing through the sand and gravel formation, had been substantially renovated. (See Table 1)

Before land application, the primary effluent averaged 192 mg/1 COD and 122 mg/1 BOD_5. These levels were reduced to 10–20 mg/1 and 1.0/2.5 mg/1 in the groundwater samples.

Concentration of total nitrogen in the primary effluent averaged 47 mg/1, which was divided equally among the organic and inorganic forms. The observation wells indicated total nitrogen, primarily as nitrate-nitrogen in the 10 to 20 mg/1 range.

This was a reduction of about 60 to 80% in total nitrogen levels. Changes in the concentration and form of nitrogen showed that applied nitrogen was nitrified, with substantial nitrogen removal due mostly to denitrification.

Table 1.   Chemical Characteristics of Primary Effluent Compared with Water Quality in Wells 3, 4, 5, and 6 at Fort Devens. (Average Values).

Parameter[a]	Effluent	Well			
		3	4	5	6
pH (Standard Units)	6.2–8.0	6.3	6.9	7.0	7.1
Electrical conductivity (umhos/cm)	511	360	441	502	466
BOD_5	122	2.5	1.5	1.6	1.9
COD	192	19	29	28	34
Total Nitrogen	47	19.5	20.6	22.1	22.2
Organic-nitrogen	23	2.8	7.9	11	8.0
NH_4-N	21	1.3	6.4	7	8.4
NO_3-N	1.3	15.6	5.9	3.8	5.7
NO_2-N	0.02	0.3	0.4	0.3	0.1
Total PO_4-P	11	0.9	0.9	0.8	1.0
Ortho PO_4-P	9	0.2	0.3	0.1	0.2
Cl	150	257	157	159	155
SO_4	42	46	43	47	46

[a]mg/l unless otherwise noted.

Source: Satterwhite, Stewart, Condike, and Vlach, 1976.

Phosphorus levels in the primary effluent averaged 11 mg/l, 80% of which was orthophosphate. Total phosphorus levels in the groundwater were 1.0 to 2.0 mg/l, slightly above the 0.7 mg/l background level. Orthophosphate was generally less than 0.4 mg/l in wells located around the treatment area but was higher than the 0.1 mg/l background level.

Chloride, sulfate, pH and hardness levels varied little from observed effluent levels, although conductivity and alkalinity were substantially less. Analysis of groundwater samples for fecal coliform bacteria proved negative. Mean numbers of total coliform bacteria in the groundwater were less than 200/100 ml, although 2 wells showed mean counts of 400 to 600 organisms/100 ml of samples.

The cation exchange capacity (C.E.C.) of soils also has been characterized. Background C.E.C. values from unamended soils range from 2.0 to 8.0 meq/100 g in surface horizons and about 0.5 meq/100 g at depths greater than 1.6 feet. Cation exchange capacities of soil samples taken in treatment beds were relatively constant throughout the 9.8-foot sampling depth, ranging from 0.79–15.1 meq/100 g. The C.E.C. of the beds has increased over the 6 years since the beds were last renovated, presumably due to accumulations of organic matter.

An attempt was made in 1974 to increase denitrification by increasing the application rate. To achieve this, the application cycle was modified from inundating 3 beds for 2 days, followed by a 14-day recovery period, to inundating 9 beds for 7 days, followed by a 14-day recovery period. It was found that an increase in the inundation period continued to renovate the primary effluent to the same degree as before. The total nitrogen levels of the groundwater continued to be 20 mg/l. But when the treatment basins were inundated for 7 days, the percentage of total nitrogen removal was greater than when the basins were inundated for 2 days. By increasing the inundation period, total nitrogen additions were increased by 54% from about 32 to 50 lb/acre/day. Although total nitrogen additions were larger during the 1974 study, a proportional increase in groundwater nitrogen levels was not observed, indicating a greater percentage of nitrogen removal.

However, after 6 months of increased inundation period, the infiltration capacity had been reduced so much that the basin surfaces were still wet at the beginning of the next cycle of inundation and recovery. This gradual decline in the basin infiltration capacity over several months was attributed to clogging of the surfaces of the basins by accumulating organic matter. It was found that an occasional extended recovery period of 60 consecutive days will rejuvenate the infiltration capacity of the treatment basins so that the 7-day application, 14-day recovery cycle can once again be used. The restoration of infiltration capacity during the extended recovery period is attributed to the aeration of the surface and the subsequent oxidation of accumulated organics.

Denitrification was increased at Fort Devens site by increasing the period of inundation. Increased inundation periods resulted in a greater accumulation of organic matter, thus reducing infiltration capacity of the site. This was alleviated by allowing an occasional extended recovery period of 60 days which rejuvenated the infiltration capacity.

Conclusions of study of Fort Devens system:

1. The rapid infiltration system has operated effectively throughout the year. Greater ponding of effluent was observed during winter than during warmer periods of the year.

2. The 2 days wet/14 days drying operation cycle has maintained infiltration and percolation capacities of the treatment beds after six years of field operation.

3. Levels of nitrogen, phosphorus, calcium, magnesium, potassium, iron, sodium, copper, zinc, chloride and sulfur have increased in the soil surface horizon of the treatment beds.

4. Percolate from the treatment site has increased the levels of nitrogen, chloride, sulfate, conductivity, alkalinity and hardness in the groundwater. Slight increases of BOD, COD and total coliform bacteria levels have been observed.

5. Differences in the concentration of organic-nitrogen, NH_4-N, NO_3-N, and NO_2-N between the primary effluent and the groundwater illustrate that ammonification and nitrification were occurring in the treatment beds. A total nitrogen balance showed a 60 to 80% reduction in total nitrogen applied to the treatment beds.

6. Because of the limited capacities of the other plausible nitrogen removal mechanisms and the substantial quantities of nitrogen removed, the reduction in total nitrogen levels observed may be attributed to denitrification.

7. The groundwater quality in the strongly impacted wells indicates that the unchlorinated primary sewage effluent is being renovated to a quality comparable to that achieved by conventional tertiary wastewater treatment facilities.

Fresno Wastewater Treatment
Fresno County, California

The Fresno County wastewater treatment facility originated in 1891 as a 40 acre "sewage farm" for raw sewage disposal. Expansion of facilities occurred seven times between 1907 and 1962. The 1924 expansion involved installing deep wells to draw down a prohibitively shallow water table (2 feet) caused by groundwater mounding. Water recovered from those wells was used to irrigate adjacent cotton fields and pastures. Some of that discharge occasionally ran into a nearby creek, but that was the only surface discharge. The 1960 expansion provided duplicate facilities ("Plant 1" and "Plant 2") with small oxidation ponds in addition to sludge thickeners, but discharge was still to the infiltration beds, with groundwater recharge the primary goal after waste treatment. A schematic presentation of this site is given in Figure 6.

> *Fresno County land application system has been greatly expanded since it began in 1891 as a "sewage farm."*

High wine production in recent years sent excessive amounts of winery wastes to this facility, causing complete breakdown of sludge handling equipment. Wineries now must undertake preliminary sludge screening before discharging to sewers.

> *Wineries discharging to Fresno County land application system must undertake preliminary sludge screening to lessen the load on the county's sludge handling equipment.*

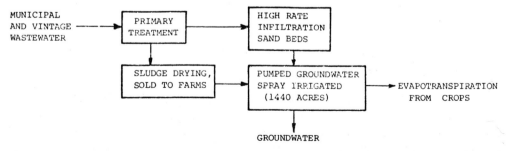

Figure 6. Schematic of the Fresno County, California, land application system for wastewater treatment.

CASE STUDY COVER SHEET

SYSTEM   Fresno Wastewater Treatment   1891 (1907)
_____   _____
              (Name)   (Date started)

LOCATION   Fresno County, Calif.   J. H. Jenks
_____   _____
                                                            (Person Involved)

FACILITY DESCRIPTION Municipal and Vintage Wastewater   rapid infiltration
_____   _____
                      (waste classification)   (application system(s))

APPLICATION _____
                        (rate)   (schedule)

CROP(S)   primarily groundwater recharge; some use on cotton and pasture

PRETREATMENT primary clarifiers

VOLUME TREATED 34 mgd

WORKING YEAR 12 mo.   CLIMATE ZONE A

SOIL "well drained", good ag. soil

COST _____

LAND AREA   1440 acres

STORAGE CAPACITY _____

COMMENT: This sanitary district in the San Joaquin Valley discharges all
           primary effluent to rapid infiltration beds. Groundwater mounding
           forces underdraining and drawdown pumping with discharge to
           adjacent pastures and cotton fields. Odors are a nuisance.
           Expansion facilities are being planned and will include
           secondary treatment. However, to control the water table, the
           practices of both recharge and irrigation will continue to be
           used.

REFERENCES: Jenks, J. H. and P. L. Adamson. 1972. Wastewater treatment
             disposal and reclamation project. Project Report, City of
             Fresno.

   The soils of the San Joaquin Valley are varied, mostly well drained alluvial deposits. Agriculture is the dominant industry. Virtually all water used comes from fine quality groundwater. Reclaimed wastewater would be too expensive to sell as irrigation water even if transmission costs could be neglected. Sludge, however, is dried and sold to local farmers as a soil conditioner. In 1968 groundwater around the facility was sampled from eight test holes and at each plant. Detailed chemical analyses of only two sampling sites are reported. Nitrate-nitrogen was measured at all sites, however, and ranged from "trace" to 213 mg/l. Potentially toxic elements are not reported. Bicarbonates, carbonates, chlorides, sulfates, sodium, hardness, Fe, Si, Mn, Mg, and NH_4^+ are reported, reflecting the primary concern of that agricultural land toward "salt" content of waters.

Evapotranspiration from existing facilities is around 10 mgd in the summer. This high rate of water loss might be expected to lead to the concentrating of salt in the effluent. However, the quality of effluent, diluted some by native groundwater, is high enough to allow its use as irrigation water without causing salinity problems.

Odor problems have caused serious complaints. Those complaints, coupled with the growth in population and industry, mandate facility expansion. To solve those problems, officials are planning secondary treatment followed by continued land application. That will expand capabilities to 68 mgd. Presumably the proposed expansion will include monitoring capabilities and an established routine to assure compliance with federal and local regulations.

Bakersfield, California

Land application of wastewater has been practiced for more than 60 years at Bakersfield in the San Joaquin Valley of Central California. Untreated wastewater was first used to irrigate crops in 1912. Since 1939, city owned lands planted with forage, fiber, and seed crops have been irrigated with treated municipal wastewater. Primary treatment plants constructed in 1939 and 1952 service about half of the metropolitan area which has a total population of 200,000. These plants supply the wastewater for the current 2,400 acre farm, soon to be expanded to 4,700 acres. The farm is leased to a grower who irrigates year-round using surface distribution methods. Year-round surface irrigation is possible because of warm arid climate. Soils have been described as "poor quality" worth $100/acre before application and have been improved with wastes application to $1,000/acre.

The land application in Bakersfield supplies irrigation water for a 2,700 acre farm, soon to be expanded to 4,700 acres.

Because certain deficiencies have developed in the operation, the existing facilities are being expanded and upgraded. The existing system consists of a network of ditches and equalizing reservoirs supplying the fields with wastewater for border strip and ridge and furrow methods of irrigation (Figure 7). Although the topography is very flat, the drainage is from north to

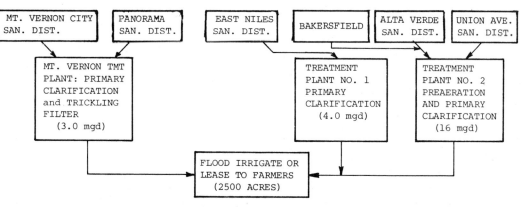

Figure 7. Simplified schematic presentation of the wastewater treatment system for Bakersfield, California.

CASE STUDY COVER SHEET

SYSTEM   Bakersfield, California _____   ___1912____
                    (Name)   (Date started)

LOCATION Bakersfield, California   Larry Grimm, Metcalf & Eddy Engineers
                                            (Person involved)

FACILITY DESCRIPTION   Municipal   agricultural flood irrigation (ridge and
                        (waste classification)   (application system)   furrow
                                                                          border strip)

APPLICATION   at grower's discretion   at grower's discretion
                    (rate)   (schedule)

CROP(S)   alfalfa, barley, corn, cotton, pasture grass (unrestricted)

PRETREATMENT primary clarification and aerated lagoons

VOLUME TREATED   19 mgd

WORKING YEAR   12 months   CLIMATE ZONE   A

SOIL   loam, clay loam, sandy loam

COST Of new system going into operation in 1978
                        $12.5 million

LAND AREA 5,700 acres of which 4,700 are under
                        cultivation

STORAGE CAPACITY 1710 MG or 90 days (under new system)

COMMENT: Bakersfield has two wastewater treatment plants, one of which will
          be closed down when the new system begins operation. Secondary
          effluent will be sent to a ditch or force mains from which irriga-
          tion water is withdrawn. All land is leased to one grower who
          must use all the water all the year but can establish his own
          management practices. Forage, fiber and seed crops are grown.
          The new system is currently under construction and will be opera-
          tional by Fall, 1979.

REFERENCES: Crites, R.W. 1974. Irrigation with wastewater at Bakersfield,
             California. In: Wastewater Use in the Production of Food and
             Fiber, EPA-660/2-74-041. pp. 229-239.

             Crites, R. W. 1975. Wastewater irrigation: This city can show you how.
             Water and Wastes Engineering, 12 (July) 49–50.

             Metcalf and Eddy, Inc. 1973. Preliminary investigation of
             wastewater treatment and disposal for southeast Bakersfield.

(continued on next page)

CASE STUDY COVER SHEET (continued)

Prepared for the City of Bakersfield and Mount Vernon County
Sanitation District,

Process Design Manual for Land Treatment of Municipal
Wastewater, U.S. Environmental Protection Agency, U.S.
Army Corps of Engineers, U.S. Department of Agriculture.
October 1977.   EPA 625/1-77-008.   pp. 7-18 to 7-26.

south with sump pumps along the southern end to return tailwater to storage ponds. Soils are generally alkaline and poorly drained with dense clay lenses at depths ranging from 10 to 15 feet below the surface. This clay barrier produces perched water in areas where it is continuous and reduced percolation in areas where it is not.

Two permanent groundwater aquifers exist at approximate depths of 100 to 200 feet and at 300 feet. They are separated by a clay barrier, and the confined lower aquifer is used for water supply. The deep wells on the farm produce water to supplement irrigation needs. The quality of this water, however, is inadequate for potable uses as a result of naturally occurring high total dissolved solids and nitrates.

Liquid and nitrogen loading rates, and nitrogen requirements for the principal crops grown on the farm are shown in Table 2. The nitrogen applied meets the nitrogen requirements of all crops. For cotton, the nitrogen loading is more than twice that which can be utilized. Yields for all other crops are about equal to, and in some cases higher than, the county-wide averages. Crop yields resulting from irrigation with primary effluent and the economic return are shown in Table 3.

Management of water has been a problem due to lack of storage and increasing flows. This will be resolved under the new system with its 90-day storage facilities. Ponding of excess water has occurred on some areas of the pastureland in winter. Although flies and mosquitoes are attracted to the stagnant water, no diseases have been traced to effluent use. The equalizing reservoirs and the storage pond for tailwater are periodically sprayed to control mosquito propagation. No disinfection of the effluent is required and none is provided at the two treatment plants. Normally, corn and barley are green chopped for cattle fodder and not harvested for grain. Dairy cows are not allowed to graze pastures irrigated with nondisinfected effluent so they are fed with green chop and hay. Beef cattle are allowed to both graze pastures and be fed on the green chop and hay.

Table 2.   Crops, Irrigation Land, and Nutrient Uptake at Bakersfield, California (Crites, 1973).

Crop	Liquid Load Rate (ft/yr)	BOD Load Rate (lb/acre/yr)	N Load (lb/acre/yr)	N Uptake (lb/acre/yr)
Barley	1.8	730	139	75
Corn	3.3	1300	252	150
Cotton	3.7	1500	277	100
Pasture Grass	4.9	1985	371	150–250
Alfalfa	4.9	1985	371	360–480

Conversion factors: lb/acre = 1.12 kg/ha;
                      ft $\times$ 30.5 = cm

Table 3.   Existing Crop Yields and Economic Return, Bakersfield Land Treatment System.

Crop	Yield (lb/acre)	Typical Price ($/lb)[a]	Economic Return ($/acre)
Alfalfa	16,000	0.025	400
Barley	3,000–5,000	0.045	135–225
Corn	36,000–60,000	0.0075	270–450
Cotton	600–800	0.35	210–280

[a]Based on 1973 prices.

1 lb/acre = 1.12 kg/ha
  1 $/lb = $2.2/kg
  1 $/acre = $2.47/ha

Source: Metcalf and Eddy, 1977.

The problem of managing large volumes of wastewater and balancing flow with irrigation needs will be resolved by the installation of 90-day storage facilities at Bakersfield.

Although primary effluent is suitable according to the California Department of Health, the Central Valley Regional Water Quality Control Board has set limits of 40 mg/l on BOD and suspended solids prior to forage crop irrigation. Their rationale is that such an effluent can be stored without causing a nuisance and will reduce the potential for odors in system management.

Under the proposed system, the existing preapplication facilities will be upgraded and a concrete pipe distribution system for continued surface irrigation of crops will be built. One of the treatment plants will be shut down and its flow redirected to the remaining plant where new primary clarifiers and aerated lagoons will be constructed. There will be no chlorination because surface application to forage, fiber and seed crops does not require disinfection.

The new 4,700-acre system will have as its principal objective to produce crops rather than to treat wastewater. Thus, double cropping with corn and barley is proposed. This combination requires less water than is presently applied.

The main objective of the new Bakersfield system will be to produce crops rather than to treat wastewater; double cropping of corn and barley will be used.

Flexibility of operation will be provided by storage reservoirs, which will hold flows during periods of low irrigation demand. Automatically operated tailwater return stations will control runoff from irrigated fields. Outlets from the distribution laterals will consist of orchard-type valves which can be adapted to gated surface pipe, open ditches with siphon pipe, or direct flooding of border strips. Telemetered alarms will continuously scan the operation of the system to alert the operator of malfunctions at any of the pumping stations.

Deer Creek Lake
Recreational Area, Ohio

The Deer Creek Lake system treats the wastewater from one of the camping sites at the Deer Creek Lake Reservoir. The site accommodates trailers and tents. Sanitary facilities include a

CASE STUDY COVER SHEET

SYSTEM Deer Creek Lake   1973
   (Name)   (Date started)

LOCATION 30 mi. S.W. Columbus, Ohio   D. J. Lambert/Corps of Eng.
                 (Person involved)

FACILITY DESCRIPTION   domestic   spray irrigation
       (waste classification)   (application system(s))

APPLICATION 0.1 in. per hour   10 hr day. Maximum load 1 in. per week
                 over entire site
      (rate)   (schedule)

CROP(S) alfalfa, reed canary grass, wheat/soybeans, tree seedlings

PRETREATMENT   lagoon

VOLUME TREATED .046 mgd

WORKING YEAR 12 months   CLIMATE ZONE D
   "poorly drained", moderately slow
SOIL to slow permeability

COST

LAND AREA   12 acres

STORAGE CAPACITY 9.0 x 10^6 gal

COMMENT: This site serves a 232-unit camping area having peak visitation of
16,500/month and annual visitation of 1.6 million persons. It was
designed and constructed by the Army Corps of Engineers and is now
operated by the Ohio Department of Natural Resources. It provides
two lagoons and a spray irrigation field. The field is underdrained.
Underdrain and overland flow effluent is returned to lagoons or,
if high enough quality, to nearby Deer Creek Lake. A 1000-2000 ft
buffer of vegetation separates spray field from camp site. The
system has performed adequately to meet all point discharge requirements under PL 92-500. The crop management program has shown that
grasses, alfalfa, and soybeans can be grown when the application
rate for these low permeable soils does not exceed one inch per week.
The system removes nitrogen, phosphorus, and BOD sufficiently to
meet drinking water standards in the percolating water. The monitoring system has performed satisfactorily and a detailed data base for
product water quality has been established.

(continued on next page)

CASE STUDY COVER SHEET (continued)

REFERENCES: Lambert, D. J. and W. R. Dawson. 1975, The living filter
comes to Deer Creek. Water Spectrum. 6(1):1-8.

Lambert, D. J. and H. L. McKim. 1977. Deer Creek Lake -
on-land wastewater treatment system, pp. 79-93 In
R. C. Loehr, ed. Food, fertilizer and agricultural
residues. Proc. 9th Cornell Univ. Agricultural Waste
Management Conference.

central sewage dump station with multiple slop drains for trailers, six comfort stations, and four wash houses. The wastewater sources feed into two lift stations located at the camping site. Wastewater then passes through underground drains and is pumped to the stabilization lagoon.

At Deer Creek Lake campsite, partially treated wastewater is pumped from a hold-ing basin to a 12-acre site where it is sprayed onto slowly permeable soil planted in alfalfa, reed canary grass, wheat, soybeans, and tree seedlings.

The complete treatment system is composed of a stabilization lagoon, chlorine contact chamber, holding basin, pump intake, distribution piping and four three-acre spray fields. Runoff is diverted by a berm located around the entire spray area. Runoff from the spray area flows through a series of ditches and is collected at the lower end of the 12-acre field. An underdrainage system which collects the water that percolates through the soil was installed at a depth of 3 feet. The soils comprising the majority of the land in the treatment area have neutral to alkaline pH and have moderately slow to slow permeability rates as classified by the Soil Conservation Service. The clay content below 30 inches always exceeds 36%.

The stabilization lagoon and holding basin were part of the original two-lagoon sewage treatment system installed at Deer Creek Lake in 1973 to handle a flow of 46,000 gpd, which was the anticipated maximum weekend flow to be pumped from the 232 campsites at the Deer Creek Lake camping area. The primary lagoon was designed to hold 73 days of maximum flow at normal depth and could be raised up to 2 feet to store an additional 60 days. A secondary lagoon, originally intended to polish the effluent from the stabilization lagoon, was converted to a holding basin capable of storing 62 days at maximum flow. The chlorination point is located between the stabilization lagoon and the holding basin.

The partially treated wastewater is pumped from the holding basin at 560 gpm to the 12-acre spray field for an average application rate of 0.1 in./hr. The pumping is limited to 10-hour periods to ensure that no more than 1 inch of effluent is applied per week. The natural slope of the spray field, averaging 1%, was left undisturbed in order to maintain the existing soil profile except for the trenching required to install the underdrain system.

Flexibility is designed into the spray system. Any two of the three units in the pump house can accommodate the design flow of 560 gpm, leaving the third as a standby pump. The entire flow of 280 gpm from one pump can be sprayed into any of the four equally sized three-acre parallel sections into which the spray field is divided. Furthermore, each pump is equipped with individual intake screens so that each intake can be back-flushed by the flow from the other pumps if the screens become clogged. All header pipes and supply lines are placed underground, not only to make the area more aesthetically acceptable, but also to decrease the time involved in the cutting, trimming, and harvesting of the vegetative cover.

Underdrains allow the application of wastewater in early spring. These drains were placed parallel to the spray header lines on 30-foot centers. Each drain consists of a 6-inch corrugated, flexible plastic pipe with a filter sleeve. All the percolating water can be analyzed and discharged to the reservoir or primary holding lagoon based on the water quality analyses.

The monitoring system ensures that water entering Deer Creek Lake meets water quality goals. It also provides a data base that will enable more accurate assessment of management and cropping practices required for design and construction of cost effective land treatment systems.

Wastewater is monitored at eight critical locations in the land treatment system. Raw sewage is monitored by a device activated by the start-up of sewage flow which collects a composite sample for water quality analysis. An automatically activated timing device provides for representative samples of the holding lagoon effluent. Composite samples are collected at the point when the pump that transports wastewater to the spray irrigation field is activated. Accurate flow rates and water quality analyses are needed at this point to ensure that water and nutrient mass balances for the spray area can be calculated. Overland runoff and subsurface drainage are measured by automatic flow recording devices. Since the system was designed and is operated to ensure that the wastewater applied will infiltrate into the soil, any runoff from the site is attributed to rainfall. When runoff occurs, grab samples are collected at these points and analyzed for water quality. The quality of the renovated wastewater in subsurface drains indicates whether the water meets advanced treatment requirements allowing discharge into Deer Creek Lake, or must be recycled to the stabilization lagoon for further treatment. Other monitoring points consist of shallow wells where the level of phreatic water surface is visible. These wells are sampled to determine the effect of spray irrigation on groundwater quality. Table 4 indicates water quality at five of these monitoring locations.

If the quality of renovated wastewater in subsurface drains does not meet requirements for discharge into Deer Creek Lake, it is recycled to the stabilization lagoon for further treatment.

Table 4.   Characteristics of Wastewater Collected from Various Points at Deer Creek Lake Land Treatment System. (Adapted from Lambert and McKim, 1977).

Constituents	Raw Sewage (ppm)	*Point 3 (ppm)	Point 4 (ppm)	Point 5 (ppm)	Point 6.1 (ppm)
Chlorides	269	49–76	6–25	4–73	6.0–19.6
Phosphate	6	0.11–0.25	0.00–2.34	0.0–0.10	0.02–1.96
Total nitrogen	50.6	1.9	0.2–2.5	–	0.4–2.2
NH_4^+-N	33.8	0.0–0.3	0.0–2.7	0.0–0.6	0.3–0.5
NO_3^--N	1.5	0.0–0.4	0.0–0.4	0.0–2.0	0.2
Total solids	1250	320–430	193–505	93–1000	300–1462
Volatile solids	330	86–229	22–249	23–180	145–219
pH	8.3	8.5–8.7	7.6–8.2	7.1–8.2	7.5–7.6
BOD	134	2.6–3.4	2.4–10	0.3–7.9	1.8–7.2
Fecal coliforms			30×10^0–5.5×10^4		
MPN/100 ml	1.3×10^7	0–240		0–600	0

*Point 3: Wastewater used as spray irrigation (pumping site)
  Point 4: Surface runoff
  Point 5: Drainage water
  Point 6.1: Water collected from one of the shallow wells

Winter Spray Irrigation
Big Bromley Ski Area
Manchester, Vermont

This full-scale demonstration/research project was undertaken to determine the feasibility of wastewater renovation by winter land application. The site selected represents a major ski area providing from 20,000 to 60,000 gpd with an established secondary treatment system (lagoon). The land for application was a nearby abandoned ski slope. The area selected was about 50% forested and 50% open field. Slopes ranged from 10 to 25% (average 17%) and soils were shallow, no more than 3 feet.

Wastewater at the rate of 20,000 to 60,000 gpd receives secondary treatment and is sprayed on an abandoned ski slope throughout the ski season at Big Bromley Ski area.

Monitoring was done using three plywood-lined pits, downslope from the spray zone. Perforated pipes were pounded through the walls of the pits into the soil to act as sample collectors. In addition, surface runoff from below the spray zone and an adjacent brook were sampled on weekdays. Parameters examined included pH, BOD, COD, TDS, PO_4^{-3}, NO_3^-, Cl^-, and SO_4^{-2}. The pH averaged about 6.9 to 5.6 in the field and 6.2 in the woods. The BOD, was 4.7 to 2.0 mg/l in the field and 1.7 mg/l in the woods. The PO_4^{-3} averaged 17.0 to 0.7 mg/l in the woods. No NO_3^- removal occurred. Concentrations of all parameters increased sharply at spring runoff. However, there are no wells within a 20-mile radius.

A special feature of winter spraying is that effluent storage occurs in the forms of large ice mounds. However, renovation occurs only after the effluent passes into the soil. Renovation, then, depends on the slow but steady melting which occurs beneath the insulating layers of ice. Larger volumes of effluent are released to soils during periods of winter melt. If soil capacity is not exceeded during such periods, application by spraying may be increased temporarily to encourage ice melt and allow more effluent to be processed before spring thaw.

Effluent stored in large ice mounds throughout the winter is renovated only after it passes into the soil. Although steady melting occurs in winter, the largest volumes are released during spring thaw when concentrations of BOD, COD, PO_4^{-3}, NO_3^-, Cl^-, and SO_4^{-2} sharply increase.

At the time of spring thaw, soils experience excessive hydraulic loadings due to snow melt and rains. Effluent stored in ice mounds will be diluted and lost to surface runoff, but the larger and thicker the ice mounds, the more slowly they will melt. Thus, winter spraying must rely on spring dilution instead of soil renovation to process the remaining effluent.

Non-chlorinated effluent was sprayed on occasions to test the spread of air-borne pathogens from the spray area. The conclusion was that pathogens were present but significantly reduced after 150 to 200 feet downwind from the last nozzle. None were detected beyond 300 feet.

A number of spray nozzles were used and some icing and pipe-freezing problems were reported, but it was felt that there was nothing that could not be handled with experience. Aesthetic considerations were not forgotten. Spraying from fixed nozzles was silent and the spray so finely atomized that visitors were genuinely disappointed with the apparent lack of action. Risers in the wooded portion of the site were well camouflaged.

CASE STUDY COVER SHEET

SYSTEM   Winter Spray Irrigation (Bromley)   1972
                    (Name)   (Date started)

                                         Peter Andrews, Dufresne-Henry
LOCATION Big Bromley Ski Area   Eng. Corp, Springfield, Vt.
                                              (Person involved)

FACILITY DESCRIPTION 1.7 in/week for 24-36 hr continual   winter ski season
                              (rate)   (schedule)

CROP(S)   none

PRETREATMENT   aeration/lagoon

VOLUME TREATED 20,000 - 60,000 gal/day

WORKING YEAR   12 weeks   CLIMATE ZONE E

SOIL   mountain forest/clearing

COST $25,000 grant

LAND AREA   2.47 acres

STORAGE CAPACITY

COMMENT: A research and demonstration project in which chlorinated secondary
          effluent is sprayed onto forest and clearcut land during Vermont
          winters. Many different types of nozzles have undergone experiment-
          ation including fixed and rotating. Sprinklers remain ice-free
          day and night. Icing on trees and branches and formation of ice
          "chalices" around sprays is a problem. Chalices are donut-shaped
          ice structures which form around the nozzles. On one occasion about
          90% of the system was blocked by such icing. Chalicing may be
          controlled by downward spraying. Renovation of water is acceptable.
          Dufresne-Henry calls the system "ice piling". Effluent is sprayed
          sometimes at -20°F. The spraying creates ice piles which melt in
          the spring, creating a large runoff. Movement of effluent through
          the soil is more horizontal than vertical. Large amounts of surface
          runoff are not a problem because there are no wells within a 20-mile
          radius of the site.

REFERENCES: Dufresne-Henry Egn. Corp. 1972, Winter spray irrigation
             demonstration Bromley Ski Area, Vermont. A report on
             water quality effects by the Vermont Dept. of Water Resources,
             Project No. D-H #2140 (August 17, 1972).

Campbell Soup Company
Paris, Texas

In the early 1950s, the Campbell Soup Company gained experience in overland flow operation from handling its 0.75 mgd tomato waste in Napoleon, Ohio. That experience with seasonal flow encouraged the development of a plant in Chestertown, Maryland (1959), which processed poultry wastes throughout the year. Based on these two studies, Campbell began an overland flow system in Paris, Texas, in 1960, going into full operation in 1964.

When the company acquired the site in 1960, most of the topsoil had been stripped away, much of the area was covered with brush and small trees, and the old erosion gullies had cut deeply into the red clay subsoil. The trees were cut down and destroyed; the erosion features were eliminated with heavy earthmoving equipment. The slopes were then smoothed with a land plane and planted to water tolerant grasses. When the grass became established, terraces were spaced at 200- and 300-foot intervals across the slope. Underground force mains were installed with automatic valve take offs located 135 feet or more upslope from each terrace. From these, surface irrigation lines extended across the slope. For more than a year, while the factory was being built, the grass on the slopes was fertilized and irrigated with fresh water to establish a good growth of sod.

The overland flow site at the Paris Campbell Soup plant was prepared by removing all trees, eliminating erosion features with earthmoving equipment, smoothing slopes with a land plane and planting water tolerant grasses.

The Paris plant prepares a complete line of heat-processed soups as well as beans and spaghetti products. Effluent is screened and degreased, then sent to a storage tank for distribution. Lateral sprinkler lines are designed to operate 8 hours on and 16 hours off, allowing for a rest period between wastewater application. Water containing suspended and dissolved organic impurities is sprayed along the top of the slope by conventional irrigation sprinklers. As it percolates through the dense sod to the soil surface, it leaves behind most of the suspended solids. From here the water trickles downslope in a thin sheet and the dissolved impurities are subjected to biological degradation. The purified water is collected in the terrace at the foot of the slope whence it flows to the receiving stream via prepared waterways. A schematic presentation of this treatment system appears in Figure 8. Table 5 shows removal efficiencies of the Paris system.

The biological and agricultural response to waste loading has been studied by North Texas State University and an extensive study on the climatology, agriculture, biology, hydrology and chemistry of the site was done by C. W. Thornthwaite Associates of Elmer, New Jersey.

What is the fate of the applied wastewater in the Pairs system? Results indicate that 20% percolates down through the soil, 10 to 30% is lost by evaporation and transpiration, and the remaining 60% returns to the surface stream as runoff.

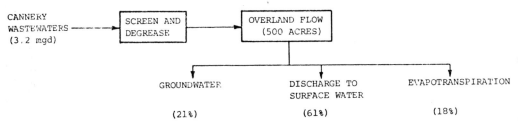

Figure 8. Presentation of land application system used for cannery wastewaters by the Campbell Soup Company, Paris, Texas.

Table 5.   Treatment Efficiency of Campbell Soup System, Paris, Texas. (Source: Gilde, 1976).

| Parameter | Mean Conc. (mg/l) | | % Removal | |
	Inf.	Eff.	Conc.	Mass
TSS	263	16	93.5	98.2
BOD	616	9	98.5	99.1
P	7.6	4.3	42.5	61.5
N	17.4	2.8	83.9	91.5

CASE STUDY COVER SHEET

SYSTEM   Campbell Soup Company   1964
                (Name)   (Date started)

LOCATION   Paris, Texas   Charles H. Neeley
                                            (Person involved)

FACILITY DESCRIPTION   Cannery wastes   Overland flow
                   (waste classification)   (application system(s))

APPLICATION 2 to 3 in/wk   Three 6-8 hr days per week
              (rate)   16 to 18 hours off
                                            (schedule)
        primarily reed canary grass, red top, perennial rye grass,
CROP(S) bermuda grass, tall fescue, native vegetation

PRETREATMENT   screen and degrease

VOLUME TREATED   6 mgd

WORKING YEAR 12 months   CLIMATE ZONE C

SOIL Sandy loam, clay, clay loam

COST   28c/1000 gal.

LAND AREA   900 acres

STORAGE CAPACITY   none

COMMENT: A sprayed effluent is allowed to flow down 150-200 ft slopes ranging
          from 2% to 6% over highly eroded, nearly impervious soils. Grasses
          are harvested two or three times a year as cash hay crops. Reed
          canary grass was found to be an exceptionally good hay when harvested
          early. Up to 90% N and 61% P removal is achieved. Effluent BOD is
          always 10 ppm, representing a 99% reduction in BOD.

REFERENCES: Gilde, L. C., A. S. Kester, J. P. Law, C. H. Neeley, and
             D. M. Parmlee. 1971. A spray irrigation system for treatment
             of cannery wastes. J. Water Poll. Control Fed. 43(10):2011-2025.

             C. W. Thornthwaite Associates. 1969. An evaluation of cannery
             waste disposal by overland flow spray irrigation. Publications
             in Climatology Vol. 22, No. 2. 73 p. Laboratory of Climatology,
             Elmer, N.J.

The system removes nutrients efficiently, 99% of the applied BOD and up to 90% of the applied nitrogen and phosphorus can be removed under favorable conditions. Early observations revealed that the removal of phosphorus was disappointingly low—about 45%. Later a change in the operating procedure to provide a longer rest period between applications, with no change in the total volume, increased phosphorus removal to nearly 90% without affecting the BOD or nitrogen removals.

Investigations showed that the Paris system operated as efficiently in winter as in other seasons. This is due to a tenfold increase in the population of microorganisms in winter. It has long been recognized that an overland flow system would continue to purify water when temperatures were near freezing, but since it is also known that respiration of microorganisms slows down as temperature decreases, it was believed that the impurities were being adsorbed upon the surface of the vegetation and held there until the weather warmed up again. The studies showing increase of microorganism numbers during winter indicate a constant level of activity of the microbial mass, which should account for the continued high removal efficiency.

The Paris overland flow system operates as well in winter as in other seasons; research shows that the population of microorganisms increases tenfold in winter thus compensating for any decrease in respiration of microorganisms under cold temperatures.

Chemical analyses of the soil indicate that while the concentration of sodium salts is increasing, it has not reached a level injurious to plants and is not expected to do so in the future. Similarly, nitrates percolating into the groundwater reserve are not expected to build up to the point of concern.

Young grasses, particularly reed canary grass, grown on irrigated lands have nearly twice the phosphorus and protein of non-irrigated grasses. This makes irrigated grasses nearly as nutritional as alfalfa. Furthermore, if cut while still tender, irrigated grasses are readily eaten by cattle. Thus two or even three harvests of hay are taken each year as a normal, cash-producing asset of the Paris system.

Muskegon County
Muskegon, Michigan

This $44 million project has won engineering awards and is often considered to be a significant demonstration of a fine land application system. The county received 45% of its funding from federal sources. Wastes are collected from 14 municipalities and 200 industries, transported through a 13-mile interceptor system to an 11-mile force main and then to three 8-acre aeration lagoons. The lagoons may operate either in parallel or series. After a 3-day retention time, discharge is to one of two 850-acre storage lakes where settling occurs. Effluent from the storage lakes (capacity equal to 6 months flow) is chlorinated and sprayed onto 7,500 acres of agricultural land through 55 center pivot rigs.

The county-wide system has two separate wastewater treatment areas, a 10,500 acre site near Muskegon and a 600-acre site near Whitehall. The crops vary, but corn is the most extensively grown. The land is underdrained with tiles buried 7 to 11 feet. Percolate is discharged to Lake Michigan via Mosquito Creek or Black Creek. It is hoped that one by-product of this system will be to reduce the pollution in Mona and White Lakes and allow them to recover from their eutrophic condition.

This project moved 154 landowners, 30 tenants, 2 farm owners, 4 businesses, and 2 non-profit organizations from the acquired land. Moving costs were unexpectedly high. Land clear-

CASE STUDY COVER SHEET

SYSTEM Muskegon County   1974
      (Name)   (Date started)

LOCATION Muskegon, Michigan   Mr. Ralph Precious, Adm.
                                     (Person involved)

FACILITY DESCRIPTION municipal/industrial   spray irrigation
                    (waste classification)   (application system(s))

APPLICATION 2.1 in./week   7 days per month
             (rate)   (schedule)

CROP(S) Winter wheat, corn, rye, oats, legumes, grass cash crops

PRETREATMENT _____ lagoon _____

VOLUME TREATED _____ 43.4 mgd _____

WORKING YEAR 212 days CLIMATE ZONE E

SOIL Sand (some poorly drained)

COST $44 x 10^6 (tot); $40/10^6 gal 1st year

LAND AREA   10,000 acres

STORAGE CAPACITY 30,000 acre ft.

COMMENT: Widely discussed system for treating wastes of 14 municipalities
and 200 industries of a west central Michigan region. Influent
goes into three 8-acre aeration lagoons, two 850-acre storage
lagoons, and an 8-acre solids settling pond. Effluent is spray
irrigated by center pivot rigs onto underdrained agricultural
land. System is monitored by some 302 wells, stores effluent
over winter, chlorinates before spraying, has minor odor problems
at influent.

REFERENCES: Forestell, W. L. 1973, Sewage farming takes giant step
forward. The American City, October: 73-74.

Chaiken, E.I., S. Poloncsik, C. D. Wilson. 1973, Muskegon
sprays sewage effluents on land, Civil Engineering. ASCE.
May. (reprint by U.S. EPA, Region V, Wacker Dr., Chicago,
Illinois 60606).

Anonymous. 1973. Muskegon County's bold agri-approach to
wastewater disposal. Michigan Contracter and Builder.
April 28. pp. 8-16.

Anonymous. 1975, Literature from conference on the
Muskegon County, Michigan Wastewater Management System.
September 17-18, 1975. Muskegon County Community College.

(continued on next page)

CASE STUDY COVER SHEET (continued)

Armstrong, J. M., R. Canale, R. Kelly. 1975. An analysis
of the effects of the Muskegon County Land Wastewater
Treatment System: a brief synopsis of research to date and
proposed combination of work. Presented at Conference on
the Muskegon County, Michigan Wastewater Management System.
Sept. 17-18, 1975. Muskegon County Community College.

Bauer, W. J. 1975. Review of design parameters for
Muskegon County Wastewater Management System No. 1 after
two years of operation. Presented at Conference on the
Muskegon County, Michigan Wastewater Management System.
Sept. 17-18, 1975. Muskegon County Community College.

Demirjian, Y. A. 1975. Land treatment of municipal
wastewater effluents. Prepared for the U.S. EPA
Technology Transfer Program (Oct.)

EPA. 1976. Wastewater: is Muskegon County's solution
your solution? EPA-905/2-76-00. Region V, Chicago,
Illinois.

ing was expensive because air pollution regulations prevented burning of felled trees. A strong citizen suit was also fought by filing a countersuit. Citizen groups feared gross environmental pollution from the proposed land treatment facility. Of particular interest is the fact that this project originated as an effort to attract industry to an economically depressed region with unemployment at 11 to 13%, twice the national average. Adequate wastewater treatment was seen as a key issue, and that led to the present system.

The 10,000 acre Muskegon County Wastewater System, which has won engineering awards, necessitated the moving of many landowners, farmers, and businesses, and was accomplished in the face of strong citizen opposition.

The soil at the site is very sandy with a 10 in./hr infiltration rate, which is considerably decreased upon plowing. The available water capacity is 0.02 to 0.05 inch per inch of soil. The soil is underlain by impervious clay slanting upward and emerging at the south end of the site. The clay layer, water table, and low capacity for holding water require underdraining. Discharge is to easily maintained open channels before going to nearby creeks. Before construction, the groundwater table was very close to the soil surface in many of the fields. Tile drainage or drainage wells were installed and the water table lowered. The drainage network now collects the sprayed renovated wastewater after it has percolated through the crop soil system and discharges it into the receiving stream. The drainage network, along with interception ditches around the storage lagoon, is designed to protect the quality of the groundwater. Another interesting aspect of the site-drainage system is the bypassing of all drainage from lands upstream, and construction of berms to prevent storm water runoff from the site.

A shallow groundwater table was lowered at the Muskegon site by installing tile drains or drainage wells.

Soil pH ranges from 4.5 to 6.0. Soil C.E.C. and toxic element load are not specified in the literature cited. The site has a 250 foot buffer zone around its entire periphery which is used as a sanitary landfill. The flow design for this facility is given in Figure 9.

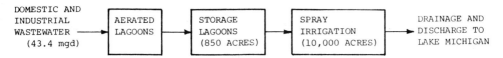

Figure 9. Illustration of the land application system for the treatment of wastewaters used by Muskegon County, Michigan.

After reaching the treatment site, wastewater can be aerated in each of the three 8-acre, 42-MG capacity aeration cells. There are 6 50-horsepower mixers and 12 60-horsepower aerators in each cell. Research and operating experience justified reducing the amount of aeration needed. This cut down drastically on electrical energy used. The aeration mode most often used at this time is treatment with 8 aerators in Cell 1 followed by treatment with 4 aerators in Cell 2. With the current 27 mgd flow, the average retention time is about 1.5 days in each cell.

After aeration in winter, the water flows into the storage lagoons. The two storage lagoons have a combined capacity of 5 billion gallons. During the summer, the aerated water may either be sent into storage or retained briefly in an 8-acre solids settling cell before application on land through the irrigation system.

Before water is irrigated onto the land, it enters a discharge cell. Prior to entering irrigation ditches that supply water to pumping stations, the water is chlorinated as necessary to meet health standards.

The pretreated wastewater is distributed to center pivot irrigation rigs via buried asbestos cement pipes. The operating pressure is from 30 to 70 psi depending upon the location of the rig. The rigs were especially designed for spraying wastewater with downward pointing low pressure nozzles. There are 54 center pivot irrigation rigs located in circular fields of 35 to 140 acres.

Fifty-four pivot irrigation rigs spray chlorinated, treated wastewater onto circular fields of 35–140 acres, primarily planted in corn.

No specific facilities monitor the leachate from the sanitary landfill zone. However, an extensive monitoring system is used to sample surface and groundwaters associated with the storage and irrigation operations. Around the wastewater treatment system, 29 surface water stations are monitored monthly, 30 seven-well sets, south and west of the lagoon dikes, are monitored daily.

Monitoring protocol includes analysis of three water quality parameters. Evidence after two full years of operation suggests that removal of BOD and SS and phosphorus is 98%, and nitrogen is 70%. No virus or coliform organisms are recorded in the final outfall.

After two years of operation at Muskegon, removal of BOD and SS and phosphorus is 98%, removal of nitrogen is 70%.

While operating costs for the first year ran to about $40 per million gal processed, it is felt that crop revenues will reduce this cost in the future. More than a quarter million bushels of corn were harvested in 1975. Predicted crop income was between $240,000 to $360,000 a year but reached $330,000 in the first year, $700,000 in the second year and is estimated at $1 million for 1977. The sale of corn reduced the $1.9 million operating cost for wastewater treatment during 1975 by about one-third. Nitrogen fertilizer was injected into the wastewater daily during the active part of the corn growing season (2 months) to increase corn growth and yield and to stimulate increased removal of phosphorus, potassium, and other wastewater nutrients. From 0 to 89 pounds per acre of nitrogen fertilizer was added to the different irrigated fields, depending upon the amount of wastewater applied and corn crop's needs.

Sale of corn irrigated with wastewater at the Muskegon site reduced operating costs by 1/3 in 1975.

Crops are grown and sold for animal consumption. Crops are grown in circular areas of from 1500 to 2800 feet in diameter, with some overlap in places. Spray is from center pivot rigs rolling on pneumatic tires. Head pressure is 35 psi with 10 psi nozzle pressure. This provides a raindrop effect rather than a fine spray, providing better groundwetting and less aerosol effect. The maximum application rate is set at 4 in./wk but presently averages about 2.1 in./wk. The approximate application loadings of NO_3^- and PO_4^{-3} are 150 lb/acre-yr and 50 lb/acre-yr, respectively.

Average yields on 5,000 acres of corn irrigated with wastewater increased from 60 bushels per acre in 1975 to 81 bushels per acre in 1976. This increase occurred despite dry weather in 1976 which reduced the county average from 65 to less than 50 bushels per acre. The estimated increase in income from sale of corn kept pace with dramatically higher energy costs, so that the operating costs in 1976 (including debt retirement) remained about equal to the 1975 treatment cost of 24c per thousand gallons of wastewater. Table 6 summarizes the increased corn yield and income at Muskegon County's Wastewater System.

A careful examination of data from a 3-year study has shown that diversion and treatment of wastewater flows have brought about significant improvements in water quality in Mona and Muskegon Lakes. Such improvements, and the likelihood that pollutant levels in surface streams and lakes will decline further with time, have important implications for new recreational and industrial developments in the community. Muskegon County has established an office for planning and developing these new potentials. In 1976, several industries selected Muskegon as the site for new operations. The County's wastewater treatment system was an important factor in their decision.

The Muskegon land treatment system has improved water quality in Mona and Muskegon Lakes and has been a major factor in the decisions of several industries to move their operations to Muskegon.

Initial operating difficulties have been irritating, but not major. It is felt that the basic design is sound and the system should perform to all expectations. Specifically, that means serving the

Table 6.   Increased Agricultural Productivity by Renovation/Reuse of Wastewater in Muskegon (EPA, 1976).

	Crop Yield and Income		
	1974	1975	1976
Wastewater site (bu/acre)	28	60	81
County average (bu/acre)	55	65	45–50
Gross crop revenue ($ $\times$ 10^6)	0.35	0.7	1.0 (est.)

needs of a population of 170,000 by 1992 and providing wastewater renovation equal to or in excess of then prevailing water quality standards for the entire anticipated 43.4 mgd flow.

Campbell Soup Company
Napoleon, Ohio

The Campbell Soup Company of Napoleon, Ohio, began using a complete containment spray irrigation system in 1954, and gradually evolved into a spray irrigation-overland flow system. The present system utilizes five natural sub-watersheds ranging from 11 to 56 acres in size, for a total area of 165 acres. Each watershed is graded to uniform 5% slopes. The slopes are divided with collection waterways to provide slope runs of 100-200 feet. One sub-watershed retains remnants of an old tile underdrainage with five outlets. Effluent of screened tomato wastes is sprayed from fog nozzles (14-20 gpm) or spray nozzles (7-25 gpm) at the top of the slopes and ultimate discharge is to a nearby river.

At Napoleon, Ohio effluent from screened tomato wastes is sprayed from fog nozzles or spray nozzles at the top of 5% slopes; wastewater is treated through 165 acres of natural subwatersheds and ultimately discharged to a nearby river.

Soils are calcareous clay or clay-loam till, outwash, and river alluvium that is underlain by black shale at about 50 feet. Infiltration rates are fairly high but subsurface permeability is low, giving "imperfect" to "very poor" natural drainage. Agricultural soils of the area are generally underdrained. Other soil characteristics are not specified. The estimated fate of the hydraulic load is about 40% to runoff, 30% to evapotranspiration, 25% stored in the upper 3 feet of soil and eventually percolated to greater depths, and about 5% is lost directly by spray drift/evaporation. A schematic diagram of this system is given in Figure 10.

Water renovation is monitored to some extent, but how much is standard routine and how much was unique to the research effort is unclear. Waste removal on a mass basis was: COD, 81-90%; BOD, 98.7%; Total-N, 73-93%; phosphates, 65-84%; and suspended solids, 89-97%. In all cases, the underdrained slope outperformed other slopes. The water quality from the run-off area was compared to the quality of runoff from agricultural watersheds as given in Table 7.

The overland flow treatment system at Napoleon's Campbell Soup plant was substantially improved in 1973 based on experience gathered at the company's plant in Paris, Texas. Table 8 gives a comparison of the characteristics of the original system and of the improved system.

Land utilization at the Napoleon treatment system was increased by investing approximately $300 per acre in earthmoving. In this way the wetted surface was increased to 80%. The land utilization at Napoleon formerly was about 35%. Available land must be utilized efficiently in this area because land values are exceeding $1,000 per acre and the piping of the disposal system adds another $700 to the costs.

Wastewater renovation was enhanced by increasing the wetted area to 80% at the Napoleon site by earthmoving.

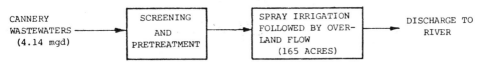

Figure 10. Schematic flow diagram of the land application system for wastewater treatment employed by the Campbell Soup Company of Napoleon, Ohio.

CASE STUDY COVER SHEET

SYSTEM   Campbell Soup Company   1961
                    (Name)   (Date started)

LOCATION Napoleon, Ohio   P. T. DuByne (Campbell Soup Co.)
                                                      (Person involved)

FACILITY DESCRIPTION   Cannery (Tomato)   Overland flow
                        (waste classification)   (application system(s))

APPLICATION 1.2-1.4 in./day   spray 6 hrs, rest 6, on 24 hr schedule
                    (rate)   (schedule)

CROP(S)   Reed canary, seaside bent, red top

PRETREATMENT   screened

VOLUME TREATED   5.20 mgd

WORKING YEAR   50 day   CLIMATE ZONE D

SOIL   clay, clay loam

COST

LAND AREA   165 acres

STORAGE CAPACITY   none

COMMENT: A tomato soup cannery which sprays screened effluent onto five
          graded slopes. Renovation is by overland flow and some
          infiltration; discharge is to nearby river. Average COD load is
          916 mg/l, BOD is 548 mg/l, organic-N is 26.8 mg/l and pH
          ranges from 4.9-9.3.

REFERENCES: Bendixen, T. W., R. D. Hill, F. T. DuByne, and G. G. Robeck.
             1969. Cannery waste treatment by spray irrigation-runoff.
             J. Water Poll. Contr. Fed. 41(3)-part 1: 385-391.

             Urban, D. R. 1963. Evaluation of the soils resources,
             Campbell Soup Farm, Napoleon, Ohio. Conserv. Farming Guide.
             Soil Conserv. Dist., Defiance, Ohio.

**Table 7.   Water Quality Comparisons. Data from Two Watersheds,
Campbell Soup Company, Napoleon, Ohio. (Bendixen, *et al*., 1969)**

Item	Agricultural Watershed (lb/acre-yr)	Spray-Runoff Watershed (lb/acre-yr)
COD	480–1300	410–2080
Total-N	11–237	18–72
PO_4^{-3}	1–28	11–54

Conversion factors: lb/acre-yr × 1.12 = Kg/ha-yr.
Bendixen, T. W., R. D. Hill, F. T. Dubyne and G. G. Robeck, 1969. Cannery waste
treatment by spray irrigation runoff. *J. Water Pollut. Contr. Fed.* **41**, (3) Part I:
385-391.

Table 8.   Napoleon, Ohio Plant

Characteristics of Spray System—Initial Design, 1961-1965

	Volume Sprayed[a]		Volume of Runoff		COD Applied		COD of Runoff			
	mil gal	gal/ acre-day	mil gal	% Flow	mg/l	1000 lb	mg/l	% Red.	1000 lb.	% Red.
1961	152.3	19,700	86.5	57 (29)[b]	576	732.6	94	84	67.7	91
1962	158.2	18,800	99.9	63 (36)	523	691.5	81	85	67.6	90
1963	203.0	27,900	86.6	43 (36)	369	625.5	94	75	67.8	89
1964	208.1	23,400	84.0	40 (29)	661	1208.0	136	79	95.3	92
1965	316.7	32,500	152.6	48 (26)	500	1319.3	94	81	119.9	91

Characteristics of Spray System—Improved Design Based on Paris, 1973-1976

					BOD Applied		BOD of Runoff			
1973	211.3	16,611	97.5	46.2	430	757.8	11.0	97.4	8.9	98.8
1974	182.6	17,552	67.1	36.7	458	697.5	10.1	97.8	5.6	99.3
1975	188.1	20,436	125.7	66.8	471	738.8	10.0	97.9	10.5	98.8
1976	260.8	19,622	136.7	51.3	390	848.3	5.0	98.7	5.7	99.3

[a] Avg. season was 50 days.
[b] Percentage after correction for rainfall.
Source: Gilde, 1977.

Flushing Meadows Project

This project indicates that nitrogen removal is highly dependent on application schedules. Nitrogen loadings range from 24,000 to 32,000 lb/acre-yr. far more than could be taken up by crops, so removal depends on anaerobic denitrification, achieved by flooding. However, to facilitate mineralization of organic-nitrogen, and allow conversion to NO_3^-, "resting" periods must be programmed so that the needed soil aeration would occur before inundation. Trial and error methods suggested that a 14 day wet, 10 (summer) or 20 day (winter) dry schedule reduces total N to about 30-60% of influent concentrations and NO_3-N to near zero except at the start of inundation. That anomaly at the start of inundation occurs, it is felt, because water held by the soil during dry periods becomes aerated, NH_4^+ is oxidized to NO_3^- and, on inundation that NO_3^- is flushed out too rapidly for any denitrification to occur. Over a period of years it was found that alternating application periods from long to short and back again was not only most effective but necessary to keep soil C.E.C. from becoming saturated with NH_4^+.

Filter basin clogging occurred with application schedules involving 2-3 weeks of continual flooding or when suspended solids rose to 50-100 mg/l during the winter. Severe clogging was remedied by "shaving off" the filter beds each spring.

23rd Avenue Project Based on Flushing Meadows Results.   The 23rd Avenue Project, a large-scale rapid infiltration system, was designed based on engineering criteria developed at Flushing Meadows. This 40-acre project was constructed in 1974. It was necessary to supplement the present water resources in the Phoenix area, and the 23rd Avenue Project was intended to demonstrate the *feasibility of rapid infiltration* on a scale that could partially meet this need for water. If this initial demonstration project shows that wastewater can be economically renovated, the system could be expanded to reclaim all of the effluent discharged in the Phoenix

CASE STUDY COVER SHEET

SYSTEM   Flushing Meadows Project   1967
                    (Name)   (Date started)

LOCATION   Phoenix, Arizona   H. Bouwer
                                                   (Person involved)

FACILITY DESCRIPTION Municipal   rapid infiltration
                          (waste classification)   (application system(s))

APPLICATION   Average 1-2 ft/day application   mixed for research purposes
                        (rate)   (schedule)

CROP(S)   Bermuda grass, Mexican "sprangle top", barnyard grass

PRETREATMENT   activated sludge

VOLUME TREATED   average 0.67 mgd

WORKING YEAR 12 months   CLIMATE ZONE   B

SOIL   fine loamy sand over coarse sand

COST   Estimated $5.00/acre foot

LAND AREA   2 acre

STORAGE CAPACITY none

COMMENT: Pilot study and feasibility demonstration on the bank of the dry
          Salt River bed. Six parallel infiltration beds, 700 ft x 20 ft,
          with ground water at 10 ft, were inundated at schedules ranging
          from 2 days flood, 3-5 days drying to 2 to 4 weeks each.
          Renovated water was pumped to surface storage for recreational
          and industrial reuse. Denitrification was relied upon for nitro-
          gen removal.

REFERENCES: Stevens, L. A. 1974. Clean water. E. P. Dutton & Co.,
             New York. pp. 189-194.

             Bouwer, H. 1973. Renovating secondary effluent by ground-
             water recharge with infiltration basins. In W. E. Sopper
             and L. T. Kardos. Recycling Treated Municipal Wastewater and
             Sludge Through Forest and Cropland. Penn State University
             Press. University Park, Pennsylvania. pp. 164-175.

             Bouwer, H. 1970. Groundwater recharge design for renovating
             wastewater. J. Sanitary Engr. Div., ASCE, Vol. 96SA1, 59-74.

             Bouwer, H. 1968. Returning wastes to the land, a new
             role for agriculture. J. of Soil and Water Conservation.
             Sept-Oct. 164-168.

             Pound, C. E., R. W. Crites. 1973b. Wastewater treatment
             and reuse by land application. Vol II. Prepared for

(continued on next page)

CASE STUDY COVER SHEET (continued)

Office of Research and Development, US EPA, EPA-660/2-73-006b.
pp. 195-197, 205-216.

Metcalf and Eddy, Inc. 1977. Process design manual for
land treatment of municipal wastewater. U.S. Environmental
Protection Agency, U.S. Army Corps of Engineers, U.S.
Department of Agriculture. EPA 625/1-77-008.   p. 7-44.

area. A significant portion of the treated flow would be used for nuclear power plant cooling water. The rest could be made available for irrigation and an extensive aquatic park development.

The 23rd Avenue Project is a large scale rapid infiltration project in Phoenix intended to demonstrate the feasibility of economically renovating all effluent discharged in Phoenix area, making it available for reuse for nuclear power plant cooling, irrigation, and development of aquatic parks.

The new rapid infiltration site is located on the north side of the bed of the Salt River and east of 35th Avenue. Secondary effluent from the 23rd Avenue wastewater treatment plant flows through a concrete channel to the site. The soil profile at the site is similar to the Flushing Meadows site, consisting of loamy sands, sand, gravel, and boulders to a depth of more than 200 feet. On the basis of results learned at Flushing Meadows, infiltration rates of at least 2.5 ft/d were expected.

When the 23rd Avenue Project is fully operating, about 13 mgd of secondary effluent will be applied to the four rapid infiltration basins. The renovated water will be recovered by a series of three 24-inch diameter wells equipped with pumps of 3000 gal/min capacity. Two 6-inch diameter observation wells and sampling wells have been built, these to be used to sample renovated water quality and monitor the groundwater level. The project will be operated so that the groundwater level will be the same as that in the aquifer adjacent to the project to prevent the movement of renovated water away from the site.

In addition to the quality and level of groundwater, the direction of groundwater movement will also be checked by monitoring the total dissolved solids concentration in the observation wells. If no native groundwater enters the project, the total dissolved solids of the reclaimed water should be approximately the same as that of the wastewater effluent.

A special objective of the 23rd Avenue Project is to determine how air pressure buildup in the soil beneath large infiltration basins affects the infiltration rate. The effects of high algae loading on surface clogging will also be studied.

A special objective of the 23rd Avenue Project is to determine how air pressure buildup in soil beneath large infiltration basins affects the infiltration rate.

Research at Flushing Meadows has dealt with the fate of viruses in wastewater as they enter the soil. However, the emphasis of the most recent research at Flushing Meadows is aimed at maximizing nitrogen removal. Increased nitrogen removal has been realized by reducing the hydraulic loading rate to the basins and using optimum flooding and drying periods. Preliminary results indicate that by reducing the annual hydraulic loading to the basins from 300 to 173 feet, nitrogen removal increased from 30 to 60% and phosphorus removal increased from 70 to 90%. The application schedule was 9 days flooding and 12 days drying.

Padre Dam Municipal Water District
Santee, California

The Padre Dam Municipal Water District is a public agency which provides water and sewerage service for the unincorporated community of Santee, California. The District has no local water supply and must depend on water from the Colorado River, some 300 miles away, and from the Feather River which is part of the California State Water Project. The customers of the District currently use 8,000 acre feet of water per year. The wholesale cost of this imported water has more than quintupled in the past 20 years from $17 an acre foot in 1957 to $90 in 1977. It is expected to increase further during the next decade to a price of more than $190 per acre foot.

The Padre Dam Water District aims to reclaim water from sewage and reuse it primarily for recreational purposes thus reducing the amount of expensive "imported" water purchased.

The intention of the water district is to reclaim water from sewage and reuse it for recreational, agricultural and industrial purposes, thus reducing the amount of expensive imported water purchased. The major difficulties faced were acquiring appropriate land and assuring public acceptance of reclaimed wastewater for recreational use. According to water district officials, the project has been successful because of a "fortuitous governmental cooperation, dedicated employees and good management." A former manager of the Water District said, "One reason the project has been so enthusiastically accepted by our community is because we have always tried to be completely honest with the people and have kept them informed throughout the progress of the project." Public acceptance was achieved through several tactics. A major public education campaign was conducted both in the immediate community and in surrounding communities for considerable distances. The lagoon site and all other parts of the system were landscaped, seeded with grasses, and made attractive. Picnic tables were installed, the grounds were mowed, and swans were purchased to live at the site. Access roads were opened. However, the immediate water area was securely fenced to prohibit entrance by the public. People could still come, see, smell and appraise the facility from the other side of the fence. A public protest arose; citizens demanded access to the attractive recreational facility, but authorities assured the public that there would be no public access until the health safety could be guaranteed. This conservative approach helped to build public confidence in the safety of the project.

Public acceptance of using reclaimed wastewater for recreation was achieved through a gradual, conservative public education campaign.

The potential hazard of the operation was evaluated by the Santee County Water District in conjunction with the U.S. Public Health Service, the California Department of Public Health, and three other state and county agencies. This effort provided the necessary information, including proof of virus removal, that assured the safety of the waters. Gradually and systematically, the lakes were opened to public boating (1963), fishing (1964) and swimming (1965). Although swimming was allowed for five years, the high degree of chlorination caused the build-up of iron and manganese in the water. Special devices were purchased to filter out these

CASE STUDY COVER SHEET

SYSTEM   Padre Dam Municipal Water District   1959
                     (Name)   (Date started)

LOCATION   Santee, California   Edwin W. Houser
                                                     (Person involved)

FACILITY DESCRIPTION   Municipal waste   slow percolation, lakes
                       (waste classification)   (Application system(s))

APPLICATION   flood
                 (rate)   (schedule)

             naturally occurring chaparral, sycamore trees
CROP(S)   in percolation area

PRETREATMENT   tertiary, chlorinated

VOLUME TREATED   3.6 mgd

WORKING YEAR   12 months   CLIMATE ZONE   A

SOIL   clay, sand, gravel

COST $2,224,944

LAND AREA 3-acre percolation area, 100-acre
             recreation area

STORAGE CAPACITY   22 MG

COMMENT: The Santee project represents a deliberate attempt to convert municipal
           wastewater to water suitable for recreation. Chlorinated secondary
           effluent is filtered through sand before passing in a series through
           three abandoned gravel pits converted to lakes. The system now in-
           cludes seven recreational lakes representing 75 water surface acres
           and 25 ground acres. Boating and fishing are allowed. A golf course
           also uses the reclaimed water for irrigation and water hazards. The
           system has become a major source of fresh water for recreation in
           this semi-arid region.

REFERENCES: Houser, E. W.   Santee project continues to show the way.
              May, 1970. Water and Wastes Engineering Municipal and
              Industrial.

              Merrell, J. C., W. F. Jopling, R. F. Bott, A. Katko, H. E. Pintler.
              The Santee recreation project, Santee, Calif. Final Report.
              U.S. Dept. of Interior, Federal Water Poll Control Admin, Cincinnati,
              Ohio. 1967. 165 p.

              Ormond, R. Reclamation bonanza In American County Government.
              Official Publication of the Nat. Assn. of Counties.
              San Diego, Calif. 1968.

(continued on next page).

CASE STUDY COVER SHEET   (continued)

Stevens, L. A. 1974. Clean Water. E. P. Dutton and Co.,
Inc. New York. pp. 143-154.

Sullivan, R. H., M. M. Cohen, and S. S. Baxter. 1973.
Survey of facilities using land application of wastewater.
Office of Water Programs Operations. U.S. EPA.
EPA-430/9-73-006. pp. 201-202.

elements. When the filtering devices wore out after five years, the water officials decided to close the swimming area rather than to purchase new equipment.

The Padre Dam system is based around abandoned sand and gravel pits underlain by an impervious layer of clay. These three nearly depleted sand pits, very near the new municipal treatment facility, were found to be suitable for surface storage. Ownership of the pits was transferred to the sanitation district. The pits were bulldozed to form three basins.

The system is located in a natural canyon, shallow with gently sloping sides. The canyon bottom is covered with an alluvial fill of sand and gravel approximately 12 feet deep and ranging from 400 to 1000 feet in width. An impervious clay underlays the sand and gravel. The effluent distribution system extends into the San Diego River basin. The raw sewage pump station is located at the mouth of the canyon. Raw sewage from this district of about 30,000 people is pumped up the canyon, past the recreational lakes, percolation basins, and oxidation ponds to the treatment plant. The effluent, after treatment in the activated sludge plant, flows back down the canyon through oxidation ponds and percolation basins, and thence is filtered through natural underground aquifers into the recreational lake system from which effluent for distribution is pumped. A schematic of this system is shown in Figure 11.

The Padre Dam system is located in a natural shallow canyon; its bottom covered with sand and gravel.

The pump station is a three-level structure, each pump capable of delivering 4,150 gallons per minute against a head of 192 feet. The basic treatment used at the plant is activated sludge with a design capacity of 4.0 mgd in the first stage. The elements of the treatment system are primary sedimentation, biochemical oxidation by aeration, final sedimentation, polishing in three oxidation ponds, and then percolation through the soil a minimum of 400 feet. Sludge and excess wastewater are sent to the San Diego Metropolitan System.

Chlorination is provided at four points: to the raw sewage influent, return activated sludge, effluent recovery water at the wet well, and final effluent. Chlorine is applied to raw sewage for odor control, to the sludge to control bulking, and to the effluent to provide disinfection as required for public health purposes.

Wastewater reclaimed for recreational lakes in Santee is chlorinated at four points before being discharged into lakes.

There is a total of 11 percolation basins which measure 50 feet by 150 feet by 3 feet each. Water is now percolated through the soil a minimum of 400 feet down into sand and gravel, and because of the underlying clay it moves horizontally in a downstream direction until it emerges into an interceptor trench located above the uppermost lake. From the trench, water flows in

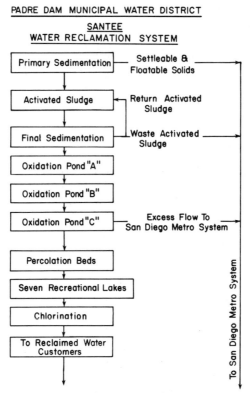

Figure 11. Schematic flow diagram of the land application system for wastewater treatment of the Padre Dam Municipal Water District in Santee, California.
Source: Padre Dam Municipal Water District, 1977.

a downstream direction until it reaches the lake adjacent to the oxidation pond. Eventually the hydraulic capacity of the percolation area will be exhausted, and it will be impossible to percolate greater volumes of water in the future. This contingency has been provided for and tertiary treatment facilities will go into operation to accomplish the full treatment job within the plant site, thereby eliminating the need for an oxidation pond and soil percolation.

> When the hydraulic capacity of the percolation basins is exhausted, tertiary treatment facilities will take over for the percolation basins and oxidation pond.

A laboratory on-site provides facilities to perform all necessary chemical and bacteriological tests for proper control of the operation and of water quality in the recreational lake system.

The surface water of this system continues to be monitored weekly. The final effluent contains 18 mg/l BOD_5, 25 mg/l SS, 19 mg/l P, and 22 mg/l NO_3^-. No monitoring wells, however, are used despite a 3 to 4 foot depth to the water table.

Extensive studies have been conducted at the Santee site on viruses, bacteria, phytoplankton, benthic organisms and fish. Further research projects have been proposed including the creation of a live stream using reclaimed water and energy-saving alternatives for reclamation of water. Among the other proposals are using reclaimed water for drip irrigation, for pet food production, for coastal wetlands and for irrigation of saline-tolerant plants in San Diego County. Among the new technologies the group proposes to investigate are efficiencies of different aquatic vascular plants in wastewater treatment systems and models for the most cost effective systems of brine disposal after demineralization in inland communities.

> *Officials of the Padre Dam Municipal Water District plan to do extensive research in a number of areas on reclaimed wastewater including creation of a live stream using reclaimed water.*

HYDIG
Hertfordshire, England

The West Hertfordshire Main Drainage Authority, located at Rickmansworth, about 20 miles north of London, England, serves an area of 210 square miles with a population of 550,000. 141,000 cubic meters/day (37 mgd) of wastewater, 80% from domestic sources, are treated in a two-stage treatment facility. Only 3% of the waste appears ultimately as sludge, and that is applied to land. To avoid public reference to sewage and its connotations the digested sludge has been given the name HYDIG.

The primary and activated sludges are held in anaerobic digestion tanks for 20–24 days at temperatures of 90–98°F. The annual production of digested sludge amounts to about 90 million gallons. The production of digested sludge is continuous; some sludge is irrigated every day except Sundays. The daily application is approximately $\frac{1}{24}$ of the contents of the digestion tanks, or from 250,000 to 500,000 gallons (all volumes are given in U.S. gallons). Capacity of the secondary sludge storage tanks is approximately $8\frac{1}{2}$ million gallons, which permits winter storage up to 6 weeks.

About 90 million gallons per year of liquid digested sludge is produced. The sludge has a solid content of about 3% and is applied to the land, either by spreading from tanktrucks or by irrigation from pits or stationary storage tanks adjacent to the fields. Approximately 1000 acres are owned by the Authority and used as experimental farmland, and the balance of the 6,000 acres is operated or owned by some 62 private farms. The cost of transporting and applying HYDIG in 1972 was about $6 per 1,000 gallons. The disadvantages of tank-truck operation are more than offset by the savings that result from having neither investment in 5,000 acres of farmland nor farm operating expenses on this land.

> *90 million gallons of digested sludge is applied to the land each year at this site 20 miles north of London; sludge is spread from tank trucks or irrigated from pits or stationary storage tanks adjacent to the fields at a cost of $6 per 1,000 U.S. gallons.*

The irrigation is done on gravel soils that are fairly firm and easily drained. The crops grown include grass, forage crops, English black beans, grains, potatoes and other root crops. There have been no build-up of toxic salts, cattle disease, objectionable odors, fly problems, or community objections. The public health officers are satisfied that the Hertfordshire irrigation procedure is not a threat to public health. There have been some individual complaints, but the majority of these has involved the use of the highways by the large tanktrucks. So far as is known, there has been no significant detectable uptake of trace metals in any of the crops grown at Hertfordshire. The principal problem appears to be speculation about what might happen after decades of sludge application. There is some concern that long-term loading of sludges may produce concentrations of potentially toxic elements in soils that will prove to be hazardous to crops. However, if crops such as certain grasses are used which tolerate the trace

CASE STUDY COVER SHEET

SYSTEM HYDIG   1952
       (Name)   (Date started)

LOCATION Hertfordshire, England

                                 Spray irrigation, surface spreading
FACILITY DESCRIPTION Municipal sludge   from stationary tank and trucks
                      (waste classification)   (application system(s))

APPLICATION
                    (rate)   (schedule)
CROP(S) grass, forage crops, English black beans, grains, potatoes, other
        root crops.

PRETREATMENT secondary

VOLUME TREATED   37 mgd
                          similar
WORKING YEAR   12 months   CLIMATE ZONE to C

SOIL   gravel, easily drained

COST   U.S. $6.00/1000 gal.

LAND AREA   6000 acres

STORAGE CAPACITY

COMMENT: A population of 550,000 is served by secondary treatment facilities.
The sludge from that treatment is applied onto 1000 acres of public
land and some 5000 acres of farm land. The sludge is called HYDIG
for public relations purposes. No odor, fly or health problems are
noted. Toxic element loading is considered to be the rate limiting
factor and is restricted to 8.3 mg/l zinc equivalent per year throughout the 30 year site lifespan.

REFERENCES: Seabrook, B. L. 1974. Irrigation of liquid digested sludge.
Movie, Wealth from Waste, Hertfordshire, England. Fact
sheet for U.S. EPA Office of Water Program Operations, Washington,
D.C. Aug. 30.

metals involved, the problem may be minimized. The most abundant potentially toxic metals
are zinc, copper and nickel.

*There has been no buildup of toxic salts, cattle disease, objectionable odors, fly
problems, community objections, nor significant detectable uptake of trace metals
by crops grown at Hertfordshire. The main problem is speculation over long term
effects of sludge application and concentrations of potentially toxic elements in soils.*

Tentatively, the Authority allows no more than 250 ppm of zinc-equivalent to build up in the topsoil of previously unamended soils over the site lifespan. It is recognized that the toxic element build-up appears to be cumulative, so the Authority has selected a 30-year period for the application of sludge to a particular piece of land. This limits the annual dressing to no more than $\frac{1}{30}$ of the 250 ppm arbitrary maximum. A further requirement is that soil pH must be maintained at > 6.5 at all times. It has been found that when the soil pH is less than 6.5 toxic effects of certain elements are accelerated. As a general precaution, livestock are not allowed to graze fields to which sewage has recently been applied until after rain has washed the edible plant sections clean. The Hertfordshire Authority points out, however, that there is no evidence to show that there has even been a problem from ingestion of such metal traces when livestock have grazed on fields that have not been washed clean by rain. In fact, palatability tests have led to observations that the cattle feed avidly upon grass which has received a fresh application of liquid digested sludge.

BIBLIOGRAPHY

Anonymous. 1973. Muskegon County's bold agri-approach to wastewater disposal. *Michigan Contractor and Builder*. Apr. 28. pp. 8–16.

Anonymous. 1975. Literature from conference on the Muskegon County, Michigan wastewater management system. Sept. 17–18, 1975. Muskegon County Community College.

Antonucci, D. C. and F. D. Schaumbur. 1975. Environmental effects of advanced wastewater treatment at South Lake Tahoe. *J. Water Pollut. Contr. Fed.*, 47 (11): 2694–2701.

Armstrong, J. M., R. Canale, and T. Kelly. 1975. An analysis of the effects of the Muskegon County land wastewater treatment systems: a brief synopsis of research to date and proposed combination of work. Presented at Conference on the Muskegon County, Michigan Wastewater Management System. Sept. 17–18, 1975. Muskegon County Community College.

Bendixen, T. W., R. D. Hill, F. T. Dubyne, and G. G. Robeck. 1969. Cannery waste treatment by spray irrigation-runoff. *J. Water Pollut. Contr. Fed.*, 41 (3) 1:385–391.

Bogedain, F. O., A. Adamczuk, and T. J. Tofflemire. 1974. Land disposal of wastewater in New York State (revised). New York Dept. of Environ. Conservation. Prepared for the Spring Meeting, New York State Water Pollution Control Association, June 13, 1973. Whiteface, N.Y.

Bouwer, H. 1968. Returning wastes to the land, a new role for agriculture. *J. Soil and Water Conservation*. Sept.–Oct. 164–168.

Bouwer, H. 1970. Groundwater recharge design for renovating wastewater. *J. Sanitary Engr. Div.*, ASCE, Vol. 96SA1, 59–74.

Bouwer, H. 1973. Renovating secondary effluent by groundwater recharge with infiltration basins. *In* W. E. Sopper and L. T. Kardos. Recycling treated municipal wastewater and sludge through forest and cropland. Penn State University Press, University Park, Pa. pp. 164–175.

Chaiken, E. I., S. Poloncsik, and C. D. Wilson. 1973. Muskegon sprays sewage effluents on land. Civil Engineering. ASCE. May. (reprint by U.S. EPA, Region V, 11 Wacker Drive, Chicago, Ill. 60606).

Crites, R. W. 1974. Irrigation with wastewater at Bakersfield, California. *In* Wastewater use in the production of food and fiber, EPA-660/2-74-041. pp. 229–239.

Crites, R. W. 1975. Wastewater irrigation: This city can show you how. Water and Wastes Engineering, 12 (July) 49–50.

Dalton, F. E., J. E. Stein, and B. T. Lynam. 1968. Land reclamation–a complete solution of the sludge and solids disposal problem. *J. Water Pollut. Contr. Fed.*, 40 (5): 789–801.

Demirjian, Y. A. 1975. Land treatment of municipal wastewater effluents. Prepared for the U.S. EPA Technology Transfer Program (Oct.).

D'Itri, F. M., T. P. Smith, H. Bouwer, E. A. Myers, and A. R. Overman. 1975. Design seminar for land treatment of municipal wastewater effluents. Prepared for U.S. EPA Technology Transfer Program. New York City. June, 1975.

Dufresne–Henry Eng. Corp. 1972. Winter spray irrigation demonstration. Bromley Ski Area, Vermont. A report on water quality effects by the Vermont Dept. of Water Resources, Project No. D-H #2140 (Aug. 17, 1972).

EPA. 1974. Land application of sewage effluents and sludges: selected abstracts. Water Quality Control Branch, Robt. S. Kerr Environmental Research Lab. EPA-660/2-74-042. Corvallis, Ore. 248 p.

EPA. 1976. Wastewater: Is Muskegon County's solution your solution? EPA-905/2-76-004, Region V, Chicago, Ill.

EPA. 1977. Selected recent reports on land application of municipal wastewaters. Wastewater Management Branch, Robt. S. Kerr Environmental Research Laboratory. Unpublished. Ada, OK. 7 p.

Forestell, W. L. 1973. Sewage farming takes a giant step forward. The American City. Oct., 73–74.

Foster, H. B. 1965. Survey of sewage disposal by hillside sprays. Bureau of Sanitary Engineering, California State Dept. of Public Health (Mar.).

Gilde, L. C. 1977. Food processing wastewater disposal by irrigation. University of Guelph, Ontario, Canada, April 26–27, 1977.

Gilde, L. D., A. S. Kester, J. P. Law, C. H. Neeley, and D. M. Parmlee. 1971. A spray irrigation system for treatment of cannery wastes. J. Water Pollut. Contr. Fed., 43 (10): 2011–2025.

Gomey, H. J. 1968. Water reuse in Monterrey, Mexico. J. Water Pollut. Contr. Fed., 40 (4): 540–545.

Guarino, C. F., M. O. Nelson, S. A. Townsend, T. E. Wilson, and E. F. Ballotti. 1975. Land and sea solids management alternatives in Philadelphia. J. Water Pollut. Contr. Fed., 47 (11): 2551–2564.

Houser, E. W. 1970. Santee project continues to show the way. Water and Wastes Engineering Municipal and Industrial.

Jenks, J. H. and P. L. Adamson. 1972. Wastewater treatment disposal and reclamation project. Project Report, City of Fresno.

Johnson, R. D., R. L. Jones, T. D. Hinesly, and D. J. David. 1974. Selected chemical characteristics of soil, forage and drainage water from the sewage farm serving Melbourne, Australia. Prepared for the Department of the Army Corps of Engineers. 54 p.

Kerfoot, W. B. 1975. Living filters and water conservation on Cape Cod. The Cape Naturalist, 4 (1): 4–12.

Kerfoot, W. B. and B. T. Ketchum. 1974. Cape Cod wastewater renovation and retrieval system, a study of water treatment and conservation. Technical Report, Woods Hole Oceanographic Institute, Woods Hole, Mass. WHOI-74-13 (unpublished manuscript).

Kerfoot, W. B., B. H. Ketchum, P. Kallio, P. Bowker, A. Mann, and C. Scolieri. 1975. Cape Cod wastewater renovation and retrieval system, a study of water treatment and conservation, first year of operation. Technical report WHOI 75-32, Woods Hole Oceanographic Institute, Woods Hole, Mass.

Ketchum, B. H., R. F. Vaccaro, P. E. Kallio, A. Mann, P. L. Deese, and C. Palmer. 1976. Cape Cod wastewater renovation and retrieval system: a study of water treatment and conservation. Technical Interim Report, June 11, 1975–June 10, 1976. WHOI-76-93, Woods Hole Oceanographic Institute, Woods Hole, Mass.

Ketchum, B. H., R. F. Vaccaro, P. E. Kallio, A. Mann, P. L. Deese, C. Palmer, M. R. Dennett, P. C. Bowker, and N. Corwin. 1977. Cape Cod wastewater renovation and retrieval system: a study of water treatment and conservation. Interim Technical Report, WHOI-77-32, Woods Hole Oceanographic Institute, Woods Hole, Mass.

Lambert, D. J. and H. L. McKim. 1977. Deer Creek Lake-on-land wastewater treatment system. In R. C. Loehr, ed. Food, fertilizer and agricultural residues. Proc. 9th Cornell Univ., Agricultural Waste Management Conference. Ann Arbor Science Pub., Ann Arbor, Mich.

Malhotra, S. K. and E. A. Meyers. 1975. Design, operation, and monitoring of municipal irrigation systems. J. Water Pollut. Contr. Fed., 47 (11): 2627–2639.

Mann, A. W., R. F. Vaccaro, and P. L. Deese. Controlled chlorination in agricultural systems irrigated with secondary wastewater effluents. J. Water Pollut. Contr. Fed. In press.

Mead, R. and R. F. Vaccaro. 1971. Sewage disposal in Falmouth, Massachusetts. III. Predicted effects of inland disposal and sea outfall on ground water. J. Boston Society of Engineers, 58 (4): 278–297.

Merrell, J. C., W. F. Jopling, R. F. Bott, A. Katko, and H. E. Pintler. 1967. The Santee recreation project, Santee, Calif. Final Report. U.S. Dept. of Interior, Federal Water Poll. Control Admin., Cincinnati, Ohio. 165 p.

Metcalf and Eddy, Inc. 1973. Preliminary investigation of wastewater treatment and disposal for southeast Bakersfield. Prepared for City of Bakersfield and Mount Vernon County Sanitation District.

Metcalf and Eddy, Inc. 1977. Process design manual for land treatment of municipal wastewater. U.S. Environmental Protection Agency, U.S. Army Corps of Engineers, U.S. Department of Agriculture. EPA 625/1-77-008.

Nutter, W. L., R. C. Schultz, and G. H. Bristor. 1975. Sewage effluent irrigation project at the station: Second annual progress report. Georgia Department of Natural Resources. (unpublished)

Ormond, R. 1968. Reclamation bonanza. In American County Government. Official Publication of the Nat. Assn. of Counties. San Diego, Ca.

Pound, C. E. and R. W. Crites. 1973. Wastewater treatment and reuse by land application. Vol. II. Prepared for Office of Research and Development, U.S. EPA, EPA-660/2-73-006b. pp. 195–197, 205–216.

Satterwhite, M. B., G. L. Stewart, B. J. Condike, and E. Vlach. 1974 (May). Rapid infiltration of primary sewage effluent at Fort Devens, Massachusetts. Draft report for USACRREL project as part of the RDTE Project 4A062112A891, Task 05, Environmental Quality for Army Construction.

Satterwhite, M. B., B. J. Condike, and G. L. Stewart. 1975 (Jan.). Treatment of primary sewage effluent by rapid infiltration. Draft report for USACRREL Project as part of RDTE project 4A062112A891, Task 05, Environmental Quality for Army Construction.

Satterwhite, M. B., G. L. Stewart, B. J. Condike, and E. Vlach. 1976. Rapid infiltration of primary sewage effluent at Fort Devens, Massachusetts. CRREL Report 76-48, Prepared for Directorate of Military Construction, Office of Chief of Engineers.

Satterwhite, M. B., B. J. Condike, and G. L. Stewart. 1976. Treatment of primary sewage effluent by rapid infiltration. CRREL Report 76-49, Prepared for Directorate of Military Construction, Office of Chief of Engineers.

Seabrook, B. L. 1975. Land application of wastewater in Australia. The Werribee farm system. Prepared for U.S. EPA Municipal Construction Division, Office of Water Program Operations (May). 27 p.

Searle, S. S. and C. F. Kirby. 1972 (fall). Waste into wealth. Water Spectrum. U.S. Army Corps of Engineers. 15–21.

Sopper, W. E. and Kardos, L. T. eds. 1973. Recycling treated municipal wastewater and sludge through forest and cropland. Penn State University Press, University Park. 462 pages.

Stephan, D. G. and L. W. Weinberger. 1968. Wastewater reuse—has it "arrived"? *J. Water Pollut. Contr. Fed.*, 40 (4): 529–539.

Stevens, L. A. 1974. Clean water. E. P. Dutton & Co., New York. 289 p.

Sullivan, R. H., M. M. Cohen, and S. S. Baxter. 1973. Survey of facilities using land application of wastewater. Office of Water Programs Operations. U.S. EPA. EPA-430/9-73-006. pp. 201–202.

Thornthwaite, C. W. and Associates. 1969. An evaluation of cannery waste disposal by overland flow spray irrigation. Campbell Soup Company, Paris, Texas. *Publications in Climatology*, Vol. 22, No. 2, 73 p.

Urban, D. R. 1963. Evaluation of the soils resources. Campbell Soup Farm, Napoleon, Ohio. Conserv. Farming Guide. Soil Conserv. Dist., Defiance, Ohio.

BIBLIOGRAPHY ABSTRACTS

Antonucci, D. C. and F. D. Schaumbur. 1975. Environmental effects of advanced wastewater treatment at South Lake Tahoe. *J. Water Pollut. Contr. Fed.*, 47 (11): 2694–2701.
Considerable data on a tertiary treatment facility and its impact on its environment. Data interesting especially in comparison to land application alternatives.

Bogedain, F. O., A Adamczuk, and T. J. Tofflemire. 1974. Land disposal of wastewater in New York State (revised). New York Dept. of Environ. Conservation Prepared for the Spring Meeting, New York State Water Pollution Control Association, June 13, 1973, Whiteface, N.Y.
A survey of individual, municipal, and industrial facilities in New York employing land application of wastes. Includes operational summary of eight land application systems (some of which are failures).

Dalton, F. E., J. E. Stein, and B. T. Lynam. 1968. Land reclamation—a complete solution of the sludge and solids disposal problem. *J. Water Pollut. Contr. Fed.*, 40 (5): 789–801.
A review of the problems and plans of Chicago with respect to handling vast amounts of sludges.

D'Itri, F. M., T. P. Smith, H. Bouwer, E. A. Myers, and A. R. Overman. 1975. Design Seminar for land treatment of municipal wastewater effluents. Prepared for U.S. EPA Technology Transfer Program at New York City. June, 1975.
Four facilities were selected by the authors for detailed analysis of their operations. The facilities include the Michigan State University Water Quality Management Project, the City of Tallahassee, Florida, Flushing Meadows (Phoenix, Arizona), and the Pennsylvania State University Wastewater Renovation and Conservation Project.

Foster, H. B. 1965. Survey of sewage disposal by hillside sprays. Bureau of Sanitary Engineering, California State Dept. of Public Health (Mar.).
Thirty hillside spray disposal plants were visited and reports are made on their design and effectiveness. Considerable amounts of specific data are given.

Guarino, C. F., M. O. Nelson, S. A. Townsend, T. E. Wilson, and E. F. Ballotti. 1975. Land and sea solids management alternatives in Philadelphia. *J. Water Pollut. Contr. Fed.*, 47 (11): 2551–2564.
Interesting comparison between land application and sea dumping in which the decision to go to sea dumping was justified on cost effective grounds.

Gomey, H. J. 1968. Water reuse in Monterrey, Mexico. *J. Water Pollut. Contr. Fed.*, 40 (4): 540–545.
Specific case study of municipal waste treatment by land application.

Melhotra, S. K. and E. A. Meyers. 1975. Design, operation, and monitoring of municipal irrigation systems. *J. Water Pollut. Contr. Fed.*, 47 (11): 2627–2639.
Review of much information included in modules of this book, but exemplified with references to ten specific land application systems. Specific data are provided.

Nutter, W. L., R. C. Schultz, and G. H. Bristor. 1975. Sewage effluent irrigation project at the station: Second annual progress report. Georgia Department of Natural Resources. (unpublished)
A second annual report on a specific spray irrigation system of secondarily treated municipal sewages in the Georgia mountains. Specific data on chemical and biological effects.

Pound, C. E. and R. W. Crites. 1973. Wastewater treatment and reuse by land application. Vol. II. Prepared for Office of Research and Development, U.S. EPA, EPA-600/2-73-006b. 249 pages.
A wide ranging publication which often illustrates points by discussing appropriate aspects of specific case studies. Starting on page 185 there are summaries of numerous specific sites visited during the preparation of the manuscript.

Sopper, W. E. and L. T. Kardos, eds. 1973. Recycling treated municipal wastewater and sludge through forest and cropland. Penn State University Press, University Park, Pa. 462 pages.
A symposium report documenting the Penn State Wastewater treatment program, but also presenting papers on the Flushing Meadow Project (Phoenix, Arizona), The Mt. Sunapee State Park Project (New Hampshire) and others.

Stephan, D. G. and L. W. Weinberger. 1968. Wastewater reuse—has it "arrived"? *J. Water Pollut. Contr. Fed.*, 40 (4): 529–539.
A summary of 163 land application systems around the United States, identifying each and giving some generalities and some particulars.

Stevens, L. A. 1975. Clean water. E. P. Dutton & Co., Inc., New York. 289 p.
A general summary of land application systems written in advocacy style for general readership. Non-technical but many interesting tidbits of different systems. Several good photographs.

Sullivan R. H., M. M. Cohen, and S. S. Baxter. 1973. Survey of facilities using land application of wastewater. Office of Water Program Operations, U.S. EPA, EPA-430/9-73-006. 377 pages.
Reports of 100 field surveys of facilities where land application of domestic and industrial wastes has been attempted. There are many colored pictures of sites, reviews of general information, and documentation of specific data.

INDEX